TANKS
and other Armoured Fighting Vehicles
of World War II

TANKS
and other Armoured Fighting Vehicles of World War II

by
B. T. White

Illustrated by
JOHN WOOD
Brian Hiley
J. Pelling
E. Bruce

Exeter Books

NEW YORK

75-28306

CONTENTS

Book I
TANKS
and other Armoured Fighting Vehicles
of the Blitzkrieg Era 1939–41

Introduction to Book I: 1939-41

Blitzkrieg, 1939-41

Blitzkrieg ('lightning war') was the term which came to mean, in 1939-40, the successes of German arms, led by tanks, beginning with the invasion of Poland in September 1939 and followed, in April-June 1940, by the conquest of Denmark, Norway, Holland, Belgium, Luxembourg and France.

Britain narrowly escaped defeat in 1940 only because the major part of the British Expeditionary Force was evacuated from Dunkirk, but without its tanks and heavy equipment.

Before this, in northern Europe, Russia, which had joined in the attack on Poland in 1939, had moved against Finland at the end of November. Although the end was not in doubt, the Finns succeeded in capturing much Russian equipment, including tanks, before surrendering in March 1940.

Italy entered the war on Germany's side in June 1940 and the defeat of the Italian Army in Libya between November 1940 and the early part of 1941 was the first of a string of Allied victories. This was, however, only the beginning of a long series of North African battles, in which the German Afrika Korps joined in March 1941.

Then, following the final abandonment of 'Operation Sea Lion', the planned German invasion of England, came the massive attack on Russia in June 1941. Some of the greatest tank battles of all were to take place on Soviet territory before the war ended.

The two other great powers, the U.S.A. and Japan, came into the world conflict at the very end of 1941.

However, apart from token U.S. equipment covered in this volume, the armour of these countries is better dealt with later in the series.

Technical Development

The wide range of A.F.V. designs from all the countries involved in a world war cannot satisfactorily be summarised in a short introduction like this, and only broad trends can be mentioned, more detail being left to the descriptions and illustrations of A.F.V.s in the main part of the book.

The widest single influence in A.F.V. design in 1939 was probably still that of the British firm of Vickers-Armstrongs Ltd. Light tanks ranging from 2 to 7 tons supplied by Vickers-Armstrongs, built under licence, or inspired by Vickers-Armstrongs' designs, formed a high proportion of the armoured forces of the U.S.S.R. (T-26 series), Poland (TK series and 7 TP), Germany (PzKpfw IA and B, derived from Vickers-Carden-Loyd designs), Italy and France (L.3/35 and Renault UE, both based on a Carden-Loyd design), as well as of Britain. These tanks were all of simple and relatively cheap but reliable and effective design. Most were lightly armoured but some, such as the Russian T-26s, were very well armed for their size. The British Cruiser tanks Marks I and II and the Valentine (the British tank built in the greatest numbers in the Second World War) were also Vickers-Armstrongs' designs.

The American Christie designs were another, and more enduring, influence on A.F.V. development, and Russia,

Poland and Britain used J. Walter Christie's principles of a good cross-country suspension system with a high-powered engine for fast medium tanks. The Russian BT series (the most numerous Soviet tank in 1939) and the British Cruiser Mark III were successfully developed into the T-34 and later cruiser tanks respectively, used to the end of the war and after.

Other medium tanks ranged from the German PzKpfw III, intended as the basic tank of the Panzer divisions, which was armed with a 3·7-cm. gun and was fairly mobile but armoured only to a maximum of 30 mm., to the French Somua S.35. This tank had cast armour up to 55 mm., a 47-mm. gun and a quite good performance, and was considered one of the best of its class in the world in 1939, although, unlike the German tank, it probably lacked the potential for much further development. French tanks, whose development was to cease after June 1940, had relatively poor suspension systems but in many cases had advanced transmissions and steering and, except for the light cavalry reconnaissance vehicles, were well armoured, much use being made of large castings for hulls and turrets. Welding techniques were also successfully applied to armour in, for example, the F.C.M.36. Good examples of well-balanced designs of light-medium tanks were the Czech LT-35 and LT-38, both of which were sold commercially before 1939. Supplies of these tanks, and their production lines, were invaluable to Germany's later plans when Czechoslovakia was annexed in March 1939. Britain's Infantry Tank, Mark II, although often limited in use by the official infantry supporting concept to which it was designed, was in 1939-40 one of the best tanks in the world in the medium category. Although compact, it was very well armoured, well armed and reasonably mobile.

Self-propelled artillery was mainly a German speciality in 1939-40, with both improvised mountings on PzKpfw I chassis and specialised 'assault guns', although the French Char B and the Russian KV II were different approaches to the problem of bringing artillery into action close to the centre of the battle.

Armoured car design of the older school was characterised by the Polish wz 34 which used a conventional 4×2 chassis, and by the Russian BA-10 which, because of its six-wheeled chassis, had a rather better cross-country performance. The German SdKfz 231(6-rad) series was also in this category, but exhibited a much more advanced design of ballistically thought-out armoured hull. Ahead in their mechanical concepts were the rear-engined Dutch DAF six-wheeler (which was well armed and had a good hull design), the French Panhard 178, which first came into service in 1935, and the Swedish Pb. m/39-40. Britain's modern armoured car was the Guy Tank, Light (Wheeled) Mark I which was similar in layout to the Panhard and also had 4×4 drive with 'solid' axles. The large German eight-wheeled armoured cars, the small British Scout Car, Mark I and the Italian AB.40 all showed more advanced mechanical features for suspension and all-wheel-drive transmission.

Armoured personnel carriers for the transport of infantry accompanying the tanks were employed significantly only by the Germans in 1939–40, the vehicle type being the half-tracked SdKfz 251 and, later, the SdKfz 250 series. These vehicles were rather complicated in design but highly efficient, and were also used for many other purposes. The French were the only other country to employ half-tracks in action at this time, although the armoured ones were represented principally by the Schneider P.16 used as an Auto-mitrailleuse de Combat alongside full-tracked light tanks. The only Allied armoured personnel carrier during this period was the wheeled American White Scout Car (so called) supplied to Britain in 1941. However, the British full-tracked carriers performed some of the same functions as the German half-tracks. The Russians simply carried infantry on the backs of tanks.

Armoured Command Vehicles were represented by modified German tanks on PzKpfw I and III chassis, together with wireless versions of the armoured half-tracks and armoured cars. All British tanks were wireless-equipped (unlike some German and Russian tanks at the early stages of the war) so command was relatively easy, but British A.C.V.s like the Guy Lizard did not appear until late 1940 and, at a lower command level, the White Scout Car was used for this purpose from 1941 onwards.

Designs for special forms of tanks or other assault vehicles were called for to meet particular problems. The breaching of the Siegfried Line could, it was hoped in 1939–40, be carried out by the British A.22 (later known as Infantry Mark IV), or by T.O.G. heavy assault tanks, or by the N.L.E. Trenching Machine. A French approach was a design for a special version of the Somua-Coder bridging device, although this was never built. The German 'Operation Sea Lion' required the use of amphibious tanks and a Schwimmpanzer II was built, together with submersible versions of PzKpfw III and IV. The United Kingdom was never invaded, but the submersible tanks were used in crossing the River Bug at the opening of the invasion of Russia in June 1941. To counter the expected German landings, Britain produced in a matter of months large numbers of improvised armoured cars to help fill the gap left by the loss of the British Expeditionary Force's tanks. All used standard lorry or passenger car chassis and some of the more important are shown in this book. Others were 'armoured' with concrete or with boxes filled with pebbles.

The Irish Republic also built in 1940–41 armoured cars (similar in layout to the Polish wz 34 and many others of this type) to defend their neutrality, and another neutral, Sweden, continued the development of the Landsverk series of armoured cars and tanks. Swedish armoured fighting vehicles were, at this time, well up to the standard of their contemporaries in the bigger countries, the tanks having torsion-bar suspension and geared steering.

Power plants were diverse in British and French tanks in 1939–40, varying from slightly modified commercial engines to specially designed tank engines. Some were diesels, but these were in the minority. Germany had concentrated solely on petrol engines for all her tanks and had standardised on a range built by Maybach, with advantages in the supply of components and spares. The Italians, on the other hand, chose a diesel for their medium tanks and this was one of their best features. The Russians had a fairly wide range of engines in use in 1939 but they concentrated their efforts on the development of a good twelve-cylinder diesel engine of around 500 h.p. This powerful engine was successfully used in the KV and T-34 tanks and lasted throughout the war.

Suspension systems varied widely in most countries over this period, only the Italians continuing to favour the leaf springs controlling groups of road wheels which were common in the pre-war Vickers designs. The French tended to prefer coil-spring systems of various sorts (sometimes using rubber washers in compression instead) and Britain (after the Cruisers Marks I and II and Infantry Marks I–III) generally used independent coil-spring suspensions of one type or another, the Christie system being standardised for Cruiser tanks. After many experiments with all the early versions of their principal tanks in use by 1939, the Germans settled on transverse torsion bars for the PzKpfw III and quarter-elliptic leaf springs, in different layouts, for the PzKpfw IV and standard models of PzKpfw II. The Russians had various suspension systems on their older tanks in use in 1939 but retained the Christie system of the BT in developing the T-34 (omitting the ability to run on wheels) and used torsion bars for the KV series and also for new light tanks.

Steering systems generally tended to advance from the crude clutch and brake (skid-turn) type to geared arrangements of varying degrees of sophistication. The British Bren Carrier's track-bowing system for gentle turns, before bringing in the clutch and brake, is worthy of mention here because it was one of the few of its kind.

Armament and armour have been left to last because, given that a tank has some degree of mobility, they are the most important features.

Armour increased steadily in thickness between 1939 and 1941 but although some effective designs, such as the DAF armoured car, had shown the way, little real attempt to improve its arrangement on tanks for maximum effect seems to have been made before the appearance of the Russian T-34. An example of these increases is the British Cruiser Mark I, which had a 14-mm. armour maximum, whereas the Cruiser Mark V (Covenanter) had nearly trebled this to 40 mm. before the end of 1940. An exceptionally well-armoured tank in 1939, with a 60-mm. maximum, was the British Infantry Mark I, but for the Infantry Mark IV, prototypes of which appeared before the end of 1940, 102 mm. was considered necessary. British armour protection was to some extent accelerated because of the delay in production of a heavier offensive weapon than the 2-pounder, but on the German PzKpfw III, the original 14·5-mm. maximum went up to 30 mm. on Ausf.E and climbed to 50 mm. on some models before the end of 1941. Armament also showed a steady increase between 1939 and 1941 in calibre and/or penetrative ability. Even for light tanks after 1940 the heavy machine-guns or rifles that served as anti-tank guns generally could no longer be regarded as worth while, although they continued in use for armoured cars. Perhaps the most dramatic contrast was between the 45-mm. gun, generally used as an armour-piercing weapon in many older Russian tanks in 1939, and the powerful 76·2-mm. gun (L/30·5 calibre, soon to be increased to L/41·2) of the KV I and T-34. This gun was capable of firing solid armour-piercing shot and high-explosive ammunition, a feature absent in the British 2-pounder (40-mm.) gun which was in its time an excellent armour-piercing weapon.

The German encounter in 1941 with these two powerful Russian tanks, and particularly the T-34, marked a watershed in A.F.V. design because they were so much better in all essentials than tanks of other countries on both sides.

Armoured Formations

The successes of the German Panzer forces in 1939–41 are attributable to a high degree of training and organisation and not just to numbers of tanks or their quality.

In Poland, where only some 700 tanks (the majority tankettes of the TK type), mostly dispersed among various unarmoured formations, were mobilised and available to oppose about 2,000 German tanks (many of which were, admittedly, also light) organised into seven Panzer Divisions and four light divisions, the final outcome was predictable.

The Panzer forces for the campaign in the West in May 1940 had no such overall superiority, however. The French had a quite considerable armoured force of about 3,000 modern tanks, of which some 800 were medium or heavy tanks. There were two types of armoured formation, the Divisions Légères Méchaniques (D.L.M.) of which three existed in May 1940, and the Division Cuirassée (D.C.R.) of which there were also three, with a fourth still in the process of formation when the campaign began.

These two types of formation were specified for strategic reconnaissance on the one hand—and the D.L.M. was a mobile and fairly well-balanced formation, although with a preponderance of light tanks and armoured cars—and for the set-piece breakthrough on the other. The D.C.R. was well provided with powerful tanks but lacked both mobility and adequate supporting arms. Some 1,500 tanks of all sizes were contained in formations of this type and the balance of the modern French tanks was distributed in groups of tank battalions attached to the various French Armies along the frontier and behind the Maginot Line defences.

The British Expeditionary Force in France had only one Army Tank Brigade of two battalions of infantry tanks, one armoured division (of which only one of the two armoured brigades arrived in time for the main battle), and numbers of light tanks included in the divisional mechanised cavalry regiments in each infantry division.

Against this Allied force the Germans used some 2,500 tanks, nearly all included in ten Panzer divisions, nine of which were concentrated on a narrow front. The French armoured formations were committed piecemeal and apart from slight temporary set-backs such as the attacks of the 1st Army Tank Brigade and de Gaulle's 4e D.C.R., the Panzer division had it all their own way and the campaign was virtually over in a fortnight.

The same well-tried German tactics were used again in Russia in June 1941, this time with about 3,000 tanks, some 2,000 being PzKpfw IIIs and IVs. To oppose them, the Russians probably had at least 20,000 tanks of all types, although only a relatively small proportion were organised in formations actually at the front. In five months the Germans destroyed or captured around 17,000 Russian tanks against their own losses of 2,700. Almost at the gates of Moscow and almost, it seemed, within sight of final victory, the offensive was halted by the combination of supply problems in the vast country, stubborn Russian resistance and finally, the Russian winter.

THE COLOURED ILLUSTRATIONS

A description of each coloured
plate is given between pages
89 and 146.

NOTE

The side views of the Finnish Vickers 6-ton tank (No. 22) and the Polish light tank 7TP (No. 17) have been constructed by the artist. In both cases, the proportions of the suspension should, in fact, correspond closely with that shown in the side view of the Russian T-26B (No. 36).

By a Publisher's error, the Russian T-26B (No. 36) and the Finnish Vickers 6-ton (No. 22) tanks were transposed out of the sequence intended by the author.

Poland

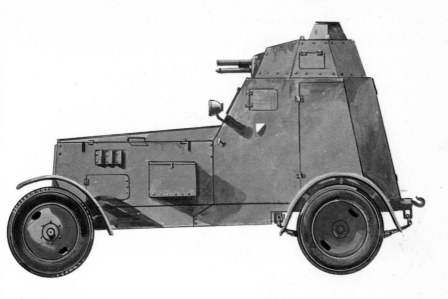

1   Armoured Car wz 34

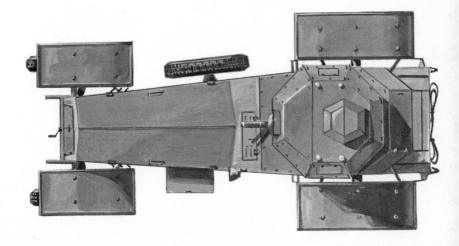

Poland

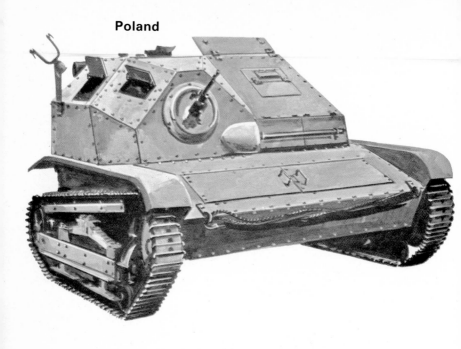

2 Tankettes TK3 (with 20-mm. gun) (*below*) and TKS

3 Char Moyen Renault D.2

France

4 Chars de Bataille Renault B.1 (*below*) and B.1 bis

France

5   Char Léger Renault R.35

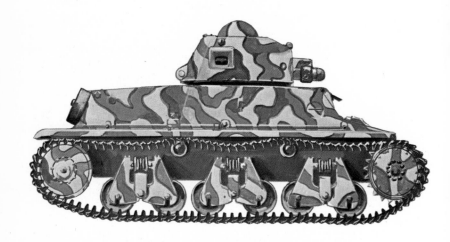

6 Chars Légers Hotchkiss H.35 (*below*) and H.39

7   Char de Cavalerie Somua S.35

France

8 A.M.C. 1935, Renault type ACG 1

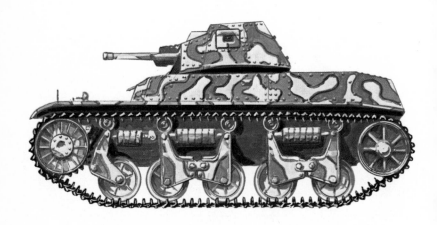

France

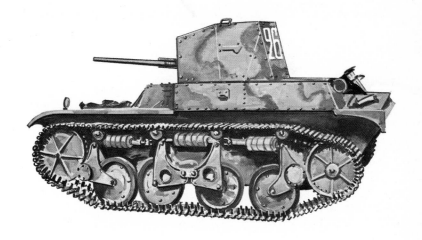

9 A.M.R. 1935, Renault type ZT

France

10   A.M.D. Panhard type 178

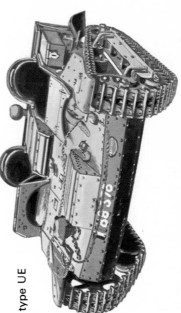

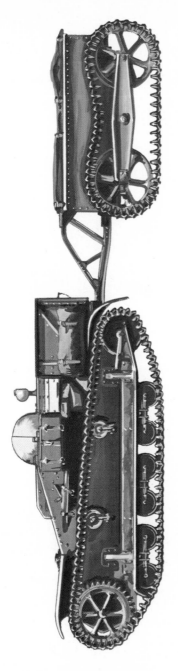

France

11   Chenillette d'infanterie Renault type UE

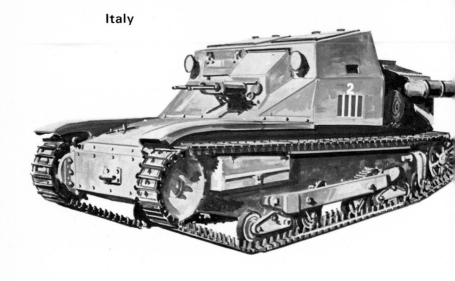

12   Carro Armato L.3/35

Czechoslovakia

13 Lehký Tank LT-35 (*above*) and Panzerkampfwagen 35(t)

14   Char Léger, Vickers-Carden-Loyd, Modèle T.15

Germany

15   Panzerkampfwagen I, Ausf. B

France

16 Char Léger F.C.M. 36

17 Light Tank 7TP

Poland

18   Medium Tank 10TP

Germany

19 Schwerer Panzerspähwagen (6-rad) SdKfz 231 (*above*)
and Schwerer Panzerspähwagen (6-rad) (Fu) SdKfz 232

20 Panzerkampfwagen II, Ausf. c

21   BA-32-2 (Armoured Car)

Finland

22 Tank, Vickers 6-ton (T-26E), with 37-mm. Puteaux gun (*above*) and with 37-mm. Bofors gun

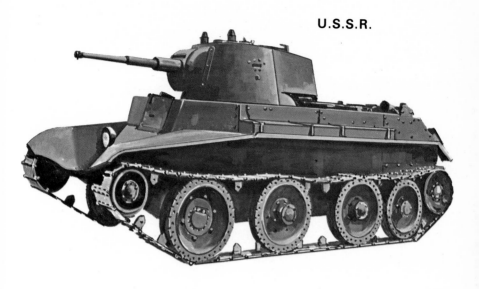

23 BT-7 ('Fast Tank'): BT-7-1 (*below*) and BT-7-2

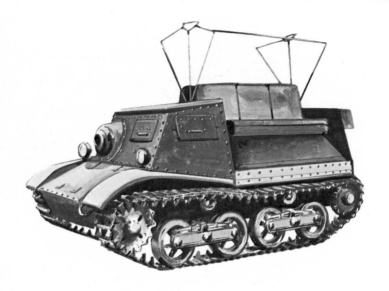

24 STZ-3 Komsomolets (Armoured Tractor)

25   Carrier, Bren

U.K.

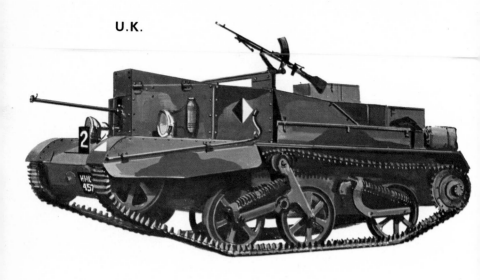

26 Carrier, Cavalry, Mark I (*below*) and Carrier, Scout, Mark I

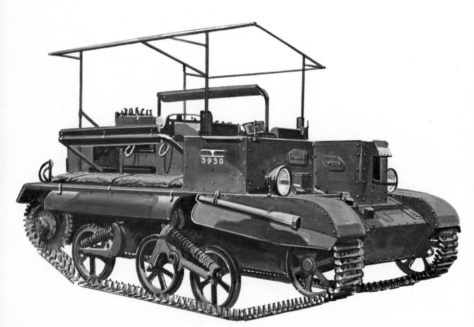

27 Armoured Car, Reconnaissance, Morris (Model CS9/LAC)

28 Schwere Panzerspähwagen (8-rad) Sdkfz 231 (chassis) (*below*) and Schwere Panzerspähwagen (8-rad) (Fu) Sdkfz 232

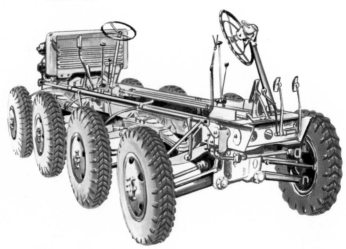

29 Schwerer geländegangiger gepanzerter Personen-
kraftwagen, SdKfz 247 (6×4) (*above*) and SdKfz 247 (4×4)

Czechoslovakia

30 Panzerkampfwagen 38(t) (LT-38)

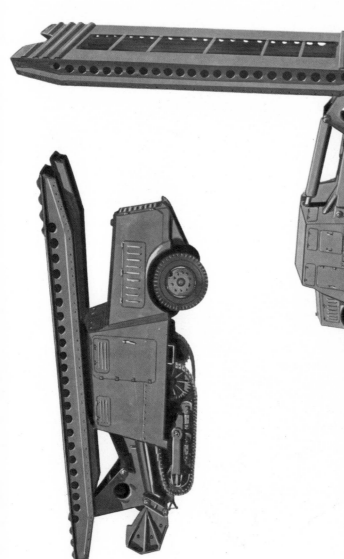

31 Porte-Pont, Somua-Coder MSCL-5

32 T-28C (Medium Tank)

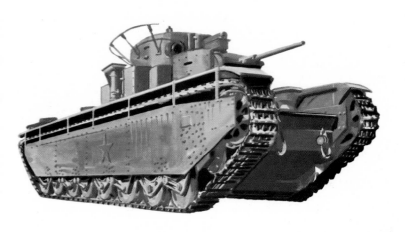

33 T-35 (Heavy Tank)

Sweden

34 Pansarbil m/39-40

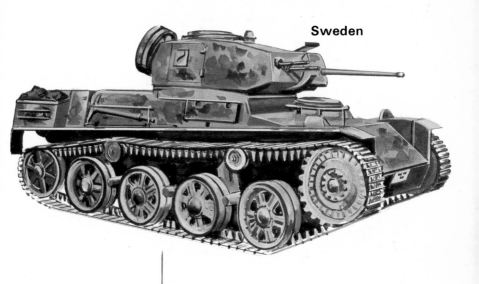

Sweden

35 Stridsvagn m/39

36 T-26B (Light Tank)

37 Tank, Light, M2A4

38   Scout Car, M3A1

39   Tanks, Light, Mark VIB (*above*) and Mark VIC

40 Tank, Infantry, Mark I

41   Carro Armato M.11/39

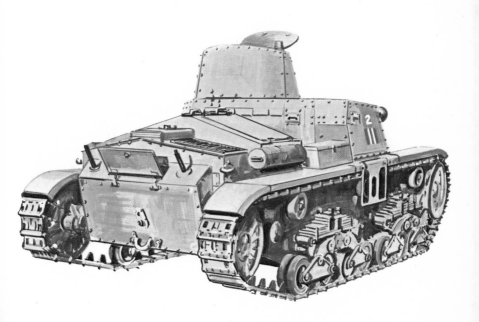

42 Mittlerer Schützenpanzerwagen SdKfz 251/1 (*above*) and Mittlerer Schützenpanzerwagen (Funkwagen) SdKfz 251/3

Germany

43 Kleiner Panzerbefehlswagen I

44   Panzerkampfwagen III, Ausf. E (*below*) and G

Germany

45 Panzerkampfwagen IV, Ausf. A (*below*) and B

46 15-cm. s.I.G. on Panzerkampfwagen I, Ausf. B

Germany

47 Panzerjäger I

Holland

48   Pantserwagen M'39 (DAF)

49 Tanks, Cruiser, Mark I (*above*) and Mark ICS

50 Tank, Cruiser, Mark IIA

51 Tanks, Cruiser, Marks IV (*below*) and IVA

52 Tank, Infantry, Mark II, Matilda I

53   Tanks, Light (Wheeled) Marks I (*below*) and IA

54   Car, Scout, Mark I

55   KV I(B) (Heavy Tank)

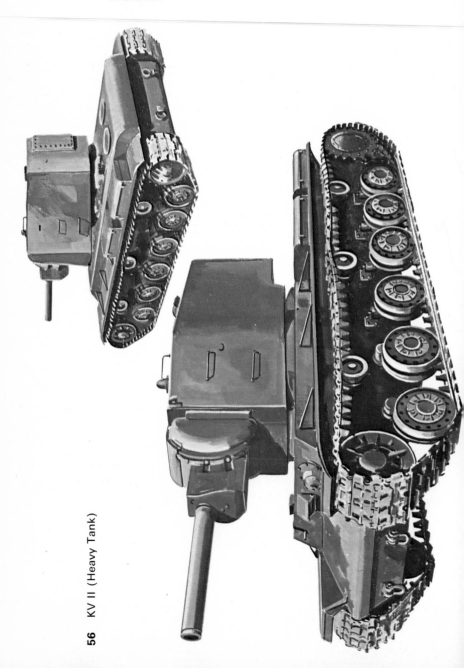

56   KV II (Heavy Tank)

South Africa

57 South African Reconnaissance Car, Mark II

58 Leichter Panzerspähwagen SdKfz 222

Germany

59 Leichter Schützenpanzerwagen SdKfz 250/1 (*above*) and leichter gepanzerter Munitionstransport Kraftwagen SdKfz 252

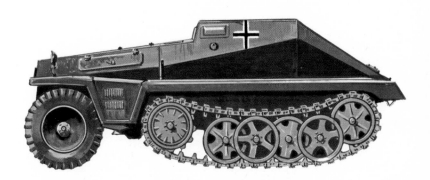

60   Sturmgeschütz III

U.S.S.R.

61 T-34 ('T-34/76A') (Medium Tank)

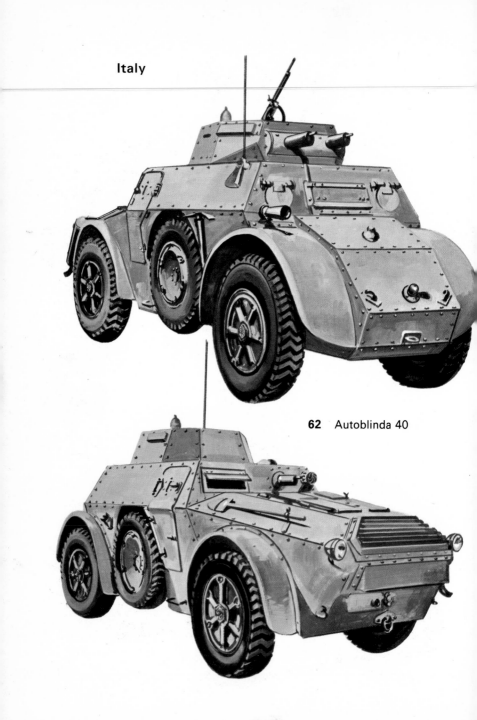

62 Autoblinda 40

Italy

63 Carro Armato L.6/40

64   Carro Armato M.13/40

65   Tank, Infantry, Mark III*, Valentine II

66 Cars, 4×2, Light Reconnaissance, Standard, Marks I (*above*) and II (Beaverette I and II)

67 Car, 4×2, Light Reconnaissance, Humber Mark I (Ironside I) (*above*) and Car, 4-seater, Armoured Saloon, Humber (Special Ironside)

68 Armoured Car, Dodge (*above*) and Lorry, 30-cwt, 4×2, Armoured Anti-tank, Bedford

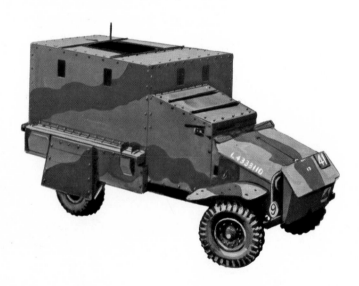

Germany

69 Panzerkampfwagen II (Schwimm.)

70   Panzerkampfwagen II (Flamm.)

71   Tank, Heavy, T.O.G. I

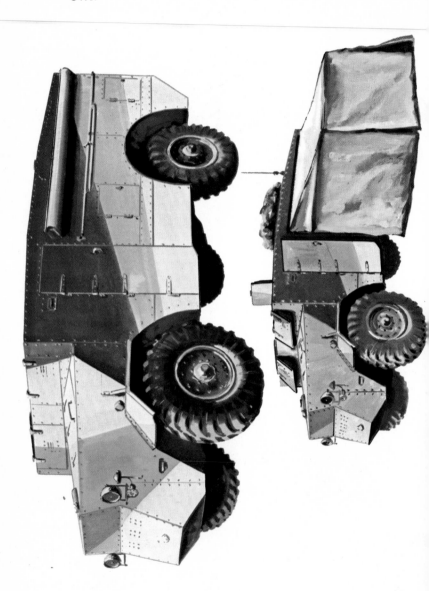

72 Armoured Command Vehicle, Guy 'Lizard'

73 Armoured Carrier, Wheeled, I.P. Mark I

74 Tank, Cruiser, Mark V, Covenanter I

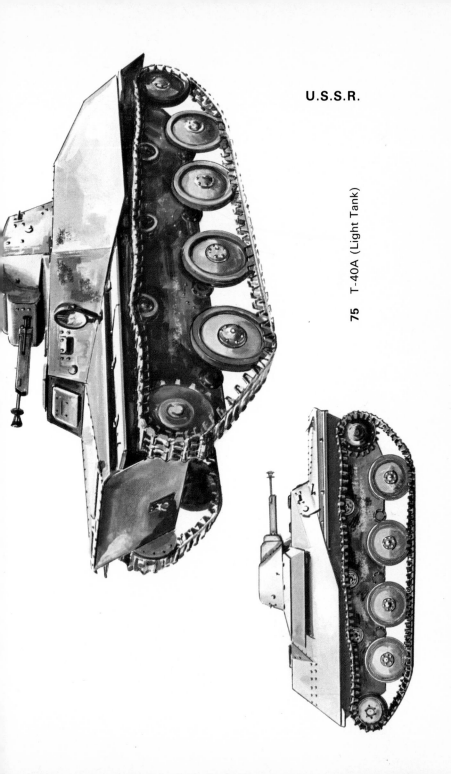

U.S.S.R.

75   T-40A (Light Tank)

Irish Free State

76 Armoured Car Mark IV (Ford)

77 Cockatrice (Bedford) (*below*) and Heavy Cockatrice (A.E.C.) Flamethrowers

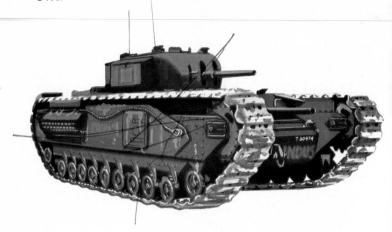

78 Tanks, Infantry, Mark IV, Churchill I (*above*) and Mark IVA, Churchill II

U.K.

79 N.L.E. Trenching Machine, Mark I

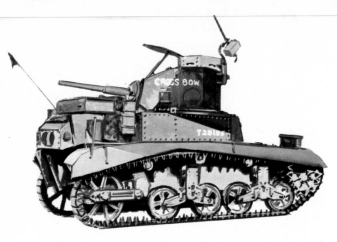

80 Tank Light, M3 (Stuart I)

TANKS AND OTHER ARMOURED
FIGHTING VEHICLES OF THE BLITZKRIEG ERA

1 Armoured Car wz 34, Poland.

Eighty-six of these light armoured cars were built in Poland in 1934, using commercial chassis and the turrets and some of the armour from half-tracked armoured cars that had been constructed in Poland in 1928 on Citroen-Kegresse chassis purchased in France. The layout was conventional for armoured cars of the period, although with only a two-man crew the wz 34 was more compact than some (if rather tall in relation to its length), and the car had a good ground clearance. The suspension consisted of quarter-elliptic leaf springs at the front and semi-elliptics at the rear, where there were dual wheels. The engine was originally a six-cylinder 20-h.p. Citroen with three-speed gearbox, although in later versions (wz 34—I and wz 34—II) 23-h.p. and 25-h.p. Polish Fiat engines with four-speed gearboxes were used instead.

The armament consisted of either one short 37-mm. gun or one 7·92-mm. machine-gun in the turret. The armour protection was only 6-mm., though this kept the weight down to under 2½ tons.

The wz 34 armoured cars, together with a smaller number of the older wz 29 pattern, were employed in reconnaissance squadrons in each of the eleven Polish horsed cavalry brigades during the invasion of Poland. The armoured cars were too weak and too few in numbers, however, and were no more able to stand up against the well-equipped German Panzer divisions than were the mounted cavalry.

2 Tankettes TK 3 and TK S, Poland.

A total of nearly 700 of these two-man light tanks or 'tankettes' was built in Poland during the 1930s and at the time of the German invasion the type was by far the strongest in numbers in the Polish armoured forces.

The basic models of the TK 3 and TK S were very much alike in external appearance and both were closely derived from the British Carden-Loyd Mark VI under the licence of which they were built. The chief difference between the two was that the later model, the TK S, had a four-cylinder Polish-built Fiat engine in place of the four-cylinder Ford Model A engine which was used in the TK 3 and the Carden-Loyd. Both the Polish tanks had an enclosed roof of a different design to that of the later enclosed Carden-Loyds and the armour was up to a maximum of 8 mm. in the TK3 and 10 mm. in the TK S. The standard armament was, in both cases, a 7·92-mm. machine-gun mounted in the front right-hand side of the hull.

Various experimental models of the TK 3 and TK S were produced with improvements in the armament, and the best of these was a version of the TK 3 in which a 20-mm. cannon, mounted in a slightly extended gunner's compartment, replaced the machine-gun. It was planned to have at least a proportion of the tanks in each company of TK 3s or TK Ss rearmed with 20-mm. guns, but only relatively few tanks of this version were in service by September 1939. At this date each of eighteen infantry divisions and eleven (horsed) cavalry brigades had a company of TK 3 or TK S tanks, and the two motorised cavalry brigades included two companies each. Although numerically fairly impressive, this equipment was completely outclassed by the German tanks which it encountered when Poland was invaded.

3 Char Moyen Renault D.2, France.

Direct in line of descent from the light Renault FT of 1917 through the NC 27 and NC 31 (sold abroad but not used by France), the Char D.2 was one of the first modern types of infantry medium tanks to be supplied to the French Army after the First World War.

The Renault-designed D.2 had a rear-mounted engine—a six-cylinder Renault of 150 h.p.—with transmission via a four-speed gearbox to rear sprockets. The crew compartment and turret were set fairly well forward, the cast turret mounting a 47-mm. gun and one 7·5-mm. machine-gun. Armour was to a maximum of 40 mm. and the top speed was 15 m.p.h. The suspension, protected by hinged side skirting plates, consisted on each side of three bogie units of four road wheels and sprung on vertical coil springs. Additionally there were single road wheels each side in front of and behind the bogie groups. First appearing in 1933, the Char D.2 was largely superseded by the Char B series by 1940. Nevertheless, the D.2 still remained in first-line service and formed part of the

equipment of General de Gaulle's 4e Division Cuirassée.

4 Chars de Bataille Renault B.1 and B.1 bis, France.

Chars B represented the principal striking force of the four French armoured divisions (Divisions Cuirassées—D.C.R.) that were in existence by 15 May 1940 (the last, under the command of General de Gaulle, created on this day) and, as such, were perhaps the most significant Allied tanks of the era. Each of these divisions had an establishment of four battalions of combat tanks, organised by 1940 in a demi-brigade of two battalions of Chars B.1 bis and a demi-brigade of two battalions of much lighter tanks, in most cases H.39s.

The specification for the Char B had its origin as far back as 1921, but this was not agreed in a final form until 1926 and three prototypes were built between 1929 and 1931. From trials of these emerged the first production model, Char B.1, the earliest of which were completed about 1935.

The Char B showed the influence of the First World War traditions in its long, high profile, but its armour was good for its time, and its armament—a short 75-mm. gun, a 47-mm. gun and two machine-guns—was powerful, although the heavy weapon was limited in use by its mounting low in the hull front. Mobility, too, was not neglected because a six-cylinder Renault engine of 250 h.p. gave a top speed of 17 m.p.h. Steering was by means of an advanced regenerative controlled differential system, by means of which also the 75-mm. gun, which had no independent traverse, could be laid.

The second production model, Char B.1 bis (all of which went to the four D.C.R.), had a 47-mm. turret gun model SA 35, with a longer barrel than the model SA 34 of the B.1, and a 300-h.p. engine which increased the overall performance generally and the top speed slightly, although the radius of action was reduced. The maximum armour protection of 40 mm. in B.1 was increased to 60 mm. in the B.1 bis. A third model, B.1 ter (of which only five were built), had a 350-h.p. diesel engine, the incorporation of limited independent traverse for the 75-mm. gun and redesigned side armour.

Production of the Char B series was undertaken by Renault, Schneider, F.C.M., F.A.M.H. (Saint Chamond) and AMX and about 380 were built, all of which were B.1 bis except for thirty-five of the earlier B.1. Some of those that remained intact after the Campaign of 1940 were used by the Germans as training vehicles, flame-throwers or self-propelled mountings.

5 Char Léger Renault R.35, France.

Designed and produced by the Renault company to replace its famous predecessor, the FT 17, the R.35 appeared in 1935. A two-man light tank of just under 10 tons, the R.35 was intended to re-equip the tank regiments supporting infantry divisions and, as such, had relatively heavy armour protection (to a maximum of 45 mm.—greater than that of many contemporary medium tanks of other countries), and a short-barrelled low-velocity 37-mm. gun with coaxial 7·5-mm. machine-gun.

This was at the expense of mobility, because a speed of only 12 m.p.h. was attained with the Renault four-cylinder 82-h.p. engine.

The general layout of the R.35 was conventional, although the use of castings for the turret (pioneered in the Renault FT 17) and parts of the hull was uncommon outside France at the time. The rear-mounted engine drove sprockets at the front of the track and the suspension consisted, each side, of five road wheels and a low-mounted idler wheel at the rear. The road wheels were mounted in two articulated bogies, each of two wheels, and a single. The wheel movement was controlled by springs made up of horizontally mounted rubber washers.

Although production of the R.35 was insufficient completely to replace the FT 17 in the infantry tank regiments, this tank equipped twenty-three battalions and was an important element in the French rearmament programme: it was certainly one of the best-known tanks of its era. Some were also employed in the Divisions Cuirassées in lieu of H.39s.

An improved model of the R.35 had the longer-barrelled SA 38 37-mm. gun and a further development, known as R.40, had an entirely new suspension system designed by AMX with armoured skirting plates. This tank had a far better cross-country performance than the R.35 but only two battalions had been equipped with it by 1940.

6 Chars Légers Hotchkiss H.35 and H.39, France.

This light tank was produced at the same time as the Renault R.35 and was adopted by the cavalry, just as the

R.35 was used to re-equip the tank units of the infantry.

The Renault and Hotchkiss tanks were rather alike in appearance and had identical armament of one 37-mm. gun and one 7·5-mm. machine-gun. The H.35, however, had the special characteristic required by the cavalry of a better speed and this was attained to some extent at the expense of armour protection, which was at a maximum of 34 mm. compared with the infantry tank's 45 mm. The Hotch-kiss H.35 had a similar suspension system to the Renault's but using coil springs instead of rubber washers and with one extra road wheel each side: the longer-track base contributing to a better performance cross-country at speed.

In the course of production of the H.35 the original Hotchkiss six-cylinder 75-h.p. engine was replaced by one of 120 h.p. and this increased the maximum speed from $17\frac{1}{2}$ m.p.h. to $22\frac{1}{2}$ m.p.h. The rear hull deck over the engine was higher in this model, known as H.39. Finally, the turret in the later H.39s to be produced was equipped with a long 37-mm. gun.

One of the most important types of French tank of its era, over 1,000 Hotch-kiss H.35s and H.39s were produced and with the Somua S.35 they formed the backbone of the cavalry Divisions Légères Méchaniques (DLM) as well as subsequently equipping most of the light battalions in each of the Divisions Cuirassées (DCR) formed in 1939–40.

7 Char de Cavalerie Somua S.35, France.

The Somua S.35 was regarded as the best French tank of the early part of the Second World War and, indeed, was considered by some as one of the best medium tanks of its era in the world. Certainly, after the surrender of France in 1940 this was one of the few types of French tank to be used by the Germans to equip some of their own tank units.

Produced by the Societé d'Outillage Méchanique et Usinage d'Artillerie (SOMUA), the S.35 first appeared in 1935. Intended for the mechanised cavalry, it was originally classified as an Automitrailleuse de Combat (AMC) but later was designated Char de Cavalerie and became one of the principal fighting vehicles of the Divisions Légères Méchaniques. Each of these mechanised cavalry divisions had one regiment (two squadrons) of S.35s in its tank brigade, together with a regiment of Hotchkiss H.39s.

The Somua S.35 shared a common turret design with the Char B.1 bis but had few other similarities with the heavier vehicle. The S.35 had a good road speed of 25 m.p.h. without undue sacrifice of armour protection, which was up to 55 mm, and although the hull was somewhat high the armour was rounded and well-shaped to a design facilitated by the cast form of manufacture used.

The armament of one 47-mm. gun and one 7·5-mm. machine-gun in an electrically traversed turret was as good as or better than that of the majority of German tanks in 1940, although the tank's performance in action was retarded by the fact that the commander was also the gunner.

Power was supplied by a Somua V-8 engine of 190 h.p. linked to a synchromesh five-speed gearbox which transmitted the drive to the tracks via rear sprockets. The steering was of the double differential type offering one radius of turn for each of the five forward gears. The suspension consisted of small road wheels in pairs sprung on leaf springs and protected by side armour skirting.

8 A.M.C. 1935, Renault type ACG 1, France.

This light combat cavalry tank ('Automitrailleuse de Combat') was one of the most advanced French tanks for its size in that as well as being equipped with a good gun it had a two-man turret—the first French tank to do so—with all the advantages in command it conferred.

Designed by Renault, the AMC 35 used suspension of similar design to that of the R.35, but the hull and turret were redesigned and used a bolted or riveted form of construction instead of cast. As required of a cavalry tank, a reasonably good maximum speed of 25 m.p.h. was attained, thanks to the satisfactory power/weight ratio conferred by the 180-h.p. Renault six-cylinder engine. The armament consisted of a 7·5-mm. machine-gun and either a 47-mm. gun (as shown in the pictures) or a high-velocity 25-mm. cannon.

Manufacture of the AMC 35 was undertaken by l'Atelier d'Issy les Moulineaux (AMX) and, somewhat surprisingly, for in retrospect this seems to have been one of the best pre-war French light tank designs, only 100 were built. Twelve tanks of this type were supplied to the Belgian Army.

9 A.M.R. 1935, Renault type ZT, France.

Designed by Renault for the French cavalry, this light tank was a battle reconnaissance vehicle in the category of 'Automitrailleuse de Reconnaissance' (AMR), to follow the earlier Renault model 33, type VM.

Known by its manufacturers as type ZT, the AMR 35 had the main characteristic demanded of this class of tank of high speed (37 m.p.h.), although at the expense of armour protection which was in the 5–13 mm. range. The armament was, however, an improvement over its predecessor in that the second model (shown in the illustrations) had a 13·2-mm. heavy machine-gun (in place of the 7·5-mm. machine-gun of the AMR 33 and first model of AMR 35). In the final model of AMR 35 a 25-mm. gun was fitted.

The mechanical layout of the AMR 35 was similar to that of most French light tanks of the period—a rear-mounted engine (four-cylinder Renault, 80-h.p.) with drive to front sprockets. The suspension consisted, each side, of one pair of road wheels and two singles controlled by rubber washers in compression—a system also used in the R.35 and H.35. The two-man crew occupied the centre part of the vehicle, the driver at the left. The turret was also at the left-hand side of the hull, the engine being at the right.

Nearly 200 of these tanks were built and many were still in service in 1939–40, although it was the intention to replace them with the slower but much better-protected Hotchkiss H.35.

10 A.M.D. Panhard type 178, France.

This Automitrailleuse de Découverte, which was designed in 1933, first entered service with the French Army in 1935, and today still looks modern in appearance, was one of the best armoured cars of its kind in the world in the early part of the Second World War.

Known as the Panhard type 178 to its manufacturers and as AMD Panhard modèle 1935 by the French Army, this was the first four-wheeled, four-wheel-drive rear-engined armoured car to go into series production for a major country and the same layout was subsequently adopted by the United Kingdom, Germany, the United States and Italy, among others.

Power was provided by a four-cylinder Panhard-type S.K. engine of 105 h.p. and transmitted through a gearbox with four forward and four reverse speeds. The maximum speed was 45 m.p.h. The crew of four included a second driver at the rear, and a speed of 26 m.p.h. could be attained in reverse.

Early examples of the Panhard 178 had a short-calibre gun or, in some cases, two machine-guns but the standard armament was a 25-mm. high-velocity gun and one 7·5-mm. machine-gun mounted coaxially in the turret. A command version had a fixed structure replacing the turret and was without armament. The armour protection of the Panhard was in the range 20 mm. maximum and 7 mm. minimum.

The Panhard armoured cars were used by the mechanised cavalry for long-distance reconnaissance in the reconnaissance regiments of the Divisions Légères Méchaniques (D.L.M.), and in the so-called reconnaissance groups of infantry divisions (G.R.D.I.): in both types of unit they were grouped with cavalry full-tracked or half-tracked armoured vehicles. After the defeat of France in 1940, the Germans acknowledged the merit of the Panhard 178 by taking all those available into service in the German Army, where they received the designation of Pz. Spähwagen P.204(f).

11 Chenillette d'infanterie Renault type UE, France.

This small tracked vehicle was produced in large numbers from 1931 onwards as an armoured supply tractor for the French infantry. Weighing only about 2 tons, its own carrying capacity was slight, but a tracked trailer was normally towed. Both tractor and trailer were derived from Carden-Loyd designs and a very similar vehicle, the Carden-Loyd Mark VI, was widely used by the British Army in the 1930s although, unlike its French contemporary, it had been superseded by the outbreak of the Second World War.

Although a version of the Renault UE with a mounted machine-gun for the co-driver was built, the great majority were unarmed and intended purely as front-line supply vehicles. They were fully enclosed, with light armour protection up to a maximum of 7 mm. The trailer, which could carry about 500 kg., was open and unprotected, and could be used with or without tracks.

The Renault UE was powered by a four-cylinder Renault 35-h.p. engine mounted between the two members of the crew.

12 Carro Armato L.3/35, Italy.

Yet another member of the family of the Carden-Loyd Mark VI, which, by direct sales and the granting of manufacturing licences, spread to many of the countries of the world in the 1930s, was this small Italian tank.

Twenty-five Carden-Loyd Mark VIs were purchased by the Italian Army in 1929 and, based on these, a model known as Carro Veloce ('fast tank') C.V.28 was built by the Fiat motor works in conjunction with the Ansaldo armaments concern. This was followed by further models, C.V.29 and C.V. L.3/33. The Carro Veloce L.3/35 was the final model and included some improvements over the L.3/33, although up-dated examples of the earlier model existed and so the differences between the two are often small.

Although still bearing a superficial resemblance to its Carden-Loyd prototype, the L.3/35 was, in fact, greatly improved mechanically and also in several respects as a fighting vehicle but, even so, by 1939 it was heavily outclassed by the tanks of other powers.

The L.3/35's engine was a four-cylinder Fiat of 43 h.p., mounted transversely at the rear with the radiator—a circular type with centrifugal fan—behind it. The transmission was led forward to the clutch and gearbox (with four forward speeds) in front of the driver, with final drive to front track sprockets. The suspension consisted of two three-wheel bogie units

and a single, unsprung, road wheel (just in front of the rear idler wheel) each side. Each bogie unit was sprung on a quarter-elliptic leaf spring.

The fighting compartment of the L.3/35 was in the centre of the vehicle with the two crew members—driver on the right and gunner on the left—sitting side by side. The armoured superstructure varied in that in the earlier tanks built it was constructed of plates riveted on to angle girders whereas in later vehicles bolts were employed. Maximum armour thickness was 13·5 mm. The standard armament was two 8-mm. Breda model 38 machine-guns with a total traverse of 24 degrees, elevation of 15 degrees and depression of 12 degrees. There was also a flamethrower version in which the flame projector replaced one of the machine-guns.

Large numbers of these Carro Veloce (the maximum speed was in fact only 26 m.p.h.; later the designation Carro Armato was used) were built for the Italian Army and were used in the North African Campaigns and, although easily knocked out by the smallest anti-tank gun, were even employed in the Russian campaign.

The illustrations show both flush-riveted and bolted hull types. Both tanks are shown in desert paint and the colour marking in both cases represents the third tank of the 1st platoon, 1st company of a tank battalion.

13 Lehký Tank LT-35 (Panzerkampfwagen 35(t)), Czechoslovakia.

The Czechoslovak arms industry was one of the strongest in Europe in March 1939 when Czechoslovakia was annexed by Germany. The tanks in particular that were built or being made for the Czechoslovak forces or for export were an extremely useful accession to the new German armoured divisions then being formed.

There were three main centres of tank production in Czechoslovakia: the famous Skoda works at Pilsen; Ceskomoravska-Kolben-Danek (CKD —builders of Praga lorries) at Prague; and Adamov in the Brno region. All three concerns were, however, linked in the exchange of designs and in the sharing of production orders.

The LT-35 was one of the two principal Czechoslovak tank designs when Germany took control of the country. It was a 10-ton tank developed by Skoda from an earlier and lighter model, P.II, apparently originated by CKD, which had been adopted for production by the Czechoslovak army as Lehký Tank (light tank) LT-34. Skoda gave the works designation of S.IIa to the LT.35, which differed from the LT-34 mainly in having thicker armour and a more powerful engine of 120 h.p.—nearly double that of its predecessor. One of its principal features was its relatively simple, rugged design in which more attention than usual was given to ease of operation. A twelve-speed gearbox combined with a pneumatic-servo-mechanical steering unit made the vehicle easy to drive and the suspension, consisting of two four-road-wheel bogie units each side—each unit sprung on a single leaf spring—was exceptionally hard-wearing. An uninterrupted compartment for the four-man crew was achieved by adopting a rear sprocket drive combined with a rear-

engine layout. The armament—common to most of the Czech tanks of this period—consisted of a 37-mm. gun (in this case the Skoda A.3) with a coaxial 7·92-mm. machine-gun which could, if required, be elevated independently. There was a second machine-gun in the hull front.

About 160 LT-35s were built for the Czechoslovak Army and these were taken over by the German Army in 1939. The 6th Panzer Division received 106 of these tanks and these formed the greater part of its equipment for the campaign in the West in May 1940. The LT-35 had not achieved anything like the commercial success of the LT-38 and also was less popular with the Germans than that tank. Production was not continued under German control and after front-line service in the Western campaign, it was phased out of service as a battle tank, although the chassis continued to be used as mortar-carriers or tractors.

The coloured illustrations show a LT-35 in 1939 Czechoslovak Army markings and a PzKpfw 35(t) (as the LT-35 was designated by the German Army) of the 6th Panzer Division in 1940.

14 Char Léger, Vickers-Carden-Loyd, Modèle T.15, Belgium.

Belgium relied mainly on French and British equipment for her small mechanised force and several different types of light tracked vehicle were purchased from Vickers-Armstrongs Ltd in the years leading up to the Second World War.

These British vehicles included versions of the Carden-Loyd Mark VI, both as an anti-tank gun tractor and as a self-propelled mounting for a 47-mm. gun, two other types of armoured tractor mounted with 47-mm. guns (known as Canons Automoteurs, T.13 Type 1 and Type III), and some light tanks.

The military vehicles offered for sale commercially by Vickers-Armstrong had, by arrangement with the War Office, to be of different design to those supplied to the British Army. However, the Vickers-Carden-Loyd light tank, 1934 model, purchased by Belgium, had many features in common with the Light Tanks, Marks II, III and IV, of the British Army.

The main features of the Vickers-Carden-Loyd 1934 model were a two-man crew, with engine mounted at the right-hand side of the hull and the turret at the left. The suspension was of the Horstmann type with two two-wheel bogey units each side, controlled by coil springs; front drive sprockets and rear idler wheels. The engine was a Meadows six-cylinder in-line unit of about 90 h.p., used with a five-speed gear-box.

The armament of the Belgian Vickers-Carden-Loyds, which had special turrets, was fitted after delivery and consisted of a 13·2-mm. Hotchkiss long-barrelled heavy machine-gun.

Forty-two machines of this type were delivered to the Belgian Army by the end of 1935. A batch of similar vehicles to the T.15 (the Vickers-Carden-Loyd 1936 model, with one or two machine-guns) was supplied to the Dutch East Indies Army and others were to have been sold to the Dutch Home Army. The latter were, however, retained in Britain in 1940 and used in the defence of the United Kingdom. An improved model, the so-called Vickers-Carden-Loyd Command Tank with a three-man crew and equipped with a 40-mm. gun, was to have been produced under licence in Belgium, but none had been built there by 1940.

15 Panzerkampfwagen I, Ausf. B, Germany.

Over 500 of these light tanks and of the earlier model PzKpfw IA took part in the campaign in the West in 1940. Before this they had taken an even more prominent part in the Polish campaign. However, it had never been the intention of the German High Command, when these light-machine-gun-armed tanks were put into production, to employ them in major campaigns in this way.

When the expansion and re-equipment of the Reichswehr was decided on in 1932 the main need, initially, was for a supply of tanks that could be built cheaply and issued to the troops for training. For this purpose the firms of Krupp, MAN, Rheinmetall, Henschel and Daimler-Benz were asked to submit prototypes on the lines of the British Vickers-Carden-Loyd light tanks that, by then, had reached a fairly satisfactory state of mechanical development. The Krupp design known as L.K.A.1 was selected as the first production model in 1934, eventually becoming known as, PzKpfw IA. A second prototype, L.K.B.1, in which a more powerful engine (a Maybach Krupp air-cooled model) replaced the original Krupp air-cooled type, was also put into production as PzKpfw I, Ausf. B.

The earliest versions to appear of both these models had open-top hulls and no turrets. This, and the designation—landwirtschaftliche Schlepper (La.S.) (agricultural tractor)—was intended to disguise their true purpose, although in this form they were still entirely suitable for driver training and tactical exercises.

The layout of both the A and the B models was the same—a rear-mounted engine with the transmission led forward to front driving sprockets. The crew compartment was in the centre of the vehicle, with the driver at the left. The turret, mounting two machine-guns, was off-set to the right on the roof of the hull. In the suspension the front road wheel was sprung independently on a coil spring and the remaining wheels in pairs on leaf springs linked by a girder for extra rigidity. In the PzKpfw IB an extra road wheel was added each side to carry the lengthened hull made necessary by the larger engine.

Production of the PzKpfw IA was limited to about 500, but nearly 2,000 of the IB, which was the much more important model, were built. In 1936 both types were tried out in combat in the Spanish Civil War when the shortcomings of a two-man crew and the lack of an anti-tank gun were brought out. By 1939 tanks of more powerful type had not been built to replace them, and for this reason they had to be used both in Poland and the following year in France. A few were still in service even in the campaign in Russia in 1941.

16 Char Léger F.C.M.36, France.

Built by Forges et Chantiers de la Mediterrannée in conjunction with Automobiles M. Berliet (which provided the engine) the FCM 36 came into production in 1936 to help increase the supply of tanks for the French infantry-support units. As such, it was a tank in the same broad specification as the more widely known Renault R.35, but the FCM 36 had some unusual features for French tanks of its time and some of these were in advance of developments elsewhere.

Of fairly conventional general layout, the FCM 36 had the engine at the rear, driving rear sprockets, but it was uncommon in that this was a diesel (of Ricardo design and built by Berliet under licence). Only two other French tanks produced around this time (the AMX 38 and B1 ter) shared this feature, which gave the FCM 36 a range of 200 miles—double that of most of its contemporaries in the French Army.

The armour protection was to the 40-mm. maximum standard required of French infantry tanks of this period, but another rare feature for the time was that for both hull and turret welded construction was used—an achievement which anticipated the method of welding armour plate in the United Kingdom, for example, by several years. The angles of the armour plate were (except for the suspension skirting plates) well thought out and the flat surfaces were able to offer the same sort of protection as the rounded cast armour that was used in most other French infantry tanks. The armament was one 37-mm. gun and one 7·5-mm. machine-gun.

Only 100 FMC 36s were built and this number, allowing for reserves, was sufficient for the equipment of two units—4^e and 7^e Bataillons de Chars de Combat.

17 Light Tank 7TP, Poland.

About forty Vickers-Armstrongs 6-ton tanks were purchased from England between 1932 and 1934. These tanks were widely popular in the 1930s and they were sold to many countries at this time. They were of a straight-forward but effective design and it was decided to build them in Poland in a slightly modified form, which became known as 7TP.

The Vickers-Armstrongs tanks appeared in two versions, one with two turrets armed with two machine-guns, and the other with a single turret mounting a gun and a single machine-gun. The 7TP also appeared in two versions at first, but the later production models, incorporating improvements, were built only in the single-turret version. The final model, in production up to 1939, is shown in the illustrations. This type had the normal Vickers suspension but incorporated a special Polish turret (built in Sweden) with a 37-mm. gun and a coaxial machine-gun. The general appearance was much the same as the Vickers-built tanks, but a 110-h.p. Saurer-designed diesel engine was used in place of the 80-h.p. air-cooled petrol engines of the former. This helped to maintain a similar performance to that of the earlier tanks although the armour had, in the final Polish model, been increased to a maximum of 40 mm. on the hull and 30 mm. on the turret.

Approximately 170 7TPs of all types were built (in addition to the Vickers tanks bought from England) and they formed the backbone of the Polish armoured forces in September 1939. Somewhat old-fashioned compared with the German tanks against which they were opposed, the 7TPs were nevertheless better in armament than the PzKpfw Is and IIs which formed the bulk of the German armour.

18 Medium Tank 10TP, Poland.

This interesting tank, which existed only in prototype form, was a Polish version of the Christie model 1931 medium tank. Five vehicles of this type were ordered from J. Walter Christie for the United States Army together with two for the Polish Government. Two further chassis, together with the manufacturing licence, were sold to the U.S.S.R. and these formed the basis of the BT ('fast tank') series which was eventually developed into the T-34.

The Polish Government defaulted on their order for the two Christie tanks and these vehicles were, accordingly, delivered to the U.S. Army where they were designated Medium Tanks T.3E1. However, the knowledge gained by the Poles from examination of Christie's prototypes and specifications was put to good use, because a prototype tank was built in 1936–7 which closely resembled the T3.E1.

The main characteristics of the Christie design were high speed, attained by means of a high power/weight ratio and an effective suspension system, and the ability to run on wheels as well as tracks. These features were reproduced in the 10TP, the Polish version, in which the engine was a German twelve-cylinder Maybach of 300 h.p., giving a reported speed of 31 m.p.h. on tracks and 47 m.p.h. on wheels.

The suspension was of the normal Christie type with four large road wheels each side, each wheel independently sprung on a leading or trailing arm, controlled by a long coil spring, all the springs being contained between the inner and outer skins of the side armour. For running on wheels, the tracks were removed and the second pair of road wheels was raised. The front pair of road wheels was steerable and the transmission was transferred from the rear drive sprockets to the rear road wheels.

The armament of the 10TP prototype consisted of a 37-mm. gun and a coaxial machine-gun in a turret which was identical to that of the contemporary version of the 7TP—a light tank already in service with the Polish Army. In addition there was a second machine-gun in the front of the hull. Armour was on a maximum of 20 mm. for the hull and 16 mm. for the turret.

A battalion of 10TP tanks was intended to form the main fighting element in each of the Polish motorised cavalry brigades, the formation of which began in 1937. Two of these brigades were in existence on 1 September 1939, but without their 10TPs, since production of this tank had not been started, and so it never had the opportunity of being tested in action.

19 Schwere Panzerspähwagen (6-rad) SdKfz 231 and 232, Germany.

The six-wheeled German armoured cars in service in 1939–40 and used in the campaigns in Poland and the West were the product of experiments begun ten years earlier with standard six-wheeled lorry chassis.

In the late twenties, the most effective way of obtaining a reasonable cross-country performance without excessive cost was to use a six-wheeled lorry with drive transmitted to all four rear wheels. The commercial vehicle manufacturers of Daimler-Benz, Büssing and C. D. Magirus all made available chassis of this type and, with some modifications, including duplicate steering controls at the rear, all three types were produced as armoured cars. The armoured hulls in the first vehicles of the three makes differed from each other but eventually a standardised form was developed with only slight modifications (such as the bonnet length and form of radiator protection) for each chassis manufacturer. The armoured hulls were supplied by Deutsche Edelstahl of Hanover and Deutsche Werke of Kiel and were ballistically much in advance of those of most British armoured cars of the period.

The chassis were conventional with front-mounted engine and drive transmitted to the rear bogie (all the rear wheels were dual): suspension was by means of longitudinal leaf springs. The engines were petrol units of between 65 and 70 h.p.: six-cylinder in the case of the Daimler-Benz and Magirus and four-cylinder for the Büssing.

One disadvantage of six-wheeled chassis of this kind with a relatively long wheel-base was that the underside of the body between the front and rear wheels was liable to ground when going across rough country. To counter this tendency, the Magirus models (which were the last in production) had a roller added midway between the front wheels and the leading pair of rear wheels.

Sufficient of these cars were produced to re-equip the German Army and they performed useful service in pre-war training and exercises and even in the campaigns of 1939–40. Their deficiencies in performance were well realised, however, and from about 1938 onwards they were progressively replaced by their eight-wheeled counterparts.

The six-wheeled armoured cars were built in three versions: SdKfz 231—the normal gun car, armed with one 2-cm. gun and one machine-gun; SdKfz 232—similar to SdKfz 231, but with the addition of a frame wireless aerial; SdKfz 263 Panzerfunkwagen—a command vehicle with a non-rotating turret with one machine-gun only and having a crew increased to five men instead of four.

20 Panzerkampfwagen II, Ausf. c, Germany.

The plans for the re-equipment of the Reichswehr were based on medium tanks armed with shell-firing guns. These were expensive and took longer to produce than light tanks, however, and it was decided to build a 10-ton tank as an interim measure to supplement the 6-ton PzKpfw I models. An upward step was the 2-cm. cannon included in the armament specification and the command position was considerably improved by the addition of a third man to the crew.

Prototype vehicles to the new specification were completed by MAN, Henschel and Krupp—in 1934—and of these the MAN version was chosen for production. The first model of this appeared in 1935 as PzKpfw II, Ausf. a1, followed in small numbers by Ausf. a2, a3 and b which had successive improvements in engine cooling and suspension. All these earlier models had a suspension system somewhat similar to that of PzKpfw I. In the next model, Ausf. c, an entirely different form of suspension was introduced and this, together with the more powerful 6·2-litre engine (used first in Ausf. b), gave this model a far better performance than its predecessors and created the basis of the design for most of its successors.

The Ausf. c., like the earlier models, had a rear-mounted engine and transmission through driving sprockets at the front, but the suspension consisted of five medium-sized road wheels each side, each sprung independently on leaf springs.

The PzKpfw II was employed in Poland in 1939 and in France in 1940, when the Ausf. c formed an important element. Nine hundred and fifty-five PzKpfw IIs were in service at the beginning of the Western Campaign. They could be said in one sense to have formed the backbone of panzer troops because they represented the highest number of any one type out of the 2,500 German tanks used.

21 BA-32 (Armoured Car), U.S.S.R.

The only heavy armoured car to be employed by the U.S.S.R. in the Second World War, the BA-32 was a direct successor—and easily recognisable as such—to the BA-10 which first went into mass production in 1930. Very typical of their era (armoured cars of similar type were built in Britain, Germany and the U.S.A.), the BA-10 and BA-32 were built on GAZ six-wheeled lorry chassis, the GAZ being a Russian version of a Ford design. The use of a normal front-engined chassis of this kind largely dictated the armoured car layout, so that the driver was behind the engine, with a co-driver's machine-gun position beside him, and the turret was located over the rear wheels. The turrets used in this BA-10/BA-32 series were those of contemporary tanks and the armament ranged from a 37-mm. gun and coaxial machine-gun, in early versions, to the 45-mm. gun and machine-gun in the version (BA-32-2) shown in the illustrations. The armoured hull was of riveted construction in the early versions, but welding later came increasingly into use and in the final version the hull sides were more sloping and the roof at the rear was lowered, together with the turret, so that the 45-mm. gun only just cleared the part of the hull over the driver's head.

To improve its performance over snow or soft ground the rear wheels of the BA-32 could be fitted with tracks, as shown in one of the illustrations.

22 Tank, Vickers 6-ton (T-26E), Finland.

Finland was among the many countries that tested various models of Vickers and Vickers-Carden-Loyd tanks offered for sale commercially by Vickers-Armstrongs Ltd. in the 1930s. This led to an order for sixteen Vickers 6-ton tanks which were delivered in 1938,

followed by a further sixteen in 1939.

These tanks, powered by a four-cylinder 90-h.p. Armstrong Siddeley engine, were of the single-turret variation known as 'Alternative B' to the manufacturers. The standard armament was a 47-mm. gun. However, a proportion of those used by the Finns had machine-guns only and others were fitted in 1939 with a special mounting for the French Puteaux 37-mm. gun, of the type used in the old Renault FT tanks acquired by the Finns in 1919. One 6-ton tank was modified in 1940 to receive a Swedish Bofors 37-mm. gun and mounting of the pattern found in some models of the Swedish Landsverk six-wheeled armoured car, one of which had been bought by Finland in 1939. These three variants of the Vickers 6-ton tank were unique and used only by the Finns.

During the Russo-Finnish war in 1939–40 and again in 1941 quantities of Russian tanks were captured and taken into service with the Finnish Army. The most numerous of these were T-26s, the Russian-built version of the Vickers 6-ton tank. The Russian tanks, apart from their armament, were almost unchanged in design and were readily absorbed into new Finnish tank units. Eventually, the original Vickers 6-ton tanks from England were designated T-26E by the Finns.

23 BT-7 ('Fast Tank'), U.S.S.R.

The most important Soviet tank numerically in 1939, the BT-7 was the last in a series developed from an almost exact copy of the American Christie M-1931 tank.

Two Christie tanks were imported

from the United States in 1931 and given searching tests in the U.S.S.R. which were obviously satisfactory, because they were followed by the manufacture, in a remarkably short time, of the first vehicles built under licence. They were adapted slightly and simplified to meet Soviet production requirements but even the power plant—a Liberty V twelve-cylinder modified aero engine—was built in the U.S.S.R. After use in service, the series was developed through a number of models (not all of which went beyond the drawing board or prototype vehicles) up to the BT-7, which first went into production in 1935. The type had the special Russian classification of Bystrochodnij Tank ('Fast Tank').

Although superior to earlier models in engine power, armour and armament, the BT-7 retained the salient Christie features of high speed, both on and off tracks, and good cross-country running ability. These characteristics were due mainly to the high power/weight ratio of over 30 h.p./ton and the Christie suspension system, consisting of four large-diameter road wheels each side, independently mounted at the end of leading or trailing swing arms, controlled by long coil springs. The springs were mounted between the inner and outer hull side plates. Transmission from the engine mounted at the rear was to track-drive sprockets at the back. When the tracks were removed and the tank converted to run on wheels (a process which took about half an hour) the drive was transferred from the rear sprockets to the rear road wheel on each side. In this configuration the front two road wheels were used for steering instead of the clutch and brake system employed when on tracks. On wheels, the BT-7 had a top speed of 45 m.p.h., but even on tracks the maximum was 33 m.p.h.

The BT-7 in its later standardised form had armament consisting of a 45-mm. gun and a coaxial 7·62-mm. machine-gun. In some cases, there was a second machine-gun in a ball mounting in the rear of the turret, which was mainly of welded construction. Earlier models, however (like the BT-7-1, shown on wheels in one of the illustrations), retained the older cylindrical riveted turret of the BT-5. The original Liberty engine had, in the BT-7, been replaced by a 450-h.p. twelve-cylinder V-type of different design.

Still in service in large numbers at the time of the German invasion in 1941, tanks of the BT series were by then too lightly armoured and were as soon as possible replaced by T-34s, a type which owed a great deal to them.

24 STZ 3 Komsomolets (Armoured Tractor), U.S.S.R.

The Russians were one of the few countries to produce and put into service before the Second World War a similar type of vehicle to the British tracked carrier series. Although intended primarily as an artillery tractor, the STZ Komsomolets, or STZ-3 most closely resembled the configuration of the British Cavalry Carrier which also had an armoured driver's and machine-gunner's compartment at the front and longitudinal outward-facing seats at the rear for the crew, unprotected by armour. An overhead frame sometimes fitted in the STZ served both as a wireless aerial and to carry a canvas roof for the rear compartment.

Weighing just over 4 tons and with a maximum speed of 25 m.p.h., the STZ was used as a tractor for anti-tank guns or light infantry howitzers, or as an ammunition carrier. First appearing in 1937 and seeing use in the Finnish campaign in 1939–40 and the opening stages of the German attack against Russia in 1941, the STZ was succeeded as a gun tractor by later tracked, semi-tracked or wheeled vehicles of both Russian and American manufacture. However, STZ chassis only slightly modified were used as a self-propelled mounting for the 57-mm. anti-tank gun and this equipment was in service as late as mid-1942.

25 **Carrier, Bren,** U.K.

The tracked armoured carrier was one of the most characteristic vehicles of the British Army in the Second World War and around 50,000 of all types were built in the United Kingdom alone by 1945, similar vehicles being also made in quantity in Canada and the U.S.A. as well as in other Commonwealth countries.

One of the earliest types of carrier to be used in the Second World War was the Carrier, Bren, but although in this particular form relatively few were built (then being replaced by the Carrier, Universal) the name Bren Carrier continued in popular usage for all types throughout the war.

Built as a larger and more sophisticated replacement for the Carden-Loyd Mark VI, the new Carrier for the transport of infantry machine guns was evolved by Vickers-Armstrongs Ltd. from their series of Light Dragon artillery tractors. The prototype Carrier, M.G., for the Vickers 0·303-in. machine-gun, appeared in 1935 and, after trials, a pilot batch was ordered in 1936, followed in the same year by a first larger production contract. Further contracts were awarded in 1937 and the later vehicles of some of these orders were completed as Carriers, Bren, in which the mounting was adapted for the new 0·303-in. Bren light machine-gun which was just coming into service with the infantry.

The most interesting feature of the Bren Carrier (and all other carriers of the same mechanical design) was the steering system. This was operated by a steering wheel (with the consequent advantage of simplification of driver training during the expansion of the Army). When the steering wheel was turned, the front two-wheel suspension units on each side were moved laterally, being mounted on a cross-tube which ran through the vehicle. This bowed the tracks into a curve, which the vehicle followed. Further movement of the steering wheel operated track brakes on either side, causing a skid turn.

The suspension consisted, each side, of two road wheels in one Horstmann-type bogie unit, sprung on a pair of oblique coil springs, and a single wheel unit of generally similar type. The idler wheel was at the front. Power was provided by a 65-h.p. Ford V-8 engine in the first vehicles, although later 85-h.p. Canadian or U.S.-built engines were also used.

The crew of the Carrier, Bren, consisted of three men, the driver at the right and the gunner beside him at the left with an extension of the armour in front of him to facilitate operation of the Bren gun when mounted in the vehicle (normally it was intended that the gun should be operated from the ground in normal infantry fashion). The third man sat behind the gunner in a separate compartment and the armour was extended rearwards on this side to protect him. The maximum armour thickness of the Carrier was 12 mm.

Bren Carriers were used in all the campaigns of the British Army in the earlier years of the Second World War, before being replaced by Carriers, Universal.

One illustration shows a Carrier, Bren, No. 2, Mark II (the No. 2 indicates a U.S.-built engine, the Mark number indicating slight changes in the hull), from above in colours used in France in 1940. The other view is of a Carrier belonging to the 2nd Battalion The Cameronians, of the 4th Indian Division in the Middle East in 1940.

26 Carrier, Cavalry, Mark I and Carrier, Scout, Mark I, U.K.

The Carrier, Cavalry, was conceived as a vehicle for mechanised cavalry in a new role in which the troopers could be carried forward with their weapons, dismount rapidly and go into action. The chassis that was already in production as a M.G. Carrier was selected for conversion for this function. The front part of the armoured hull, including the gunner's compartment and gun-mounting, was retained, only slightly modified. At the rear, however, longitudinal seats were provided each side for the cavalrymen. There was also a curved guard over the tracks to protect the men's legs, a folding handrail each side and provision for an overhead canvas hood. There was no armour protection for the passengers at the rear. Only fifty Cavalry Carriers were built (by Nuffield Mechanisations Ltd) and although some were taken to France by the British Expeditionary Force and employed as personnel carriers, the role for which they were designed was by then realised to be impractical in modern warfare.

The Scout Carrier also was designed as a vehicle principally for the cavalry, although in this case it was anticipated that the weapons carried would be used from the vehicle to a greater extent, and all-round protection was provided for all the crew. Again, the basic M.G. or Bren Carrier chassis was adapted, the front being almost identical except that the gunner's compartment was intended for the mounting of a 0·55-in. Boys anti-tank rifle. The third man of the crew was situated at the right-hand side, behind the driver, and in his compartment was carried a 0·303-in. Bren machine-gun on a mounting suitable for use against air or ground targets. To complete the armament, a 3-in. smoke discharger (similar to that carried on the light tanks with which these carriers often operated) was mounted on the right-hand side of the hull. A No. 2 wireless set was carried at the back of the rear compartment in some vehicles. Six hundred and sixty-seven Scout Carriers were built and used by the divisional cavalry regiments of infantry divisions in 1939–40 and also by motor battalions of armoured divisions in both Europe and the Middle East.

The illustration of a Carrier, Scout, Mark I, shows a vehicle belonging to the 13th/18th Royal Hussars, the divisional cavalry regiment of the 1st Infantry Division with the British Expeditionary Force in France. The view of a Cavalry Carrier shows the framework for the canvas roof in position.

27 Armoured Car, Reconnaissance, Morris (Model CS9/LAC), U.K.

Built on a modified Morris Commercial 15-cwt 4 × 2 truck chassis, this armoured car was, in effect, a stop-gap design to replace older six-wheeled armoured cars pending the development of new four-wheel-drive chassis.

After the prototype was tested in 1936, a further ninety-nine vehicles with slight modifications were ordered and these were delivered about 1938. Thirty-eight cars of this kind were taken to France by the 12th Royal Lancers, the only armoured car regiment with the British Expeditionary Force, and later, thirty were issued to the 11th Hussars in Egypt, by whom they were used in conjunction with some 1920 and 1924 pattern Rolls-Royce armoured cars, rearmed. A high performance cross-country was not expected of vehicles with conventional 4 × 2 transmission, but the 11th Hussars found that the Morris armoured cars (which were fitted with desert tyres) traversed soft sand better than the Rolls-Royce, though the springs and steering did not stand up so well.

The Morris CS9/LAC had a six-cylinder engine of 96·2 h.p., which gave it a top speed of 45 m.p.h. The armament consisted of a 0·55-in. Boys anti-tank rifle and a 0·303-in. Bren light machine-gun mounted independently in an open-topped turret. The crew consisted of four men—commander, gunner, driver and wireless operator (who sat beside the driver).

The 12th Royal Lancers' cars did useful work in protecting the flank of the British Expeditionary Force before the evacuation from Dunkirk, when they were left behind in France. The 11th Hussars used their Morris armoured cars in North Africa up to the Spring of 1941, although by this time some had been converted into light armoured command vehicles.

The illustrations show a car ('Cowes') of C Squadron, the 12th Royal Lancers and a car of the 11th Hussars as it appeared in the Western Desert campaign.

28 Schwerer Panzerspähwagen (8-rad) SdKfz 231, and 232, Germany.

The six-wheeled armoured cars produced in the 1930s for the German Army were accepted only for their relative cheapness as a means of speeding rearmament. When the time came to consider replacements for them, however, it was natural to turn for inspiration to the very advanced experimental multi-wheeled armoured cars which had preceded the six-wheelers.

The new eight-wheeled armoured car series was developed, commencing in 1935, by the Büssing-NAG firm which had built a ten-wheeled prototype in 1929. Büssing had also, of course, produced a proportion of the chassis for the six-wheeled armoured cars and these had provided a useful fund of knowledge of operational requirements.

A rear-engined layout with transmission to all eight wheels, all of which steered, was adopted for the new armoured car chassis. This made for a highly complicated transmission and steering linkage arrangement, but produced a cross-country performance as good as that of a tracked vehicle and, for an armoured car of this size (about 19 ft long), fairly good manoeuvrability. A second driver's position, with controls, was provided at the rear. The suspension consisted of a pair of longitudinal leaf springs for each 'bogie' unit of four wheels.

The armoured hull of the SdKfz 231 (8-rad) was of very similar shape (although turned round) to that of the six-wheeled armoured cars, which had proved to be of a satisfactory ballistic design. The turret was also much the same in general appearance, although the face was cleaned up and the machine-gun was transferred to the left of the 2-cm. gun. The corresponding wireless-equipped version, SdKfz 232, employed a generally similar, although simplified, frame aerial to that of the wireless six-wheeler. Only in the third basic model, the SdKfz 263 (8-rad) command vehicle, was there a wider departure from previous practice, in that the turret was dispensed with completely and the crew compartment enlarged and extended in height to accommodate five men, including a formation commander and members of his staff.

For their size the eight-wheelers of the SdKfz 231 series were only lightly armoured and armed, the emphasis being on mobility. The armour plate thicknesses were, in fact, no more than comparable with those of the German light 4×4 armoured cars, although an

extra spaced plate at the front was added in some cases to the eight-wheelers.

The SdKfz 231 and 232 eight-wheelers were first delivered to the troops in 1938 and so some were in service in the Polish Campaign the following year (one of these, of an SS unit, is shown in one illustration) and in greater numbers in the Western Campaign. As the war progressed they replaced entirely the six-wheelers in front-line units.

29 Schwerer geländegängiger gepanzerter Personenkraftwagen, SdKfz 247, Germany.

Bearing the cumbersome designation of 'heavy cross-country armoured personnel car' (sch. gl. gp. Pkw.), this type of vehicle was an armoured staff car for very senior officers and was, accordingly, produced only in very limited numbers.

The original version was built in 1937–8 on the Krupp 6 × 4 chassis, type L2H143, which had a four-cylinder engine of about 60 h.p. with a four-speed gearbox. About twenty were made and these were supplemented in 1939 by a similar number of vehicles built on the Horch 'standard chassis II for heavy passenger cars'. This chassis was used for a variety of unarmoured military vehicles and was similar in many respects to that used for the four-wheeled armoured cars of the SdKfz 221–223 series except that the engine was mounted at the front instead of the rear. The eight-cylinder engine was rated at about 80 h.p. and was used with a five-speed gearbox. Transmission was on all four wheels.

The armoured bodies for both six-wheeled and four-wheeled cars were similar in design and of roughly the same overall dimensions and they accommodated six men, including the driver. The armoured protection was on an 8-mm. basis.

30 **Panzerkampfwagen 38(t) (LT-38)**, Czechoslovakia.

One of the most successful products of the pre-Second World War Czechoslovak armaments industry, the LT-38 or closely similar versions of it were sold to over half a dozen different countries.

The design of the LT-38 originated with Ceskomoravska-Kolben-Danek of Prague in 1933 with a model known as LTL. This model was progressively improved and in 1938 150 of the current version, TNHP, were ordered for the Czechoslovak Army. In the meantime, different variants of the design had been sold to a number of countries and export orders, including those for the TNHP, eventually totalled nearly 200, a not inconsiderable number for peacetime sales. The tank was purchased mostly by smaller countries as wide apart as Peru and Sweden.

Exports ceased when Germany annexed Czechoslovakia in March 1939, although Sweden was permitted to build them under licence. One TNHP was sold to the United Kingdom and tested by the Mechanical Warfare Experimental Establishment in 1939. Their report was mildly favourable but the tank was regarded as cramped and uncomfortable for the crew. The German Army, on the other hand, considered the LT-38 to be a good tank and were extremely glad to be able to

take over all the existing stocks, both of the Czechoslovak Army and those intended for export. Production was continued and increased under German control and LT-38s, redesignated PzKpfw 38(t), were soon issued to the 7th Panzer Division (commanded by Rommel) and 8th Panzer Division, both formed in October 1939. Two hundred and twenty-eight PzKpfw 38(t)s (most of them in 7th and 8th Panzer Divisions) were available at the opening of the campaign in the West in May 1940, but by 1941 this type of tank formed about 25% of the total tank strength of the Wehrmacht.

The LT-38 was built to a layout that has since become fairly commonplace but was by no means so widespread when its design commenced in 1933. The engine (a Praga six-cylinder type) was in a compartment at the rear with the transmission carried forward through the crew compartment to the pre-selection five-speed gearbox near the front of the vehicle. In front of the gearbox was the cross shaft incorporating the steering clutches carrying the drive to the tracks via front sprockets. The suspension appeared externally to be of the Christie type but was in fact of the semi-elliptic leaf spring variety, one spring controlling a pair of road wheels each side.

The turret, mounted on the roof of the fighting compartment, was centrally placed and carried a 37-mm. gun (Skoda model A7) and a 7·92-mm. machine-gun. Another machine-gun was mounted in the front of the hull at the left-hand side, next to the driver who could, if necessary, fire this weapon by means of a Bowden cable connected to one of the steering levers.

Good general features of the LT-38 were its sturdiness, reliability and ease of maintenance. The Germans felt it worth keeping in production (with some improvements) until 1942, when 1,168 had been produced. Although by then outclassed as a gun-tank, the chassis continued to be produced for various German self-propelled mountings until the end of the war. The tanks sold abroad or produced under licence continued in service until well after the war in some countries.

Both illustrations show PzKpfw 38(t)s in German service.

31 Porte-Pont, Somua-Coder MSCL-5, France.

This interesting vehicle was designed not long before the outbreak of the Second World War by the Société Coder de Marseille to provide a quick means of placing a bridge under fire over small rivers or similar obstacles. The bridge was about 27 ft long and could take light and medium tanks up to around 22 tons.

The bridge was carried upside down over the top of the carrying vehicle and pivoted at the rear. When laying the bridge, the vehicle was backed up to the edge of the river and the bridge raised by a hydraulic ram. As the bridge moved through the beginning of its arc of about 180 degrees, its weight was taken by two quadrant-shaped supports which moved down into contact with the ground. When the bridge had completed its arc and was resting on the other side of the river it was released from the carrying vehicle.

The whole process could be carried out by the crew under cover, the carrying vehicle, a Somua half-track, being fully protected with bullet-proof plate.

32 T-28C (Medium Tank), U.S.S.R.

Believed to have been inspired by contemporary British and German designs (the A.6 Medium and the so-called 'Gross traktor' series, respectively) the T-28 was the first Russian-built medium tank to be accepted for service with the Red Army.

Designed at the Kirov Plant at Leningrad, the first prototype of the T-28 was tested during 1932. After modifications this model was put into production. Development was continued through several models and manufacture was continued until 1939 with the final standard model, T-28C, which is shown in the illustrations.

The T-28C shared the same layout and characteristics of the earlier models, but a newer, more powerful version of the 76·2-mm. main gun (of calibre L/26) was used. Also included in the main turret was a machine-gun in a ball mounting. The two auxiliary turrets, one either side of the driver, had one machine-gun each so that in the frontal assaults for which the T-28 was intended, a bewildering volume of fire could be maintained. The frontal armour of the T-28C was likewise improved, to a maximum of 80 mm., although it is likely that this was of limited distribution.

The driver's and fighting compartments of the T-28 (occupied by the crew of six) were in the front half of the tank and the engine compartment was at the rear, the transmission being to rear drive sprockets. The engine used was the M-17L (a Russian version of the American Liberty aero engine) twelve-cylinder V of 500 h.p.: this gave a top speed of about 20 m.p.h.

Although the specification of the T-28 does not appear bad on paper, the design was found to be inadequate even in the Finnish campaign and when in 1941 these tanks came up against German armour their tall silhouette (with auxiliary turrets which were virtually useless in open warfare) and relatively thin rear and side armour made them easy victims.

33 T-35 (**Heavy Tank**), U.S.S.R.

This imposing but thinly-armoured heavy tank was one of the last manifestations of the fashion set by the British A1.E1 'Independent' tank of 1926.

The idea behind the A1.E1 was that by providing the tank with a multiplicity of turrets, so that fire could be brought to bear on all sides at once, combined with mobility, independent missions could be undertaken without support by other arms. Although Russian tactical ideas may not necessarily have coincided with those of the British, a Soviet tank on the same theme as the A1.E1 (which was experimental only) was put into service about 1931. This was the T-32 and it was followed in 1933 by the T-35, which continued in production until 1939, although a total of only twenty to thirty was built.

Like its British progenitor, the T-35 had five turrets; a large turret mounting the main armament and four subsidiary turrets grouped round it. The main turret mounted a 76·2-mm gun. and one machine-gun in a ball mounting in the turret face; two of the

auxiliary turrets (the front right and rear left) mounted 45-mm. guns and the other two small turrets had one machine-gun each. Early versions of the tank had 37-mm. guns instead of 45-mm. and there were various modifications to the armament (sometimes involving the removal of the two machine-gun turrets) in the later years of the T-35's existence. Armour protection was to a front hull maximum of 30 mm. on early models and 35 mm. on later versions.

Powered by a 500-h.p. twelve-cylinder V model M-17 M engine situated in the rear half of the hull, the 45-ton T-35 had a maximum road speed of 18 m.p.h. The cross-country speed was given as 12 m.p.h. and it is likely that, because of its length (32 ft), this could be maintained by the T-35 better than most of its contemporaries. The clutch and brake steering system was said to have been unsatisfactory, however.

Tanks of this type were used in the 1939 Finnish campaign, where they were not very successful, and a number were also intended for use against the Germans in Poland in 1941 where, however, they ran out of fuel before being engaged.

The illustrations show the second model of the T-35, fitted with a frame wireless aerial on the turret.

34 **Pansarbil m/39-40,** Sweden.

Known by its manufacturers as the Landsverk Lynx, this armoured car was of advanced conception when it first appeared in 1938 and it still appears modern more than thirty years later.

A vehicle of nearly symmetrical profile, the Lynx was armed with a 20-mm. gun and a coaxial 8-mm. air-cooled machine-gun in the turret and two further 8-mm. machine-guns in the front and the rear of the hull respectively. The car had the large crew of six men, three of them gunners.

The engine of the Landsverk Lynx was a six-cylinder Volvo of 135 h.p. which gave a top speed of 44 m.p.h. Transmission was to all four wheels, which on early vehicles, like some previous Landsverk armoured cars, were of resilient rubber but not pneumatic. However, later cars had pneumatic tyres.

35 Stridsvagn m/39, Sweden.

The Swedish armaments industry is probably better known for its artillery than for its armoured fighting vehicles. There has, nevertheless, been a history of the steady development of tanks and armoured cars dating back to 1921 and in this work the AB Landsverk concern has taken a leading part.

A version of the German L.K. I light tank of the First World War was built in Sweden in 1921 and its designer, Josef Vollmer, subsequently designed the Landsverk 10 which was the first of a new series of light and medium tanks which, with successive improvements, continued in production well into the Second World War. Some of these were sold abroad and others were used at home by the Swedish Army.

The latest of this Landsverk series in 1939 was the Landsverk L-60D, a 9-ton tank armed with a 37-mm. gun which was adopted by the Swedish Army as Stridsvagn m/39. Developed from its immediate predecessor (Strv. m/38), the L-60D differed externally in that it

had the unusual armament of twin 8-mm. air-cooled machine-guns mounted in the turret coaxially with the 37-mm. gun.

The engine was a six-cylinder Scania Vabis of 142 h.p. mounted at the rear and driving front sprockets and the steering was a geared system developed from patents taken out by Landsverk in 1930/1. A torsion-bar suspension was used for the four medium-sized road wheels each side, with a trailing idler wheel of the same size at the rear.

In 1941 the Strv. m/39 was succeeded by the Strv. m/40, which was improved in that it had the conventional gearbox replaced by a hydraulic pre-selector box coupled to a low-range mechanical gearbox for cross-country work. The only external difference from the Strv. m/39 was the addition to the turret of a cupola with armoured episcopes.

36 T-26B (Light Tank), U.S.S.R.

The T-26 was the Russian-built version of the Vickers-Armstrong 6-ton Tank, fifteen of which were ordered from the United Kingdom in 1930. The original Vickers tank was available in two models, one with two turrets, side by side, and the other with a single large turret. The original T-26s built under licence were almost identical to their British-made prototypes. Both twin- and single-turret versions were manufactured in the Soviet Union, but from about 1933 onwards development of the 6-ton type of tank was concentrated on the single-turret model, in which a larger gun could be installed.

Production of the T-26 ran through

until 1939, the final standard version being the T-26S (usually known outside the U.S.S.R. as T-26C). This differed externally from earlier models in the increased use of welded armour, with sloping hull plates and a turret of more streamlined appearance than hitherto. Turrets of this later type were in some cases used to replace those of earlier pattern on earlier models of the T-26, T-26Bs with the new turret are shown in the illustrations.

Apart from this relatively minor change, the T-26 remained both in mechanical specification and general appearance very close to its prototype, the Vickers-Armstrong 6-ton tank. The engine, an Armstrong-Siddeley eight-cylinder 90-h.p., air-cooled type, built under licence, was situated at the rear, the transmission being led forwards to drive front sprockets. The gearbox (beside the driver's feet) had five forward speeds and steering was of the clutch and brake type. The suspension was of the simple robust type designed by Vickers and consisted of two groups of four bogie wheels each side, sprung on quarter-elliptic leaf springs. The crew compartment was in the centre of the vehicle with the driver at the right and the turret on the roof.

In its armament the T-26B and later Soviet models was greatly improved over the Vickers 6-ton in that the short 47-mm. gun was replaced by a long 45-mm. L/46 gun of much higher muzzle velocity. There was also a coaxial machine-gun and in some cases a second machine-gun in the turret rear.

T-26s of all models were an important factor in the building up of the tank strength of the U.S.S.R. in

the 1930s, and although mass production ceased in 1939, they were used in action against the Finns in 1939–40 and even against the Germans in 1941, although phased out of service soon afterwards.

37 **Tank, Light, M2A4,** U.S.A.

In 1939 the latest of a line of light tanks developed from 1933 onwards, the M2A4 was the first to carry a 37-mm. gun. This light tank also had the distinction of being one of the very earliest types of fighting vehicle to be supplied to Britain by the U.S.A., a small batch being shipped in 1941.

Powered by a 250-h.p. seven-cylinder Continental radial engine (a modified aero engine), giving a top speed of 37 m.p.h., armoured to a 25.4-mm. maximum and equipped with the 37-mm. gun, which was not greatly inferior to the British 2-pr as an armour-piercing weapon, the M2A4 was much better than contemporary British light tanks and comparable with some cruiser tanks. The secondary armament, in addition to the turret coaxial 0·30-in. Browning machine-gun, included two further Brownings in sponsons at either side of the driver's and co-driver's positions and another in the glacis plate. Some or all of these hull-mounted machine-guns were often removed in the tanks in British service.

The suspension consisted of two two-wheeled bogie units each side, each unit sprung on vertical volute springs. The idler wheel was at the rear, off the ground, and the drive sprocket at the front.

A total of 365 M2A4s was built. A few were used in action with U.S.

forces in the Pacific theatre in 1942. Those delivered to Britain in 1941 (only about forty or so) were used for Home Defence and training, in which role they were useful for familiarising the troops with the similar but improved M3 Light Tank.

The illustrations show an M2A4 supplied to Britain that was subscribed for by the Canadian town of Saskatoon, and an M2A4 of the U.S. 70th Armoured Regiment.

38 Scout Car, M3A1, U.S.A.

Designed as a reconnaissance vehicle for the U.S. mechanised cavalry, the M3A1 Scout Car, built by the White Motor Company, was the last in line of a series of vehicles developed from 1929 onwards. A large, open-topped armoured vehicle, with protection ranging from 6 mm. to 12 mm., the M3A1 was powered by a 110-h.p. Hercules six-cylinder engine which gave it a maximum speed of 55–60 m.p.h. Sufficient petrol was carried for a range of 250 miles and cross-country performance with four-wheel drive was fairly good: a roller mounted at the front assisted in surmounting obstacles.

Introduced into service with the U.S. Army in mid 1939, the M3A1 Scout Car was one of the first types of armoured vehicle to be supplied in 1941 by the United States to the United Kingdom. The American vehicles, although designated Scout Cars, did not correspond in size, manoeuvrability or performance to the British requirement for a scout car, although some appear temporarily to have been used as such by some units in the

United Kingdom awaiting supplies of Daimler Scout Cars. However, good use was made by the British Army of White Scout Cars, as they were usually called, as armoured personnel carriers (they carried eight men and were used chiefly in motor battalions of armoured divisions), as command vehicles and as armoured ambulances. Later the designation of Truck, 15 cwt., Personnel (White M3A1) was adopted by the War Office.

In American use, the armament usually consisted of a 0·5-in. M2 machine-gun (Browning) on a skate mounting travelling on a rail round the inside of the hull, and one or two 0·3-in. Browning machine-guns. These guns rarely seem to have been fitted in British-used vehicles in which, also, the front roller was often removed.

One illustration shows a Scout Car M3A1 of the U.S. Army; this has the canvas hood up. The other view is of a White Scout Car as used by the motor battalion (infantry) of a British armoured brigade in 1941.

39 Tanks, Light, Mark VIB and Mark VIC, U.K.

The culmination of a long series of Light Tanks stemming from the Carden-Loyd Mark VII, designed by Sir John Carden in 1928, the Light Tanks of the Mark VI series were numerically the most important armoured fighting vehicles of the British Army in 1939–40.

Designed, like its predecessors, by Vickers-Armstrongs Ltd., and also originally built by them, the Light Mark VI was one of the fighting vehicles chosen in 1935 for production by other manufacturers outside the armaments industry to familiarise them with this particular form of heavy engineering. The Mark VIB was a slightly improved version of the original Mark VI and was built in far greater quantity.

Following the pattern of its predecessors the Mark VI had the engine (an 88-h.p. six-cylinder Meadows) at the right-hand side of the hull with the transmission led forward to drive front sprockets. The driver sat at the left-hand side, and the turret, containing the commander and gunner, was also off-set to the left. The suspension consisted of two two-wheeled bogie units each side, sprung on twin coil springs, the rear road wheel acting also as a trailing idler. This form of Horstmann suspension was simple and dependable and although there was a tendency for the tracks to be shed, they could be replaced fairly easily.

The armament of the Mark VIB consisted of a Vickers 0·303-in. water-cooled machine-gun and a Vickers 0·5-in. heavy machine-gun. The Mark VIC, which followed the Mark VIB in production, was similar in almost all respects except that it lacked the turret cupola and had Besa machine-guns of 7·92 mm. and 15 mm. instead of the Vickers. In both models the maximum armour thickness was only 14 mm. and these tanks could be regarded as no more than reconnaissance vehicles. Nevertheless, Mark VIBs were employed in all the Divisional Cavalry Regiments of the British Expeditionary Force, and as headquarters tanks in the 1st Army Tank Brigade. Even in the 1st Armoured Division Light Mark VICs formed a high proportion of the tank strength because of the delay in delivery of Cruiser tanks and they were no match for most types of German tanks encountered in 1940. Mark VIBs and earlier light tanks were also employed in the earlier North African campaigns.

The illustrations show a Tank, Light Mark VIB of the 4th/7th Royal Dragoon Guards (the Divisional Cavalry Regiment of the 2nd Infantry Division, B.E.F.) and a Mark VIC of the 10th Royal Hussars, one of the tank regiments of the 2nd Armoured Brigade, 1st Armoured Division.

40 Tank, Infantry, Mark I, U.K.

Designed and built to the General Staff specification A.11 for a two-man infantry-accompanying tank, armoured against all known anti-tank guns and equipped with one machine-gun, the Infantry Mark I met all these requirements adequately. It also was relatively cheap to manufacture, another important consideration at the time.

Sir John Carden of Vickers-Armstrongs Ltd. undertook the design, and the prototype vehicle was ready by the Autumn of 1936. A small tank, the A.11 weighed 11 tons due to its heavy armour, on a 60-mm. basis. However, as only a low speed (8 m.p.h.) was required in a tank tied closely to the infantry advance it was possible to use the readily available and inexpensive Ford V-8 lorry engine and transmission. This was sited at the rear and drove rear sprockets, much of the final drive and steering systems being closely derived from other Vickers tracked vehicles. The suspension—two four-wheeled bogie units each side, sprung on semi-elliptic springs—was similar to that of the commercial Vickers 6-ton tank and Dragon, Medium Mark IV artillery tractor.

The armament of one Vickers 0·303-in. water-cooled machine-gun, mounted in the cast turret, was intended only for use against 'soft' targets, although the need for some means of attacking other armoured vehicles was subsequently recognised by substituting the Vickers 0·5-in. heavy machine-gun in some troop leaders' tanks.

An initial order placed in 1937 with Vickers-Armstrongs for sixty Infantry Mark Is was followed by another in 1938 for a further sixty and a final order in January 1939 for nineteen. These tanks were used to equip the 1st Army Tank Brigade which joined the British Expeditionary Force in France. In action, the Infantry Mark I's served their purpose quite well, within their known limitations—their armour proving to be highly effective.

The illustrations both show tanks of the 4th Battalion Royal Tank Regiment, which used an eye as its unit sign. One picture is of a tank in the 1939 plain green and the other shows a company commander's tank in France: this is one of the later production vehicles with minor changes, including the positioning of the headlamps.

41   Carro Armato M.11/39, Italy.

The principal Italian medium tank at the beginning of the Second World War, the first prototype of the Carro Armato M.11/39 was built in 1937. This tank had a suspension system scaled up from that of the L.3/35 although most of the other features of the layout of the subsequent production version were present. These were a rear-mounted engine with drive sprockets at the front; a 37-mm. gun in the front right-hand side of the hull, with the driver at the left side; and a machine-gun turret on the hull roof.

The suspension of the production model of the M.11/39 consisted of two four-wheel bogie units each side. Each group of four wheels was in two pairs, controlled by a single semi-elliptic leaf spring.

An excellent diesel engine powered this medium tank. It was an eight-cylinder model of V-form, the Spa 8T, which was rated at 105 h.p. and produced a maximum speed of 20 m.p.h.

The hull gun was a 37-mm. semi-automatic weapon based on an old Vickers design: it had only limited traverse. The turret armament was two 8-mm. Breda machine-guns in a twin mounting. Protection was at a maximum of 30 mm.

Although mechanically reliable, the M.11/39 was a poor fighting machine, with an ineffectual main armament. It was used in the campaigns in North and East Africa until about 1941, being replaced as soon as possible by the very much better M.13/40.

The illustrations show a tank in desert yellow with tactical markings representing the second tank of the second platoon of No. 2 Company of an Italian tank battalion.

42   Mittlerer Schützenpanzerwagen SdKfz 251, Germany.

Germany produced both armoured and unarmoured experimental half-track vehicles in the First World War. During the rearmament phase from 1933 onwards, however, development of this type of vehicle was, at first, concentrated on the unarmoured variety for which there was a great demand for use as artillery tractors and for other purposes.

One of the advantages of a half-track is that it is possible to have a long chassis that, in a fully tracked vehicle, might be difficult to steer. At the same time, a better general performance can usually be obtained than is possible in a full-tracked vehicle of similar dimensions. It is also usually possible to use a larger quantity of standard commercial components in a half-track than could be employed in a fully tracked vehicle.

By 1938 a wide range of half-tracked vehicles had been developed as artillery tractors, including the Borgward 3-ton model HL k/6 for towing the 10·5-cm. light field howitzer. This chassis was selected for use as a basic armoured vehicle for infantry and other troops supporting the tanks in the Panzer Divisions and Büssing-NAG were given instructions to design the armoured hull. The chassis itself needed only minor modifications, chiefly in order to reduce the height of the bonnet.

Apart from a few prototypes, all the main types of German half tracks of the Second World War had the same mechanical layout of a front engine (a six-cylinder Maybach of 100 h.p. in the case of the SdKfz 251) with transmission leading back to drive sprockets at the front of the track assembly. The front wheels were not driven and were used to support the front of the vehicle and for steering. In a gradual turn, steering was achieved by means of the front wheels only, but further application of the steering wheel automatically brought steering brakes in the track system into operation.

The whole track assembly of the German half-tracks was complicated, expensive to produce and required a lot of maintenance, although it contributed largely to the high-speed performance of the vehicle. The suspension consisted of interleaved road wheels independently sprung on transverse torsion bars. The track, which was unique to this type of German vehicle, was made up of light weight cast links bearing rubber pads on the shoes. The links were joined by needle bearings which required individual lubrication.

The open-top armoured hull in the early versions (Ausf. A and B) of SdKfz 251 (shown in the illustrations) was assembled by means of a combination of bolting and welding. Later models were all-welded and the design (notably of the front nose plate) was progressively simplified to reduce production difficulties.

A few 3-ton armoured personnel carriers (gepanzerter Mannschafts Transportwagen) were issued to the Army in time for the Campaign in Poland and by May 1940 they were in wide use for the Campaign in the West. Production continued throughout the War, during which some 16,000 in twenty-two different versions were built. Of these, the SdKfz 251/3 Funkwagen (Wireless vehicle) (shown in one illustration) was widely used by unit and formation commanders, while the standard Schützenpanzerwagen SdKfz 251/1 used by Panzergrenadiers and for a variety of other units in armoured formations was numerically the most important variant.

43 Kleiner Panzerbefehlswagen I, Germany.

The need for commanders of tank units—at least up to Battalion and Regimental level—to maintain close contact with their tanks was well understood by the leaders of the German Army armoured forces, following experience gained in exercises. Gun tanks (Pzkpfw I) were at first modified as command vehicles until a more specialised command tank was developed.

The kleiner Panzerbefehlswagen ('small armoured command vehicle') was based on the chassis and running gear of the Pzkpfw I, Ausf. B. The turret was eliminated and the crew compartment was raised in height, thus providing somewhat cramped accommodation for a crew of three, two wireless sets and a map table. An observation cupola for the commander was provided in the hull roof. The only change to the automotive specification was an increase in the capacity of the dynamo, which was required in this version to keep the wireless batteries fully charged.

One machine-gun was provided in a ball mounting in the front plate of the hull. The armour protection of the PzBefswg. was considerably increased over that of the normal gun tank version, by 17 mm. on the front plate of the crew compartment and 10 mm. on the nose plate.

The two wireless sets (models FU.2 and FU.6) enabled the unit commander on the spot to maintain contact with both sub-units and higher formation headquarters, so that effective control over the battle could be exercised. This was an important factor in the Polish Campaign when these tanks were first used. At the opening of the 1940 Campaign in the West on 10 May, ninety-six klPzBefswg. were employed—about half of the total of 200 command vehicles on PzKpfw I chassis to be built. Thirty-nine command tanks on PzKpfw II were also used at this time.

44 Panzerkampfwagen III Ausf. E and G, Germany.

A 15-ton tank armed with a 3·7-cm. or 5-cm. armour-piercing weapon was planned as the basic equipment of the Panzer Divisions. This light tank was to be supplemented by a medium tank armed with a 7·5-cm. gun: the earlier light tanks Panzer I and II armed with nothing heavier than machine-guns or a 2-cm. gun were regarded as no more than stop-gaps.

Prototypes of the 'Zugführerwagen' ('platoon commanders vehicle'—abbreviated as ZW)—the code name for the 15-ton tank—were ordered from Daimler-Benz, Rheinmetall, MAN and Krupp. These prototype vehicles were tested in 1936-7 and, as a result, the Daimler-Benz model was chosen as the basis for further development. The early models (Ausf.A, B, C and D) had varying forms of suspension (although the hull and turret were more or less standardised) ranging from five largish road wheels on coil springs per side, in the Ausf.A, to eight small wheels on leaf springs in the Ausf.B, C and D.

About eighty of these early models were made but it was not until the advent of the Ausf.E that the suspension took the familiar form that was to be continued through the rest of the production life of the PzKpfw III. This consisted of six road wheels each side on a transverse torsion-bar suspension system. The upper run of the track was carried on three rollers per side.

In the Ausf.E a more powerful Maybach twelve-cylinder engine (model HL 120 TR) was fitted—this had an output of 300 h.p., compared with the 230–250 h.p. of the earlier models. The engine was mounted at the rear of the hull and transmitted power through a hydraulic clutch and a Maybach Variorex ten-speed gearbox to the driving sprockets at the front.

The turret of the Panzer III was situated approximately in the centre of the hull and mounted the main armament of a 3·7-cm. gun. General Guderian had wanted a 5-cm. gun for the Panzer III but in order to get production under way without controversy the smaller gun of the same calibre as the standard infantry anti-tank gun was accepted. It was not, in fact, until after the French campaign that the 5-cm. gun began to be fitted to Panzer IIIs. Coaxial armament was one machine-gun (MG 34) and another was mounted in the front of the hull beside the driver.

A few PzKpfw IIIs, mainly the earliest models, but including some Ausf.Es, were used in the Polish Campaign. In May 1940, at the beginning of the campaign in the West, 349 Panzer IIIs were employed and formed the core of the attack.

Some 3,200 tanks were available at the beginning of the campaign in Russia in June 1941 and a high proportion of these were Panzer IIIs. By this time a 5-cm. gun had been introduced into the PzKpfw III by progressive replacement of the 3·7-cm. weapon in existing vehicles and as the standard equipment in new tanks produced from the latter part of 1940 onwards.

The pictures show a PzKpfw III, Ausf.E, as it appeared (with the unusual tactical number 200) in the Western Campaign and a PzKpfw III, Ausf.G, armed with a 5-cm. KwK.L/42, of the 3rd Panzer Division in Russia.

45 Panzerkampfwagen IV, Ausf.A and B, Germany.

The fourth and, as it proved, the most enduring of the main types of tank with which Germany rearmed and entered the Second World War was the Panzer IV.

This was specified as a medium tank in the 20-ton class, to be armed with a 7·5-cm. gun, capable of giving fire support to the lighter tanks armed only with armour-piercing weapons or machine-guns. The code name adopted for this type was Bataillonsführerwagen (BW for short)—'battalion commander's vehicle'.

Designs in varying forms to meet this specification were submitted by Rheinmetall-Borsig, MAN and Krupp. Some of these designs did not get off paper, but following tests with prototype vehicles in 1935–6 Krupp were awarded the order for development of the production model.

Krupp's earlier proposals for the suspension of the BW were for interleaved road wheels of the kind that were eventually to be adopted in later tanks, but the form of suspension actually used throughout the long production run of the BW, or Panzerkampfwagen IV, as it became designated, was much more simple. The eight road wheels each side were suspended in pairs on leaf springs; the idler wheel was off the ground at the rear and the top run of the track was carried on four return rollers—an easy-to-remember recognition point for the Panzer IV. As with the other main German tanks of the period, the engine was situated at the rear with the transmission led forward to final drive via sprockets at the front of the track.

The engine was the same as that used in the Panzer III (from Ausf.E onwards)—the twelve-cylinder Maybach HL 108TR. The arrangement differed from the smaller tank in that the cooling air was drawn in at the right-hand side of the hull and after passing through the radiator was expelled through grilles at the left-hand side. The power was transmitted to the drive sprockets through a dry plate clutch and gearbox which, in the Ausf.A, had five forward speeds. This was increased to six in Ausf.B and subsequent models in which also the engine was the larger Maybach HL 120 TR (HL 120 TRM from Ausf.C onwards). These mechanical changes constituted the principal differences between the first two production models of this tank. The Pzkpfw IV Ausf.A and B are shown in the pictures, but all the earlier models of the Panzer IV were very much alike externally and all (until the introduction in early 1942, in the later vehicles of Ausf.F, of the long 7·5-cm. KwK L/43) had the short-barrelled 7·5-cm. KwK L/24 as main armament. There was a coaxial machine-gun in all tanks of the series and all except Ausf.B and C also had another MG.34 in the front of the hull to the right of the driver.

The armour basis of the hull of the PzKpfw IV Ausf.A was 14·5 mm. and of the turret 20 mm. The frontal armour in the next three models, Ausf.B–D, was increased to 30 mm. Some 270 of these early models of Panzer IV were built between 1936 and 1939 and the opportunity was taken to try them out in the Polish Campaign. As a result it was decided to increase the armour thickness at the front of the hull to 60 mm. and at the sides to 40 mm., and the new model was known as Ausf.E. The design was otherwise unchanged except in minor details and 278 Panzer IVs of all models were available at the beginning of the campaign in the West in 1940. Production was stepped up in 1940 and the next year so that over 1,000 had been built by the end of 1941. In Russia, with its original armament, the Panzer IV was found to be capable of tackling the Russian T.34 only from the rear, so an emergency programme of up-gunning had to be undertaken. As a result the Panzer IV remained a useful tank even to the end of the war—a tribute to the quality of its original design.

46 15-cm. s.I.G. on Panzerkampfwagen I, Ausf.B, Germany.

The PzKpfw I, Ausf.B, chassis was used to give greater mobility to the German 15-cm. heavy infantry gun in a conversion carried out by Alkett at Berlin-

Spandau. Some of these were first employed in action in Poland and others saw service later, in the Western campaign. Thirty-eight conversions were completed and this was the first German self-propelled gun of its kind. Many similar improvisations, in which a gun on a more or less standard field-mounting with a light armoured shield was fitted on to a tank chassis with only slight modifications, were to follow later in the Second World War.

47 Panzerjäger I, Germany

This was the first German 'tank hunter' self-propelled anti-tank gun and consisted of a Czech 4·7-cm. anti-tank gun in a limited traverse field mounting on a Pzkpfw I, Ausf.B chassis.

About 170 tank chassis were converted in this way by Alkett of Berlin-Spandau between 1939 and 1941. The conversion was a relatively simple one and involved little more than removal of the turret and substitution of the 4·7-cm. Czech anti-tank gun with a three-sided shield, open at the rear. Stowage for eighty-six rounds was provided.

Vehicles of this kind were employed in infantry anti-tank units with the Afrika Korps in 1941 and in the opening stages of the Russian Campaign.

48 Pantserwagen M'39 (DAF), Holland.

The six-wheeled Van Doorne armoured car was designed in eight months in answer to a suggestion that the DAF factory should produce under licence a British design of armoured car for the Dutch Army.

The DAF armoured car proved to be a very advanced concept for its time and consequently some were ordered for the Dutch Army and twelve were built by 15 May 1940, after which the factory was taken over by the Germans.

Both well armed and armoured, the DAF was equipped with a turret mounting a 37-mm. Bofors gun and a 7·9-mm. machine-gun, and there were two further machine-guns in the front and the rear of the hull. The hull armour was exceptionally well designed, with sloping glacis plates at front and rear as well as angled side plates.

A Ford (Mercury) V-8 engine of 95 h.p. was located at the rear of the hull at the right-hand side with a transfer box alongside to take the transmission to a Trado rear axle through which the power was transmitted to all four rear wheels. The rear machine-gunner, who sat beside the engine, was provided with a second set of driving controls for driving the car backwards in an emergency.

The twelve DAF armoured cars, not all of which were fully equipped or provided with their armament when the Germans invaded Holland, took no part in the fighting. They were subsequently used by the Germans for internal security duties.

49 Tank, Cruiser, Mark I, U.K.

Designed originally as a potential replacement for the old Medium Tanks, Marks I and II, used by the Royal Tank Corps, this tank, known originally as A.9 from its General Staff specification number, became the first of the new class of Cruiser Tanks called for under the new official policy formulated in 1936.

Sir John Carden, working for Vickers-Armstrong, designed the A.9, which followed the broad layout of the Medium Mark III (which had not been produced in numbers because of its high cost at the time) but was lighter and was intended to use a commercially available engine. An A.E.C. six-cylinder 150-h.p. engine similar to that used in buses was eventually settled on for the power unit: this was a diesel engine converted for use with petrol. The gearbox was a Meadows five-speed model.

The main armament was planned as a 3-pr (47-mm.)—the standard gun in British tanks—but this was replaced in production models by the new 2-pr (40-mm.), which was smaller but had a higher muzzle velocity. The main turret incorporated power traverse—an innovation in British tanks at this time. In addition to the coaxial Vickers 0·303-in. machine-gun, two further Vickers guns were carried in two small auxiliary turrets—one either side of the driver's cab. A proportion of Cruiser Mark Is were fitted with a 3·7-in. howitzer instead of the 2-pr to act as close support vehicles able to put down high-explosive fire and lay smoke.

Following trials, during which some unreliable features in the pilot model, including a track-shedding propensity, were dealt with, a production order for fifty tanks was given to Vickers-Armstrongs in August 1937, together with an order for seventy-five to Harland and Wolff, of Belfast. Deliveries of completed tanks began late in 1939 and ran through until about the spring of 1940, although the supplies of armament did not always keep pace with the production of the vehicles.

Cruiser Mark Is were used in action by the 1st Armoured Division in France in 1940 and one of the illustrations shows a close support tank of Headquarters, 'A' Squadron, 3rd Royal Tank Regiment, of this Division. They were also employed with the 2nd and 7th Armoured Division in the earlier North African campaigns and the other illustration is of a tank belonging to 1st Royal Tank Regiment of the latter formation.

50 Tank, Cruiser, Mark II A, U.K.

The General Staff specification A.10 was for an infantry-accompanying tank. The design for this tank, produced by Sir John Carden for Vickers-Armstrong, was based very closely on that of A.9. The mechanical components of transmission and suspension were almost identical, although lower gear ratios had to be used to deal with the extra weight brought about by an increase of the armour maximum of 14 mm. on A.9 to 30 mm. (as finally specified) for A.10.

The hull design of the A.10 was simpler than that of A.9 in that the two auxiliary turrets (cramped, and highly unpopular with tank crews) were eliminated, a single machine-gun in the right-hand side of the hull, beside the driver, taking their place.

The extra armour thickness on the A.7 was achieved by bolting additional plates on to the hull and the turret. By the time the A.7 was ready for production, in early 1938, the armour maximum of 30 mm. was considered inadequate for an infantry tank (the specification for A.11 already called for 60 mm.) but it was, nevertheless, decided to produce the A.10, although as a 'heavy cruiser' tank. Limited orders were placed with Vickers-Armstrong, Metropolitan-Cammell Carriage & Wagon Co., and Birmingham Railway Carriage & Wagon Co. for an eventual total of 160 vehicles. Most of these were completed during 1940, the last in the late autumn. Early in the course of production, the Besa 7·92-mm. machine-gun was introduced in place of the Vickers and the tanks with this weapon were designated Cruiser, Mark IIA. The bulk of the A.10s built were, in fact, in this form. A proportion of all A.10s were, at the same time, fitted out as close support tanks in which the 2-pr main armament was replaced by a 3·7-in. howitzer.

The distribution of the Cruiser Mark II and IIA paralleled that of the Cruiser Mark I and they were used in France in 1940 and in the Desert Campaigns until about the end of 1941. In service, the A.10 proved rather more popular with its crews than the A.9 since, although slower, it was more reliable, better protected and lacked the disliked auxiliary turrets.

One illustration shows a Cruiser Mark IIA with which the 5th Royal Tank Regiment (1st Armoured Division) was re-equipped in the United Kingdom after the withdrawal from France in 1940. This tank has no machine-guns, which were then in short supply. The other view shows a tank of the 2nd Armoured Division as it appeared in North Africa early in 1941. The addition of sand shields over the tracks and a water drum will be noticed.

51 Tanks, Cruiser, Marks IV and IVA, U.K.

The War Office was made aware in 1936 of the potential of the American Christie tank for development as a British medium or cruiser tank. This knowledge was gained at second hand, because although the Christie tank with its unique suspension had been around since 1928, it was not until Lt.-Col. (later General) G. le Q. Martel saw a demonstration of the Russian-built version that the merits of the design were given serious consideration.

With remarkable promptitude a Christie tank was purchased for the War Office (through the medium of Morris Cars Ltd, part of the Nuffield organisation) and this arrived in England in November 1936.

This tank was tested and it was decided to adopt two salient features of the design—a powerful Liberty modified aero engine and the high-speed suspension system—for a British cruiser tank. The alternative of running on wheels, another Christie feature, was rightly decided by the War Office as being an unnecessary complication and it is worthy of note that the Russians also took this viewpoint in their later developments of the Christie design.

A specification, A.13, was drawn up and Morris Commercial Cars Ltd, (another company of the Nuffield group) were asked to build two prototypes. After trials of these and the inclusion of modifications one of which was, on Lord Nuffield's personal instructions, the substitution of shorter-pitched tracks, a first production order for what was to be designated Tank,

Cruiser, Mark III, was awarded to Nuffield Mechanisations & Aero Ltd. This contract, for sixty-five tanks, was dated 22 January 1938, and the first vehicles were delivered to the Army in early 1939. Ease of mass-production had been given some thought in the design, probably for the first time in a British tank. By this time it was decided that the original 14-mm. armour maximum was insufficient and 30 mm. was required.

The increased armour was achieved by a redesign, known ultimately as Cruiser, Mark IV, in which extra plates were added to hull and turret frontal surfaces and spaced plates (of diamond form in front view) were added to the turret sides. Some Mark IIIs were subsequently reworked, wholly or partially, to the Mark IV standard.

The armament on all A.13 cruiser tanks consisted of a 2-pr gun with a coaxial machine-gun in the turret. On the later Mark IVs to be produced, however, the original Vickers 0·303-in. machine-gun was replaced by a Besa 7·92-mm. and these vehicles were designated Mark IVA. A few tanks were fitted for close support with 3-in. howitzers instead of 2-prs but many regiments re-equipped with Cruiser Mark IVs still retained earlier cruiser tanks for this function.

The engine of the Cruiser Tanks Marks III and IV was a Nuffield-built Liberty V-12 cylinder of 340 h.p. which transmitted its power via a multiplate clutch and a four-speed gear-box to rear sprockets. Steering was of the clutch and brake type. The suspension, which, with the high power/weight ratio, was mainly responsible for the A. 13's good performance (30

m.p.h. maximum, reduced from the prototype's 45 m.p.h.), consisted of four large road wheels each side. These were mounted on trailing or leading pivot arms, controlled by long coil springs, contained between inner and outer walls of the hull sides.

Three hundred and thirty-five Tanks, Cruiser, Marks III, IV and IVA, were built. Some of all Marks were sent to France with the 1st Armoured Division in 1940 and others (Mark IVA) were used in action in the North African campaigns, where their speed was a great asset, until late 1941. One illustration shows a tank of the Queen's Bays of the 1st Armoured Division in France (this is a Mark IV or a Mark III converted to the same standard) and the other is of a Cruiser Mark IVA (with the earlier, rectangular type of gun mantlet) of the 5th Royal Tank Regiment as it appeared in North Africa.

52 Tank, Infantry, Mark II, Matilda, U.K.

It can be claimed that the Infantry Mark II was one of the best British tanks of the Second World War, because at the time of its appearance on the battle scene it was at least as well armed as the majority of its German opponents and much better armoured. The counterattack by the 1st Army Tank Brigade near Arras on 21 May 1940 was the only real tactical shock received by the Germans in the invasion of France, and even Rommel (then commanding the 7th Panzer Division) described the situation at one stage as 'an extremely tight spot'. In the early Western Desert campaigns, the Matilda was superior to all Italian tanks and ruled the battlefield.

The weakness of an infantry tank without the capability of tackling enemy armoured vehicles was realised even during the development of the Infantry Mark I, and accordingly the new specification A.12 was drawn up for a heavier tank equipped with a 2-pr gun to succeed the earlier design. Taking the experimental Medium Tank A.7 (three prototypes were built between 1929 and 1937) as a basis, the Director of Tank Design drew up for the Mechanisation Board the essential design features of the A.12, Infantry Mark II. A contract for development, followed by eventual production, was then awarded to the Vulcan Foundry Ltd.

The essentials of the Infantry Mark II (later known as Matilda) were a 2-pr gun and coaxial machine-gun in the turret, armour increased to a maximum of 78 mm., a four-man crew and a top speed nearly double that of its predecessor. The general layout was the same as that of the later Vickers Medium tanks A.6 and A.7 and the suspension—two-wheeled bogie units on coil springs—was of the kind originally used in the commercial Vickers Mark C sold to Japan. To provide the necessary power and, at the same time, to ease production problems, two standard A.E.C. diesel engines (each six-cylinder, 87-h.p.) were used in Matilda I and Matilda II, although these were replaced by Leyland diesels (total 190 h.p.) in Matilda III and subsequent models. The machine-gun coaxial with the 2-pr gun in Matilda I, the first model of Infantry Mark II, was a water-cooled Vickers 0·303-in. This was the

model used with the B.E.F. in France—all were at first issued to the 7th Battalion Royal Tank Regiment although later a few were transferred to the 4th Battalion to give fire support to that unit's Infantry Mark Is. Matilda II and subsequent models used in later actions all had a Besa machine-gun replacing the Vickers.

A feature found only in the early Matildas was a higher form of suspension than that used in later production models, where the armoured skirting gave more protection to the road wheels. This early suspension is shown in both illustrations, which are of tanks of the 7th Battalion Royal Tank Regiment. Also shown in one view is the trench-crossing tail device that was designed and built hurriedly to meet a demand in March 1940 from the troops in France.

53 Tanks, Light (Wheeled) Marks I and IA, U.K.

Following a series of eliminating tests in 1938, a modified Guy Quad-Ant chassis was chosen for production as the first British-built, four-wheeled, four-wheel drive, armoured car for the British Army. The normal version of the Quad-Ant was an artillery tractor with the engine in front, but for the armoured car the engine was placed at the rear, at the time a layout unusual in British armoured cars. The hull and turret were designed at Woolwich Arsenal with armour on a 15-mm. basis and armament consisting of a 0·303-in. Vickers machine-gun and a 0·5-in. Vickers heavy machine-gun mounted coaxially in the turret. This specification corresponded closely to that of the current Light Tank, Mark VIB, and the new official nomenclature of Tank, Light (Wheeled) Mark I, was adopted for the armoured car.

A contract for the production of 101 vehicles was awarded to Guy Motors Ltd in January 1939. The prototype vehicles followed the then usual riveted form of construction for their hulls and turrets and this was originally specified in the production contract. However, Guy Motors asked for and obtained permission to employ instead welding for the construction of hulls and turrets, and a successful technique for carrying this out was devised by the Company. When in 1940 a much larger output of all types of military vehicles was required, Guy Motors handed over the designs and production technique to the Rootes Group, by whom they were used for the Humber Armoured Cars. The last fifty-one Guy Armoured Cars to be built under the contract had the armament changed to a 7·92-mm. and a 15-mm. Besa machine-gun. The first Humber armoured cars had this armament and were almost identical in external appearance to the Guys.

The Guy Armoured Car had a 53-h.p. Meadows engine from which the transmission was taken via a transfer box to differentials on the front and rear axles. Somewhat underpowered, the maximum speed was about 40 m.p.h.

'No. 3 Air Mission' (a special G.H.Q. liaison unit with the British Expeditionary Force) included what was known as a Phantom Squadron comprised of six Guy Armoured Cars —the only ones to be used in France. Following the evacuation of the B.E.F.,

a troop of Guy Armoured Cars from July 1940 to March 1941 provided the protection for the detachment operating Humber Ironside Special Saloons and other cars for the transport of Royalty and Cabinet Ministers. Guy Armoured Cars were also used for defence (and later for training) in the United Kingdom and the illustrations show them in this role. The Guy Mark I is as it appeared in July 1940 with the 2nd Northamptonshire Yeomanry, of the Yeomanry Armoured Detachment —a formation later equipped with tanks as the 20th Armoured Brigade. The Mark IA bears the unit code sign (47) of an armoured car regiment in the United Kingdom in 1941.

54 Car, Scout, Mark I, U.K.

The Daimler Scout Car was one of the most effective items of equipment of its kind to be built and was widely used in the British Army for scouting and liaison purposes.

The original specification drawn up by the War Office early in 1938 called for a small vehicle with frontal armour of at least 25 mm. capable of resisting infantry light anti-tank weapons and able to head a column of tanks or other vehicles likely to encounter opposition. A 0·303-in. Bren light machine-gun was to be carried and the vehicle was to be able to withdraw quickly in reverse. For this reason only frontal armour was specified: for the sake of lightness no other armour was called for.

Three designs were submitted and tested in the latter half of 1938 and eventually the one from B.S.A. Cycles Ltd. was selected. During the development of this vehicle, light side armour was at first added, as much as a means of supporting the heavy 30-mm. glacis plate as for crew protection. Then, the War Office decided that the side armour must be to a 14-mm. standard, an armoured roof must be added and the bonnet of the engine (at the rear) must also be protected. The modified vehicle was ready by January 1939 and about six months later a preliminary order for fifty-two cars (later increased to 172) was given to the Daimler Co. Ltd, who, in the meantime, had taken over the project from B.S.A.

The B.S.A./Daimler (later known simply as 'Daimler') Scout Car was powered by a six-cylinder 55-h.p. engine mounted at the rear. The drive was taken forward through a 'Fluid Flywheel' and pre-selector gearbox to a transfer box in the centre of the vehicle. This box had a single differential, from one half of which propellor shafts, universally jointed, led forward to a front wheel and back to the rear wheel on the same side. Similar shafts led from the other half of the differential to the wheels on the other side of the vehicle. At each wheel station 'Tracta' joints were used. This system left more space in the centre of the hull than a more conventional transmission and enabled the overall height of the vehicle to be reduced. The suspension was independent, using coil springs at each wheel. Steering was on all four wheels, which made for a small turning circle and, incidentally, gave considerable difficulties for drivers lacking experience. A high speed in reverse could be obtained in the Scout Car and this was facilitated for the driver by the position of his seat, which was turned inwards slightly, enabling him more readily to look over his left shoulder.

The crew compartment, in which the Bren gunner sat beside the driver, was octagonal-shaped in plan, with the upper half of the side sloping inwards, and the lower half undercut. A sliding armoured roof was fitted.

Scout Cars, Mark I, were used in action in France in 1940 with two experimental platoons of the 4th Battalion Royal Northumberland Fusiliers, an infantry division reconnaissance unit, otherwise chiefly equipped with motor-cycles. A car of this unit, with its white and red pennant, is shown in one of the illustrations. They were also used in formation, regimental and squadron headquarters in the 1st Armoured Division in France in 1940 and subsequently, together with later Marks, with most other British Armoured formations. The second illustration is of a Scout Car with the 2nd Armoured Division in Libya.

A total of 6,626 Daimler Scout Cars of all Marks was eventually built; even so, the demand always exceeded the supply.

55 KV I(B) (Heavy Tank), U.S.S.R.

The KV heavy tank (the initials stand for Klementy Voroshilov, a Marshal of the Soviet Union) was the third of a trio of designs in 1938 for a modern type to take the place of the old and unsatisfactory T-35.

The first two models (T-100 and SMK) both had two turrets (reduced at the drawing-board stage from three, at the suggestion of Stalin) and the other, which later was evolved as the KV I, had only one turret. It was, again, Stalin's influence that led to the choice of this model.

The KV I was designed as a heavy tank to enjoy the maximum protection from contemporary armour-piercing weapons coupled with an effective armament, in which the total weight should not become excessive and so cut down on mobility. A prototype of this tank was completed in September 1939 and several pre-production vehicles were in use on the Finnish front before the end of the year. This helped in the perfection of several features, including the torsion-bar suspension system, a type which was taken over from the T-100 but modified for the KV I.

The main features of the layout of the KV I were a centrally mounted turret containing a 76·2-mm. gun and two machine-guns (one coaxial, one in the rear face); the driver's compartment at the front with a hull machine-gun position to the left of the driver, and a rear-mounted diesel engine. This was a V-form twelve-cylinder power unit of 550 h.p. which drove rear sprockets via a five-speed gearbox. The tracks were exceptionally wide—27½ in.— and this helped to keep ground pressure down to little more than that of the very much lighter BT-7. Armour protection was on a generous basis, to around 100 mm. on the front of the hull and turret.

During the course of production of the KV series, improvements in both armour and armament were introduced, some tanks having a longer calibre 76·2-mm. gun and others, like the KV IB (shown in the illustrations), with both hull and turret armour supplemented by the addition of extra plates. In the case of the KV IB (the suffix was added by the Germans, incidentally, as a means of identifying this model) the additional plates were welded on to the glacis and driver's plates but bolted on to the hull and turret sides. The bolt heads were a particularly prominent feature on the turret.

Although inevitably outmoded as the War progressed, the KV I proved to be a very good design which was later used for the basis of the Stalin tank.

56 KV II (Heavy Tank), U.S.S.R.

First appearing in early 1940, this massive and cumbersome vehicle was an 'artillery tank' version of the KV I. A 152-mm. howitzer (122-mm. calibre in the very earliest models) mounted in a high, square turret took the place of the normal 76·2-mm. gun turret. This turret had a 360-degree traverse but it weighed around 12 tons and the bearings were badly designed, so that it could only be traversed when the tank was on level ground. The increase in all-up weight of about 10 tons without any increase in power, coupled with much higher centre of gravity, inevitably decreased mobility, although in any case the gun could not be fired on the move.

KV IIs used the same chassis as KV Is and the later versions of the former (known as KV IIB by the Germans) had the wider tracks of the KV IB as well as a slightly different turret and gun mounting.

The KV IIs had some success when employed in the assault on the Mannerheim Line in Finland but were found to be virtually useless when meeting the German invasion of Russia in the Summer of 1941 and they do not appear to have been used after 1941. Since the chassis were identical with those of the KV I, however, it seems likely that most KV IIs which survived were converted to KV Is.

57 South African Reconnaissance Car, Mark II, South Africa.

South African-built armoured cars made a valuable contribution to the British Commonwealth war effort, particularly in the campaign in East Africa in 1940 and in the North African battles in 1941-2, when armoured cars from the United Kingdom were in short supply.

When the Second World War broke out in September 1939, it was discovered by the South Africans that little help with supplies of armoured cars or even suitable designs was available from the United Kingdom. Accordingly, work on an armoured car based on the Ford 3-ton lorry chassis, which was already in progress, was joined by further design work for a similar armoured car on a similar Ford chassis but with the Marmon-Herrington conversion to four-wheel drive. The new prototype was ready by 18 September and after extensive tests over the next few months, which brought out the need for improvements in the engine cooling and suspension, the 4 × 4 car was put into production. Orders were increased in mid-1940 when the Germans invaded France and Italy entered the war, to reach a total of 1,000 of these first two types of South African Reconnaissance Car, as

they were designated—Mark I, the original 4 × 2 type of which only 113 were built, and Mark II, the four-wheel drive version.

Armoured cars of both types were first used in action against the Italians in East Africa in 1940. The first supplies (of Mark IIs) for the Middle East for use in the North African campaigns were received about March 1941. These cars, when supplied to orders from the British War Office, were designated 'Armoured Car, Marmon-Herrington, Mark II'.

In their original form the South African Reconnaissance Cars consisted of an armoured hull, either riveted on to a mild steel frame, or welded, and mounted on the lorry chassis, which was shortened to a 134-in. wheelbase and strengthened. The welded type of hull soon predominated and replaced the riveted kind. The original armament consisted of a 0·303-in. Vickers machine-gun in a ball mounting in the turret and another Vickers in the left-hand side of the hull. This last was of little practical use and an alternative anti-aircraft mounting was provided. Cars in this form were used by the Union Defence Forces in East Africa, but those sent to the Middle East (where they were widely used by British and South African armoured car regiments) had a Bren 0·303-in. light machine-gun and a Boys 0·55-in. anti-tank rifle in the turret and an anti-aircraft machine-gun (Bren and/or Vickers). The hull mounting was often plated over.

Both illustrations show a South African Reconnaissance Car, Mark II, with welded hull and the original armament.

58 **Leichter Panzerspähwagen SdKfz 222,** Germany.

This light four-wheeled armoured car was the second model to be developed on the basis of the 'standard chassis I for heavy passenger cars'. This type of chassis (which, in spite of its designation, seems to have been used almost exclusively for armoured cars) was a rear-engined model with four-wheel drive and steering on all wheels.

The first type, SdKfz 221, was a two-man vehicle armed with a machine-gun only, but the second type, ordered in the Spring of 1940, had a hull slightly redesigned to give more room for the crew of three, and a larger turret equipped with a 2-cm. gun in addition to a machine-gun. The dual mount of these guns was intended to be fully available for anti-aircraft use and was a variant of the 2-cm. field mounting for which the turret was, in effect, a gun shield. The turret had no roof but to provide some protection against grenades was equipped with wire grilles, hinged at the sides.

The earlier light 4 × 4 armoured cars of the series had a 3,517-c.c. Horch V-8 engine but the SdKfz 222s used the Ausf.B chassis with the enlarged 3,823-c.c. engine and hydraulic instead of mechanical brakes. Weighing only about 4·7 tons, these armoured cars had a good performance and although production was ended in 1942, served well throughout the war from the French campaign onwards (the SdKfz 221 was used additionally in Poland). The performance was, to some extent, at the expense of armour, much of which was only on an 8-mm. basis. The frontal armour was to a maximum of 14·5 mm., but to supplement this a spaced shield was added experimentally in front of the nose plate of one car in the French campaign. This vehicle is shown in one of the illustrations, together with a standard SdKfz 222 in North African colours. The spaced shield was not adopted permanently for the light armoured cars although it was later a feature on some of the German eight-wheeled armoured cars.

59 **Schützenpanzerwagen SdKfz 250 and 252,** Germany.

More or less a scaled-down version of the 3-ton SdKfz 251, the 1-ton SdKfz 250 series appeared some two years after the heavier vehicle. Development of this light armoured half-track was entrusted to the firms of Demag AG, who provided the chassis, and Büssing-NAG, who designed the body.

The chassis used was a shortened version of the Demag D.7 (used as a light artillery tractor, etc.) in which one of the overlapping road wheels was eliminated each side. A Maybach six-cylinder 100-h.p. engine of similar type to that employed in the SdKfz 251 series was used, in conjunction with a seven-speed gearbox. The SdKfz 250 had a better performance (37 m.p.h. maximum speed) than the SdKfz 251 and tended to be issued more widely to reconnaissance units.

Using the same chassis as the SdKfz 250, but with an armoured hull developed separately by Wegmann, the SdKfz 252 was intended specifically as an ammunition carrier for Sturmgeschütz units. This vehicle had a fully enclosed hull with a long sloping rear plate, which helped to distinguish it from the various vehicles of the SdKfz 250 series. Also, the maximum armour thickness was slightly greater. The advantages of the special design of the SdKfz 252 were not great enough to justify an entirely different hull design, however, and the type was discontinued by 1941, when its function was taken over by versions of the SdKfz 250 series.

The SdKfz 252 did not normally carry mounted armament, but most of the vehicles of the SdKfz 250 series as armoured personnel carriers or wireless/command vehicles frequently had a light machine-gun MG.34 mounted at the forward end of the crew compartment. The crew of vehicles of this type varied between two for ammunition carriers to six for armoured personnel carriers.

The SdKfz 250 first appeared in action in the French campaign in 1940, although it is possible that the armoured ammunition carrier SdKfz 252 was issued slightly earlier to the troops. About 7,500 vehicles of the SdKfz 250/252 type were built during the War in fourteen different versions, two of which are shown in the illustrations: a standard Schützenpanzerwagen SdKfz 250/1 (as it appeared in Russia in 1941) and an armoured ammunition carrier (le. gep. Mun. Transportswagen, SdKfz 252).

60 Sturmgeschütz III, Germany.

An armoured self-propelled gun to support infantry in the attack was called for in 1936, and the firms of Daimler-Benz and Krupp were selected to undertake the development of the chassis and armament respectively.

The chassis of the Panzerkampfwagen III, then under development by Daimler-Benz was, not surprisingly, chosen for the basis of the new assault gun and the armament was the 7·5-cm. L/24. This gun was similar to that mounted in the PzKpfw IV tank but as a low silhouette was required in the assault gun and all round traverse was not considered essential it was possible to have this gun on the smaller chassis with much heavier armour (50-mm. front; 30-mm. sides and rear) at a not greatly excessive increase in weight.

The prototypes and early production models of Stu G III were based on the contemporary PzKpfw III chassis models—Ausf. E and F. Later production versions likewise used the later Panzer III chassis and so, throughout, the assault gun was mechanically the same as the tank.

The 7·5-cm. gun fitted low in the hull front plate had a traverse of 12½ degrees either side, elevation of 20 degrees and depression of 10 degrees. The short barrelled version (L/24) of the gun was fitted throughout 1940-1 and it was only in 1942 that a longer weapon began to be used.

The Stu G III was first used in small numbers in the Western Campaign in 1940, although a total of 184 was produced by the end of the year and a further 548 in 1941. Over 10,500 Stu G III of various types were completed by the end of the War. This type of vehicle was first introduced into action by Germany and was a very successful weapon. Although later in the war production difficulties caused the Germans to use some Sturmgeschütz in place of tanks, when properly employed they were very effective.

61 T-34 (Medium Tank), U.S.S.R.

The tank which had the greatest impact on the course of the Second World War was probably the Russian T-34. Although not the best in a mechanical sense, and the T-34 had several shortcomings in design, this Russian tank was nevertheless one of the most effective fighting vehicles of all time and its influence is still felt today.

Developed from the BT series through several intermediate experimental models, during which the ability to run on wheels was finally abandoned, the T-34 was designed in 1939 under a team headed by M. I. Koshkin, and the first prototypes were running early in 1940. Some modifications were made and the first production models came off the line at the Kirov Tank Plant in June 1940. As mass production got under way, increasing numbers of T-34s became available so that by the time of the German invasion of Russia in 1941, over 1,200 had been built.

The most remarkable feature of the T-34 when it first appeared was the extremely effective use of sloped armour plates for the hull. This fact, coupled with a good gun (the 76·2-mm. L/30·5 in the first production model) and a diesel engine of 500 h.p., which ensured good mobility, added up to make a tank which had a traumatic effect on the Wehrmacht. This even led to the impractical suggestion that the T-34 should be copied and made in Germany.

Few features of the T-34 were original, because most of them had appeared in one form or another in earlier Russian or foreign tanks, but it was the combination in one vehicle that was the great achievement of the designers. The general layout of the T-34 followed that of the BT series, with the engine at the rear driving rear track sprockets. The suspension was of the usual Christie type, with large road wheels on pivot arms controlled by long coil springs. The track design was unusual, though, in that the wide (19-in.) plates were held together by pins which were retained in place only by plates, attached to the hull, which pushed back the heads of any projecting pins as they passed. This system had obvious advantages in simplifying track manufacture and maintenance.

The twelve-cylinder V-form diesel engine of the T-34 was tried out in the BT-7M, the last of the BT series, and performed well in the T-34, although the transmission system at first gave trouble—faults probably of manufacture rather than design, though.

The hull of the T-34 in its early versions was 45 mm. thick at the front and 40 mm. at the sides and was divided internally by one bulkhead separating the engine from the crew compartment. The driver sat at the front with, beside him, the co-driver, who operated a machine-gun mounted in the glacis plate. The turret, mounted near the front of the hull roof, was protected mainly on a 45-mm. basis on early T-34s, and the 76·2-mm. gun shared a mounting with a 7·62-mm. machine-gun. The first 115 tanks built followed earlier practice in having an additional machine-gun in the turret rear face, but this was abandoned in later machines.

The gun mantlet in the first T-34

production model (this had no distinctive Russian nomenclature but was called T34/76A by the Germans, a practice adopted by the British) was of the external type, cast, and of a form (when used on the Sturmgeschutz III) known to the Germans as 'saukopf' (pig's head). This early T-34 (T 34/76A) is shown in the illustrations.

62 **Autoblinda 40,** Italy.

Some interesting mechanical features were included in this armoured car, the prototype of which, built by Spa, was completed by mid-1939. The most unusual point about the Autoblinda 40 was its transmission system. From the rear-mounted engine (a six-cylinder Spa of 80 h.p.) the drive was transmitted through a dry plate clutch to a five-speed and overdrive crash-type gearbox, built integrally with the clutch housing. All speeds except the fifth and overdrive sixth were also available in reverse. From the gearbox the drive was transmitted to a distribution box located approximately in the centre of the vehicle and incorporating a differential unit. The drive direct to each wheel was taken by helical bevel gear wheels through universally jointed shafts: a layout in plan which resembled a St. Andrew's cross.

The steering system operated on all four wheels and for emergency driving in reverse a second steering wheel, together with basic driving controls, was fitted. The suspension was of the independent coil spring type and the brakes hydraulic.

The hull of the AB 40 consisted of flat armour plates, varying between 8½-mm. and 6-mm., bolted or riveted

to a framework, the whole being bolted to the chassis frame. The turret (armoured to a maximum of 18 mm. and minimum of 6 mm.) was derived from an early design for the L.6/40 tank and mounted two 8-mm. Breda machine-guns. The fixed armament was completed by a further 8-mm. machine-gun mounted at the rear of the fighting compartment, at the right-hand side, to fire over the engine.

Two drivers, a commander/gunner and a rear gunner made up the crew of the AB 40. Weighing about 6½ tons and with a top speed of 46 m.p.h., the AB 40 was a suitable reconnaissance vehicle for employment in the North African desert and this was where it was mainly used, although its successor the AB 41 also saw service in Russia.

63 **Carro Armato L.6/40,** Italy.

Fiat designed a light tank in 1936 to replace the L.3 series, and after several changes were made, principally to the suspension and the armament, the design emerged as the L.6/40, which was issued to the Italian Army in 1940–1.

The L.6/40 was more or less a scaled-up L.3 with a more powerful engine (a four-cylinder Spa of 70 h.p.) and torsion-bar suspension and equipped with a turret.

With armour to a maximum of 30 mm. and armed with a 20-mm. gun and coaxial 8-mm. machine-gun, the L.6/40 was a considerable improvement on its predecessor. However, with a crew of only two men and still too lightly armed, the tank was not a great success in combat. It was used in action in North Africa from about 1941 onwards and, later, in Russia as a reconnaissance vehicle.

The illustrations both show L.6/40s in European colour schemes; one in the plain greenish-grey used in 1940–1 and the other in a camouflage pattern believed to have been used earlier in the War.

64 Carro Armato M.13/40, Italy.

Retaining the main mechanical features of the M.11/39, the Carro Armato M.13/40 was a great improvement as a fighting vehicle in that the main gun was both much more powerful and was mounted in a fully rotating turret.

The prototype of this 13-ton medium tank appeared early in 1940 and, because of the likelihood of Italy soon entering the War, production was hurried on so that the first production vehicles were ready by July of the same year.

A factor which must have greatly simplified the production of the M.13/40 was that the lower hull was almost identical to that of the M.11/39, although the Spa 8T diesel engine was improved to give 125 h.p. The opportunity was taken at the same time of redesigning some features of the steering and final drive system to make for a more compact and efficient layout. Also, in order to carry the greater weight of the M.13/40, the suspension was strengthened and an extra leaf was added to the semi-elliptic springs.

The main armament consisted of an Ansaldo-built 47-mm. gun, 32 calibres long, mounted coaxially with an 8-mm. Breda model 38 machine-gun in a hydraulically traversed turret. In addition to this, two Breda 38 machine-guns were in a twin mounting in the front right-hand side of the hull, where they had a total traverse of 30 degrees. Armour protection of the M.13/40 was on a 40-mm. basis for the turret front and 30-mm. for the hull.

During the course of production of M.13/40, about mid-1941, a more powerful eight-cylinder Spa engine, the model 15 T of 145 h.p., was introduced and this increased the maximum speed from about 20 m.p.h. to 22 m.p.h. Tanks equipped with this engine and incorporating various other improvements were designated M.14/41. The distinction, however, does not seem to have been very clear-cut and some vehicles completed in 1942 still had the earlier Spa 8T engines. At the same time, it appears that tanks built earlier, when reworked, were sometimes fitted with the Spa 15 T.

First used in action in December 1940 in North Africa, the M.13/40 and its developments were the best Italian tanks to go into service in quantity in the Second World War. Although inferior to contemporary German tanks it was at least comparable in many respects to British cruiser tanks of its era and was one of the very few types of captured tank to be used in some numbers by the British forces—both Australian and United Kingdom armoured regiments used them in Libya in 1941.

The illustrations show the 5th tank, 1st platoon, in the 1st Company of an Italian tank battalion in North Africa, about 1941.

65 Tank Infantry, Mark III Valentine, U.K.

One of the most reliable of British tanks, the Valentine was designed as a private venture by Vickers-Armstrong Ltd and gained its name from the fact that the proposal for this new infantry tank had been deposited with the War Office just before St. Valentine's Day, 1938.

The Valentine was based on the A.9 and A.10 tanks designed by Sir John Carden, who was killed in an aeroplane accident in December 1935. The 30-mm. armour of A.10 was by 1937 no longer considered adequate for an infantry support tank and was rejected for this role, although subsequently the A.10 did enjoy limited production as a heavy cruiser tank. The Valentine, therefore, started with a 65-mm. armour basis (slightly greater than that of Infantry Tank Mark I) but took other features from the A.9 and A.10, including a similar A.E.C. six-cylinder petrol engine and transmission and the same form of suspension. Both hull and turret were more compact, though, and this limited the crew to three men only.

The proposal for the Valentine was at first put aside by the War Office, but in July 1939 a first contract for 275 tanks was placed with Vickers-Armstrongs. Almost at the same time, a further 125 were ordered from the Metropolitan-Cammell Carriage & Wagon Co. Ltd. and 200 from the Birmingham Railway Carriage & Wagon Co. Ltd.

May 1940 was stipulated as the delivery date for the first Vickers-built Valentine and this target was achieved. When the first production vehicle was tested by the War Office (no pilot vehicle had been built—the order being 'off the drawing board') it was found to be generally satisfactory, although the engine cooling needed some improvements and the tracks were unreliable. It was discovered that although many components appeared to be the same as those on the A.9 and A.10, they were not in fact interchangeable. Steps were taken to correct the faults in the tracks and cooling but the war situation in May–June 1940 made it necessary to obtain new tanks urgently, and a further 600 Valentines were ordered at this time in addition to the 1,325 already by then on order. Canada had been asked in the Spring of 1940 also to participate in Valentine production and had been given a preliminary order for 300.

Output of Valentines rose steadily, while Vickers' engineers corrected their relatively simple faults, so that by mid-1941 they were being delivered at the rate of forty-five per month. They were issued in lieu of Cruiser tanks to equip some of the new armoured divisions, following Britain's build-up of armoured forces after the Dunkirk evacuation, as well as to the Army Tank Brigades—formations which were specifically intended for infantry support.

The Valentine was eventually developed through eleven different Marks, although the main types in use in 1940–1 were the Valentine I, the original model, and Valentine II (Tank, Infantry, Mark III*), in which the petrol engine was replaced by an A.E.C. six-cylinder diesel. The desire for a three-man turret was then met with in the Valentine III. All the earlier Valentines had armament of a 2-pr gun and coaxial 7·92-mm. Besa machine-gun.

Home Defence was necessarily the main role of the Valentine in 1940–1, but some were sent out to North

Africa at the end of 1941. The 8th Royal Tank Regiment was equipped with Valentines at this time and a Valentine II of this unit in desert colours is shown in one of the illustrations. Another Valentine II is shown in the other view, as it appeared with the 1st Royal Gloucestershire Hussars (6th Armoured Division) on a United Kingdom training exercise in October 1941.

66 Cars, 4 × 2, Light Reconnaissance, Standard, Marks I and II (Beaverette I and II), U.K.

Most numerous of the many varieties of improvised armoured vehicles built for the defence of the United Kingdom in the emergency after the withdrawal of the British Expeditionary Force from France, the Beaverette was produced in the first instance principally for the defence of aircraft factories. The name was derived from that of Lord Beaverbrook, then Minister of Aircraft Production.

The large quantities of armour plate required could not be spared for these cars and so protection was made up from $\frac{3}{8}$-in. or $\frac{7}{16}$-in. mild-steel plates, with 3-in. oak planks for backing at the front of the vehicle. There was no armour at the rear and no roof. The chassis used was that of the 14-h.p. (R.A.C. rating) passenger car produced by the Standard Motor Company Ltd, of Coventry. This had an engine developing 45 h.p., with a four-speed gearbox. The Beaverette weighed about 2 tons and the maximum speed was 40 m.p.h.

A Beaverette II soon followed the Mark I and this had protection at the rear added. From the front the Mark II could be distinguished by its horizontal (instead of vertical) radiator grilles.

The armament normally consisted of a 0·303-in. Bren light machine-gun firing through a slit in the front plate. This could easily be dismounted for ground action.

Beaverettes I and II were issued during 1940 for aircraft factory defence (as originally planned), to armoured regiments waiting to be re-equipped with tanks, to the Home Guard and to the Royal Air Force for airfield protection. Then, when the Reconnaissance Corps was formed in January 1941 to carry out reconnaissance for infantry divisions, Beaverettes were issued to many battalions of this Corps for home defence and training.

The illustrations show a Beaverette I of the 53rd Battalion The Reconnaissance Corps of the 53rd (Welsh) Division as it appeared in June 1941 and a rear view of a Beaverette II of the 4th/7th Royal Dragoon Guards in July 1940. This unit had been the divisional cavalry regiment of the 2nd Infantry Division in France, where it had lost its light tanks and carriers.

67 Car, 4 × 2, Light Reconnaissance, Humber Mark I (Ironside I) and Car, 4-seater, Armoured Saloon, Humber (Special Ironside), U.K.

In the emergency after the Dunkirk evacuation, the Rootes Group as well as the Standard Motor Company was asked to produce a light armoured car. A prototype, known as Humberette, based on the Humber Super Snipe car chassis, was built during June 1940. This vehicle, with some slight modifications, including W.D. pattern rims for Runflat tyres, was put into production in the following month. Two hundred were built and known as Ironside I. Weighing about $2\frac{3}{4}$ tons, armoured to a maximum of 12 mm. and powered by the Humber 75/80-h.p. six-cylinder engine, these light armoured cars had a top speed of 45 m.p.h. Open-topped vehicles, they carried no fixed armament but were usually equipped with a 0·303-in. Bren light machine-gun or a 0·55-in. Boys anti-tank rifle, as available.

Ironsides were supplied to armoured regiments in lieu of tanks and subsequently to equip armoured car regiments or the Reconnaissance Corps. They were eventually classified as Cars, 4 × 2, Light Reconnaissance.

Another aspect of the defence of the United Kingdom was the need to provide safe transport for Cabinet ministers and members of the Royal Family in the event of air attack or parachute troops landing. The Ironside was selected as the most suitable type of armoured vehicle for adaptation for this purpose, after an old Lanchester armoured car had been tried out and found unsuitable. The detachment of the 12th Royal Lancers responsible for providing the escorts for the Royal Family and Cabinet Ministers received the first Humber Special Ironside armoured saloon on 13 September, 1940, followed by a second five days later, and soon afterwards both the King and Queen and the Prime Minister had travelled in these vehicles. Although a reasonable degree of comfort was provided in the armoured saloons, they had no windows and so in the later cars built (two of which were received by the 12th Royal Lancers detachment in December) small bullet-proof windows were provided. At the same time it was no longer felt necessary to provide picks and shovels on the newer armoured saloons, since they were invariably escorted by one or two Guy Armoured Cars, which did carry such equipment.

By January 1941 the invasion emergency had lessened somewhat and in this month the first of two Humber Pullman Protected saloon cars was received. This was a conventional car in appearance but offered some protection against shell splinters or small arms fire. Being much more comfortable than the Special Ironsides, the Protected Pullmans came to be used more and more in their place, although two Ironsides were held on the strength of the escort detachment at least until the end of 1941.

The illustrations show an Ironside I and a Special Ironside of the earlier type without bullet-proof windows.

68 Armoured Car, Dodge, and Lorry, 30 cwt, 4 × 2, Armoured Anti-tank, Bedford, U.K.

Two of the more effective of the many and varied improvised armoured vehicles built in the United Kingdom for home defence in the national emergency in 1940 were these armoured vehicles on Dodge and Bedford lorry chassis respectively.

The Dodge armoured vehicle was conceived by Sir Malcolm Campbell, the racing driver and in 1940 holder of the world water-speed record, and former holder of the world land-speed record. Campbell was then Officer Commanding the Provost Company of 56th (London) Division. It was arranged that Leo Villa, Campbell's Chief Racing Mechanic, should construct a prototype at his (Campbell's) private workshop in Surrey. This prototype was built on a Fordson lorry chassis, using ⅛-in. mild steel. This prototype was then handed over to Briggs Motor Bodies Ltd, of Dagenham, to produce a pilot production model in ⅞-in. or 1-in. armour plate, using the same chassis. With some further modifications, including those necessary to adapt the design to the Dodge chassis to be used for the production order, Briggs then went ahead and built seventy of these armoured cars, the majority being completed by the end of August 1940.

Within the limits of what could be done in the time and with the materials available, the Dodge Armoured Car was a well-thought-out design, with attention paid to the arrangement of the armour for the best protection and accessibility of components. The fully-enclosed hull had several ports for the operation of crew weapons such as the 0·303-in. Bren machine-gun or the 0·55-in. Boys anti-tank rifle. One armoured regiment equipped with these cars mounted the machine-guns from a shot-down German He.111 bomber in three of them. Later (in 1942) a Home Guard battalion in Hampshire redesigned the Dodge armoured car to take a 6-pr (First World War tank pattern) gun on an all-round mounting.

These vehicles were known as Armoured Cars, Dodge, in 1940 and unofficially as 'Malcolm Campbell' Armoured Cars. Subsequently they were classified as 'Cars, four-wheeled, Light Reconnaissance', although at around 8 tons they were anything but light.

The Lorry, 30 cwt, 4 × 2, Armoured Anti-tank, Bedford, was, by contrast with the Dodge Armoured Car, a very simple improvisation on a lorry chassis. The chassis was the Bedford model OXA with a 72-h.p. six-cylinder engine, which was widely used by the British Army as a load carrier. This modification consisted of the provision of an armoured cab for the driver, behind which was mounted on the lorry platform a rectangular armoured box which constituted the fighting compartment. The only other armour was plates over the radiator and over the petrol tanks at the side. No weapons were permanently mounted but ports were provided on all sides for the operation of crew weapons and it was intended that the principal armament should be the 0·55-in. Boys anti-tank rifle, a single-shot weapon suitable for use against light armoured vehicles. A 0·303-in. Bren gun was often carried in addition to, or instead of, the anti-tank rifle.

The illustrations show a Dodge Armoured Car in the colours of one of the infantry battalions of the 47th (London) Division, one of the formations which defended southern England, and a Bedford Armoured Lorry belonging in 1941 to the 59th Battalion The Reconnaissance Corps, of the 59th Infantry Division.

69 Panzerkampfwagen II (Schwimm.), Germany.

A Panzer Battalion was equipped with a special amphibious version of

PzKpfw II for 'Operation Sea Lion'—
the projected invasion of England in
1940.

The amphibious equipment consisted of a large pontoon built in three
parts which surrounded the tank's hull
at track-guard level and projected at
front and rear. It was attached to the
hull at the return rollers. Propulsion
in water was by means of a propeller
driven by the tank's main engine
through an extension shaft and universal joint. Steering was achieved
by a rudder behind the propeller.
The engine, as well as the hull, was
water-proofed and the turret ring was
sealed by an inflatable rubber tube.
The Schwimmpanzer II was said
to be capable of a speed of up to
6 m.p.h. in smooth water and to be
able to stand up well to seas of Force
4.

Fifty-two sets of equipment were
made by Alkett (Berlin-Spandau),
Bachmann (Ribnitz) and Sachsenberg
(Roslau) and the battalion—Abteilung
A of Panzer Regiment 2—was equipped
by the end of August 1940. Experiments and trials were carried out at the
special amphibious establishment at
Putlos, near Kiel, and a full-scale
rehearsal of the amphibious tanks for
invasion (which included also submersible Panzer IIIs and IVs) was
mounted near Antwerp at the beginning of September.

'Operation Sea Lion' was eventually
cancelled and the Schwimmpanzer IIs
do not seem to have been used after
this, although the submersible PzKpfw
IIIs and IVs were transferred to the
Russian Front for the opening of the
assault across the River Bug in June
1941.

70 **Panzerkampfwagen II
(Flamm.)**, Germany.

After the design of the basic Pzkpfw II
had been stabilised and production was
in progress it was decided to produce
also a faster version ('Schnellkampf-
wagen'), considered more suitable for
issue to light mechanised cavalry
divisions.

Daimler-Benz were asked to draw
up a design for this model in which the
upper hull and turret of the standard
type was to be retained but in which a
revised form of suspension was required
in order to give the higher speeds
needed. The design was undertaken
in 1938 and by the following year 250
tanks were produced. The suspension
used by Daimler-Benz consisted of
four large road wheels each side—of
Christie appearance, but with torsion-
bar springing. This redesign succeeded
in raising the top speed of the tank by
some 5 m.p.h. although the cross-
country performance proved to be
inferior. The new model appeared in
two forms, PzKpfw II, Ausf. D and E,
between which the chief external
difference lay in the design of the front
sprocket.

The need for this fast version of the
Panzer II was not sustained, however,
and in 1940 it was decided to convert
some of these tanks (about 100) into
flamethrower vehicles. (The balance of
PzKpfw II Ds and Es were subsequently converted to S.P. guns.) The
conversion into flamethrowers was
carried out by Wegmann of Kassell.
There were minor variations in the
work done, but essentially it consisted
of the addition of two flame projectors
—one on each front track guard—and

the substitution of a smaller turret (mounting one machine-gun) for the standard turret. The flame fuel carried was sufficient for eighty bursts of 2–3 seconds from the pump-operated projectors. The range was only about 40 yards. The crew consisted of two men.

71 Tank, Heavy, T.O.G. I, U.K.

This interesting tank started life as an alternative to the A.20 (which evolved into the Churchill) as a means of breaching the German Siegfried Line defences. It was felt that the experience of the tank designers of the First World War should be drawn upon, and Sir Albert Stern, who was prominent in tank production in 1917–18, was asked to get together some of his old associates to design an assault tank. A committee was formed under Sir Albert Stern and included Sir Eustace Tennyson d'Eyncourt, Mr. H. Ricardo and General Sir Ernest Swinton and became known as 'The Old Gang', subsequently giving its initials 'TOG' to the new tank evolved in conjunction with the design staff of William Foster & Co. Ltd., who also had played a leading part in the First World War tank design and production.

The tank required was to be able to traverse shelled and waterlogged ground, to be protected against 47-mm. armour-piercing and 105-mm. high-explosive shells at 100 yards and to carry a field gun (capable of piercing 7 ft of reinforced concrete), together with armour-piercing weapons and machine-guns.

Design commenced in February 1940 and T.O.G. I was running in October, by which time its original purpose,

now that France was defeated, no longer existed. However, development was allowed to continue, if only for the sake of research into several interesting features which had been included in the design. These included a Paxman Ricardo Diesel engine of 600 h.p. (the most powerful tank engine in existence in the United Kingdom at the time) and an electric transmission and steering system. (This was later replaced by a hydraulic transmission.)

T.O.G. I as completed broadly resembled the French Char B.1 bis, which had influenced some features of its design. A 75-mm. gun was mounted in the front hull, and a Matilda turret was mounted on the hull roof. However, neither the turret armament nor the side sponsons allowed for in the design appear ever to have been fitted.

The tracks of T.O.G. I were unsprung and with a weight of about 70 tons, not surprisingly, the maximum speed was only 8½ m.p.h., although the trench crossing ability was exceptionally good and comparable to that of the Tank Mark V** of 1918. Steering was difficult because of the exceptionally high ratio of track length on ground to width between track centres.

Development of the T.O.G. series (a second tank, T.O.G. II, was built in 1941) continued sporadically into 1942, and after that they were stored. They were never used in combat.

72 Armoured Command Vehicle, Guy 'Lizard', U.K.

An armoured command vehicle, equipped with wireless, for the use of formation headquarters staff was experimented with by the 1st Tank Brigade about 1937. This was based on a Morris 15-cwt 4×2 chassis and proved to be too small for the purpose. Accordingly, following further experiment, a larger vehicle was built on the Guy Lizard 4×4 chassis. Armoured command vehicles of this type were issued to formation headquarters in the United Kingdom and in Libya towards the end of 1940 and in early 1941.

Powered by a Gardner five-cylinder engine, the Guy Lizard was unusual for a wheeled armoured vehicle in the British Army in 1940 in using a diesel engine, although the A.E.C. (Matador) Armoured Command Vehicle which succeeded the Lizard in 1941 also had a diesel.

Headquarters, 7th Armoured Division, was using Guy Lizard A.C.V.s in the Spring of 1941, and one is shown here in the Desert camouflage in use at that time. The smaller picture shows the tent extension, normally carried rolled on the side of the vehicle, in use.

73 Armoured Carrier, Wheeled, I.P. Mark I, India.

When it was decided that India's participation in the British Commonwealth war effort should include the manufacture of armoured vehicles, this relatively simple wheeled carrier was chosen as the first type to be produced.

Based on a $113\frac{1}{2}$-in. wheelbase front-engined Ford chassis, with Marmon-Herrington conversion to four-wheel drive, an armoured body of riveted construction was manufactured by the Tata Iron and Steel Works. Only ten of these vehicles were produced between early 1940 and about mid 1941 but after that production, which soon turned to a more advanced rear-engined model of armoured carrier, increased rapidly, with other manufacturers joining Tata.

The Wheeled Carrier, India Pattern, Mark I, was intended to fulfil roughly the same functions as the British tracked carrier series, such as the transport of infantry Bren-gun crews, scouting, etc. As far as is known, Carriers of this first Mark were used only for defence and training in the Indian sub-continent.

74 Tank, Cruiser, Mark V, Covenanter, U.K.

A revised specification for the A.13 led, in 1939, to the London Midland and Scottish Railway being asked to abandon work on an earlier cruiser tank, which was proving unsuccessful, and take on the A.13 instead.

The A.13 Mark III, as it became known, was basically the same specification as the Cruiser Mark IVA with the 30-mm. armour basis, but it was desired to increase the effectiveness of the protection by improved ballistic shape of the armour and by lowering the height of the tank. The suspension was to be the same as the earlier Christie Cruisers, but a new tank engine, specially designed by Meadows, was to be used.

Many difficulties developed in the design of the A.13 Mark III, which came to be known as Cruiser Mark V, to which the name Covenanter was added. These were chiefly centred on the engine, which was the only major untried feature. The cooling was the main problem and the earliest production vehicles which were running by 1940 soon had their engine air intake louvres (situated at the front left-hand side, next to the driver) modified in Army workshops, the resulting vehicles being known as Covenanter IIs. Two further basic Marks, Covenanter III and IV, appeared before the end of 1941 but the cooling problem was never solved really satisfactorily and the Covenanter was declared unfit for overseas service. This tank, nevertheless, played an important part in the defence of the United Kingdom, first in helping to re-equip the 1st Armoured Division, back from France, and later in contributing to the new armoured divisions being raised. The 9th Armoured Division's tanks were almost exclusively Covenanters by the end of 1941. In all, 1,771 Covenanters were built.

The illustrations both show a Covenanter of the 1st Fife and Forfar Yeomanry, one of the armoured regiments of the 28th Armoured Brigade, 9th Armoured Division, in 1941. This tank has the earlier type of axle-shaped external gun mantlet.

75 T-40 (Light Tank), U.S.S.R.

A light amphibious tank, intended to replace earlier models which had been in production during the 1930s, the T-40 first came into service in the early part of 1941. With a two-man crew the T-40 weighed around 6 tons and was armed with a 12·7-mm. heavy machine-gun and a 7·62-mm. machine-gun mounted in the turret, which was offset to the left-hand side of the hull. A 20-mm. cannon was sometimes mounted instead of the heavy machine-gun. Intended to utilise standard automotive parts as far as possible, the T-40 was powered by a GAZ six-cylinder lorry engine of 85 h.p.: this was located at the right-hand side of the hull behind the driver and drove front track sprockets. Independent torsion bars were used for the suspension.

For propulsion in water, a single four-bladed propeller was provided at the rear, the hull nose plate was inclined forwards and flotation tanks were built in. Even so, the armour weight had to be kept down and was to a maximum of 14 mm. only. This disadvantage, coupled with the light armament, led to the T-40's withdrawal from production in 1942.

The illustrations show the slightly modified model T-40A which differed from the T-40 chiefly in having a folding trim-vane (for use in water) just above the top of the nose plate.

76 Armoured Car Mark IV (Ford), Irish Free State.

The outbreak of the Second World War added a greater degree of urgency to the somewhat leisurely experiments that had been carried out in the Irish Republic (as it then was) with the object of re-equipping the Irish Army with armoured cars. With the fall of France, the strong possibility that a German invasion of the United Kingdom would take place and be accompanied or followed up by a violation of Eire's neutrality, made it a matter of immediate necessity to produce armoured cars. Apart from practical considerations of cost, armoured cars were considered to be more suitable than tanks for employment in the Irish terrain.

The first experimental vehicle (later known as Mark I) was built on an old Morris chassis. This was unsatisfactory and a Ford lorry chassis was used for the next design (Mark II), of which seven were built at the Great Southern Railway Workshops at Inchicore. The Mark II was built on a standard lorry chassis, with the rear of the armoured body extending over the load platform, but it was felt that a shorter wheelbase was desirable.

When it was established that the Ford chassis could satisfactorily be shortened, arrangements by Messrs. Thompson's of Carlow went ahead to produce the prototype of the Mark III car. This vehicle, which was completed on 9 August 1940, had an armoured hull made up from $\frac{1}{2}$-in. mild-steel plates, as armour plate was not available in Ireland. It was found to offer satisfactory protection against small arms fire, however, and all subsequent cars were made from mild steel. The turret of the Mark III prototype was of armour plate and mounted a Hotchkiss machine-gun. Turrets of obsolete Peerless twin-turret armoured cars which had been taken out of service were available and were used for all fourteen Mark IIIs, including the prototype, which were built.

The general war situation at the end of 1940 led the Irish Department of Defence to decide to have made a further twenty-one armoured cars similar to the Mark IIIs. A new turret and mounting for a Vickers 0·303-in. water-cooled machine-gun was de-

signed for the new cars. The first of these, which were designated Mark IV, were completed early in March 1941.

After various modifications, the Irish-built armoured cars turned out to be quite suitable for employment in Ireland, but some Mark IVs were even used in the Congo with the Irish contingent of the United Nations Force—twenty-five years after they were constructed.

77 Cockatrice and Heavy Cockatrice Flamethrowers, U.K.

The Cockatrice type of mobile flamethrower was developed during 1941 by Lagonda Ltd as a vehicle for the defence of airfields or harbours. They were based on a prototype flamethrower vehicle, using an armoured Commer lorry chassis, built by Lagonda's in the Autumn of 1940.

The Cockatrice's flame projector was mounted in a small turret on the roof of the vehicle: it used 8 gallons of fuel per second and had a range of 100 yards. Two forms of chassis were used, both lightly armoured—the 4 × 4 Bedford model QL and the 6 × 6 A.E.C. (of the type used by the R.A.F. as refuelling tenders and crane lorries). The arrangement was, however, the same for both models, the main difference being that a greater supply of fuel for the flamethrower could be carried in the heavier A.E.C. vehicle. Both types carried as supplementary armament two light machine-guns on an open anti-aircraft mounting, at the rear of the vehicle.

Sixty Bedford Cockatrices were constructed for the defence of Royal

Naval airfields and six of the A.E.C. heavy Cockatrices were built for the Royal Air Force.

78 Tank, Infantry, Mark IV, Churchill, U.K.

A General Staff Specification, A.20, for a heavy infantry tank capable of breaching the defences of the German Siegfried Line, was drawn up in September 1939. This called for 60-mm. frontal protection and a speed of 10 m.p.h. Consideration was given to various forms of armament, ranging in calibre from the 2-pr (40-mm.) anti-tank gun to a low-velocity 3.7-in. (95-mm.) howitzer. Combinations of turrets, hull mountings and sponsons were also considered but the final decision was for a turret (with 2-pr and coaxial Besa machine-gun) like that of the Infantry Mark II, a second 2-pr mounted in the front hull, and a Besa machine-gun in a sponson on each side of the hull.

Harland & Wolff Ltd., the Belfast engineers and shipbuilders, were asked to design and supply four mild steel prototypes of A.20, or Infantry Tank Mark IV. The first of these was running by the middle of 1940 and although the armament had not been fitted its mechanical performance was disappointing, both engine and gearbox turning out to be unsatisfactory.

Vauxhall Motors Ltd., manufacturers of cars and Bedford lorries, were then asked to design a new 350-h.p. engine. This was done successfully, but it was decided to replace the A.20 specification with a revised one, A.22, in which, nevertheless, the new Bedford engine was incorporated. Vauxhall Motors, assisted by Dr. H. E. Merritt, Director of Tank Design, undertook to design and produce the new version of Infantry Tank Mark IV.

The date was then July 1940, so the utmost urgency was essential so that the greatest possible number of tanks could soon become available for Home Defence. By a remarkable effort the first prototype vehicle was actually being tested by the end of 1940, and the first production batch of fourteen Tanks, Infantry, Mark IV, was completed by Vauxhall Motors in June 1941—only a year from the commencement of design. During this time arrangements were made for mass production to be undertaken by a group of eleven manufacturers, under the overall control of Vauxhall Motors.

In ordering the A.22 'off the drawing board' it was expected that faults would come to light in the production vehicles, and many difficulties did in fact arise. However, the national emergency justified the action taken and it was felt that in the event of invasion even immobile tanks used as blockhouses were better than none at all.

One of the most interesting features of the Infantry Mark IV was the Merritt-Brown four-speed gearbox (five speeds in the very earliest vehicles) through which a controlled differential steering system was provided. The Bedford Twin-Six power unit was made up of two six-cylinder Bedford truck engines—a device which produced the necessary power, and must have simplified the supply of spares, although accessibility for maintenance was not good. A new pattern of suspension for British tanks was used, consisting of small diameter steel road wheels mounted independently on short trailing arms and sprung on vertical coil springs. The hull was made up of armour plates bolted on to a riveted steel box; the turret was a casting.

The original armament consisted of a 2-pr gun and coaxial 7·92-mm. Besa machine-gun in the turret and a 3-in. howitzer, firing high-explosive ammunition, in the hull front, next to the driver. A second model, known at first as Tank, Infantry, Mark IVA, had a second Besa machine-gun in place of the 3-in. howitzer. When, in June 1941, names were adopted officially for British tanks, these two models became known as Churchill I and Churchill II respectively. In all, 5,640 Churchills were produced by the end of the War, of which something like 2,000 were built as Churchill I's or II's.

Development of a 6-pr-armed Churchill began in 1941, but the Churchill I and II were the only types in service before 1942, when they were exclusively employed on Home Defence. The illustrations show a Churchill II of the Polish Army Tank Brigade, which had begun to receive Churchill tanks in the United Kingdom by the end of 1941, and a Churchill I of the 9th Battalion Royal Tank Regiment, which formed part of one of the newly raised British Army Tank Brigades.

79 N.L.E. Trenching Machine, Mark I, U.K.

Unique, and certainly one of the most interesting devices of the Second World War, the N.L.E. Trenching

Machine was overtaken by events so that no opportunity ever occurred for its employment in the role for which it was intended.

Originating in the fertile brain of Mr. Winston Churchill (in 1939, as in 1914, First Lord of the Admiralty) as a means of cutting through enemy defence lines, instructions were given in November to the Director of Naval Construction for experiments to be carried out. A machine which could cut a trench across no-man's-land in the space of one night, through which infantry and tanks could follow, was required. Drawings were made and a scale model was built by the Bassett-Lowke model railway firm. This model was demonstrated by Mr. Churchill during December and January to Cabinet ministers and senior British and French Army officers to some effect, for in February 1940 the Cabinet approved the construction of 240 full-size machines, known under the code name of 'White Rabbit No. 6', later changed to 'Cultivator'. The Department of Naval Land Equipment was formed to control the project and overall responsibility for production was given to Ruston-Bucyrus Ltd, Lincoln, a firm with long experience in the manufacture of civilian earth-moving equipment.

There were many difficulties in the production of such a large and unconventional machine (the prototype, when completed, weighed some 130 tons and was 77 ft 6 in. long), not the least of which was the discovery, in April 1940, that the projected Rolls-Royce engines could not be used, since all Rolls-Royce engine production capacity was required for the Royal

Air Force. Then, in May, the German campaign in France so altered the situation that the bulk of the scheme was cancelled. However, work on a limited scale was allowed to proceed on the grounds that there might, in the future, be some special tactical use for the machines or that they might, in an invasion emergency, be useful for the rapid digging of defensive ditches in the United Kingdom.

The first prototype, known officially as N.L.E. Trenching Machine Mark I, was completed by July 1941: it carried the name 'Nellie I' on its side. In overall appearance, the N.L.E. Trenching Machine resembled a lengthened British First World War tank (some of Sir William Tritton's early drawings had, in fact, been referred to for various parts of the design) but without the sponsons and with a large V-shaped plough blade covering the front section, which was hinged. This front section contained a cutting cylinder, equipped with hardened steel blades.

When starting to cut a trench, the cutting cylinder was lowered and cut into the ground as the machine moved forward (at a speed of $\frac{1}{2}$ m.p.h.) and gradually downwards into the depression that had been made. A point was soon reached where the tip of the plough blade entered into the earth ahead of the cutting cylinder and as the machine got deeper the plough took the first cut and eased the work of the cutting blades. The soil removed was ejected either side of the machine by conveyor belts. The maximum depth that could be cut in loam was 5 ft, but the soil deposited on the parapets added about another 3 ft above the surface. An armoured cab was provided for the driver, but armour was not used elsewhere, since when dug in the machine had provided its own protection.

Nellie I was powered by two Davey-Paxman diesel engines, one to propel the machine and the other to drive the cutters.

In the end, only six N.L.E. Trenching Machines, including the prototype, were completed and were kept in store until after the Siegfried Line was breached in the Summer of 1945 by less unconventional means.

80 **Tank, Light, M.3 (Stuart I),** U.S.A.

Developed from the M2A4 light tank, the M.3 incorporated improvements found to be necessary from experience with the earlier vehicle. The main change, from the mechanical point of view, lay in the introduction of a large trailing idler wheel in place of the idler of the M2A4: this helped to improve stability.

Designed, like its predecessor, at the Rock Island Arsenal, the M.3 coming after the outbreak of war in Europe was able to benefit from what up-to-date information could be obtained about tanks in combat, and the 25.4-mm. maximum protection of the M2A4 was more than doubled to a 51-mm. standard. The armament remained the same as the M2A4's.

The same engine—the 250-h.p. Continental radial—was retained and, in spite of the increased weight, the M.3 had roughly the same performance as the M2A4. In some of the later vehicles to be produced, however, a Guiberson nine-cylinder diesel engine was used, because of a shortage of Continental engines.

The Light Tank M.3 entered into production in March 1941 and some of the earliest vehicles to be completed were in the hands of British tank units in the Middle East by August of the same year, where they were a valuable addition to British strength in the desert battles.

The M.3 was named Stuart I by the War Office, who classified it this time as a light cruiser tank by virtue of its armament and armour. The two sponson machine-guns were, however, removed in most cases in tanks used in action. A weak point about the M.3, particularly in the open desert fighting, was its lack of range, and this was later rectified by the addition of jettisonable supplementary fuel tanks.

The illustrations both show tanks in British use in North Africa in 1941. Tank 'Crossbow' is a Stuart I of 'C' Squadron, 8th King's Royal Irish Hussars, one of the first regiments to receive this type.

Appendix to Book I

Armoured Fighting Vehicle Camouflage and Markings 1939–41

In the coloured illustrations, considerable effort has been made to show camouflage colours as accurately as possible and tactical and other markings for specific vehicles have been included wherever practicable. However, in some cases, information has been unobtainable or, at best, sketchy. Apart from the difficulties of colour reproduction in a book, the colours used on the actual armoured fighting vehicles often varied for many reasons—the exact colours for camouflage were not always considered important and wide discretion was allowed to unit or tank commanders; the quality control on paints issued—always difficult to maintain— sometimes allowed quite wide variations; and colours, once applied, could sometimes be changed out of all recognition by ageing, frequently helped by terrain such as desert sand.

For those wishing to go further into this subject, much useful information is published in the journals *Tankette* (Editor, Max Hundleby, 4 Low Croft, Woodplumpton, Preston, PR4 OAU, England) and *AFV News* (Editor, George Bradford, R.R.No.2, Preston, Ontario, Canada).

Belgium

Overall khaki (brown) shade. Vehicle registration number carried at front and rear preceded by a small rectangle in the national colours. A small roundel in three colours was often carried on turret or hull. Sometimes unit signs, such as the wild boar of the Chasseurs Ardennais, were also shown on A.F.V.s.

Czechoslovakia

A three-colour camouflage scheme, applied in irregular blotches. Vehicle registration number carried at front and rear.

Finland

Overall dark green, for winter operations covered in white blotches or sometimes wholly in white. The Finnish swastika in medium blue outlined in white was carried on A.F.V. turrets by 1941.

France

In some cases a single overall colour was used but generally one of several more or less standard schemes, using patches of two or, more usually, three colours. Sometimes the meeting point of different colours was outlined in a dark colour. The vehicle registration number was carried at the front and rear of the hull preceded by a blue/white/red tricolour rectangle. A roundel or rectangle in the national colours was sometimes carried on the turret or hull. Tactical markings, when used, varied widely: sometimes playing card signs to denote sub-units, or large numbers to distinguish individual tanks. Most of the Chars B carried individual tank names.

A medium to dark grey, overall, was generally used throughout the greater part of this period in all European operations and even in some tanks in North Africa. The latter were usually repainted in sand yellow, however. There appear to have been some wide variations in the grey used, ranging from a very light shade to almost black.

In the Polish campaign a white cross on turret and/or hull was used as a national marking. This was retained on some vehicles in 1940 but generally had been replaced by a black cross outlined in white or, sometimes, by only the white outline of the cross painted straight on to the vehicle.

A tactical number was usually carried, originally in white on a small black lozenge-shaped plate (at the sides and/or rear of the vehicles), later to be supplemented by, and eventually replaced by, a large number on the turret or hull. The large number was either in white; in red or black, outlined in white; or simply in white outline. The system for allocating these tactical numbers was usually as follows, although there were exceptions to the general rule.

R 01	regimental commander
R 02	regimental adjutant
R 03	ordnance or signals officer
R 04, etc.	regimental staff
I 01	commander of I battalion
I 02	adjutant of I battalion
I 03	ordnance officer of I battalion
I 04, etc.	staff of I battalion
101	officer commanding 1st company, I battalion
102	2nd-in-command, 1st company, I battalion
111	Leader, 1st platoon, 1st company, I battalion
112	2nd vehicle, 1st platoon, 1st company, I battalion (113 = 3rd vehicle, etc.)
133	3rd vehicle, 3rd platoon, 1st company, I battalion
201	officer commanding 2nd company, I battalion
301	officer commanding 3rd company, I battalion
II01	commander of II battalion, and so on for H.Q. Staff
401 501 601	officers commanding 4th, 5th and 6th companies, II battalion

Self-propelled guns often carried on the hull a letter denoting the battery to which the vehicle belonged.

A divisional sign, usually small, was often stencilled on the hull of A.F.Vs, usually on or near the driver's plate. This was in yellow or, more rarely, in white or other colours. Some divisions later introduced larger, coloured signs.

Armoured cars (which usually did not carry tactical numbers) and half-tracks, but not tanks, had vehicle registration number plates at front and rear. Wehrmacht vehicles carried the prefix WH and SS vehicles the double flash of lightning symbol. Armoured cars and artillery vehicles also often carried small symbolic signs indicating the type of unit and the sub-unit within that unit.

Holland

Overall shade of olive green. Vehicle registration number plates carried at front and rear. Before mobilisation the numbers were white on dark blue plates. After mobilisation black numbers on orange plates were used.

India

Armoured vehicles built in India intended for service in the Middle East were generally painted in the schemes used in that theatre of war.

Irish Republic

Usually overall light grey. Vehicle registration numbers (of the civilian series for the City and County of Dublin) were normally carried at front and rear, in white.

Italy

A camouflage scheme of dark rust red and dark green was generally superseded by 1940 by an overall dark greenish grey for A.F.V.s in Italy. In North Africa, vehicles were painted a sand yellow.

Tactical markings consisted firstly of the regimental number in white arabic figures and the battalion number in white Roman figures. These were usually carried on rear surfaces of the tank's fighting compartment. Battalion command tanks were denoted on the turret or hull by a rectangle divided vertically into red, blue and yellow strips or, where there were only two companies in the battalion, red and blue only. The company signs, carried on the sides and rear of the turret (or hull, in turretless vehicles) were as follows:

> 1st company—red rectangle
> 2nd company—blue rectangle
> 3rd company—yellow rectangle
> 4th company—green rectangle

Platoons were indicated by one, two or three vertical white bars on the company sign, indicating 1st, 2nd or 3rd platoon, respectively. The position of the individual tank in the platoon was shown by an arabic number in white or the company colour above or below the company sign.

From early 1941 the vehicle registration number was added at front and rear. The number was in black on a white plate, preceded by 'RoEto' (Regio Esercito = Royal Army) in red.

Poland

A two-colour scheme in shades of green and brown seems generally to have been used in 1939, although there was also an earlier scheme using three colours, outlined in a darker shade.

South Africa

A.F.V.s in South Africa are believed to have been painted in a sand colour. Registration numbers when carried were prefixed by the letter 'U' (for Union Defence Force). South African-built armoured cars sent to the Middle East were usually painted in the colours used there.

Sweden

A camouflage system of patches in grey, brown, green and black, in winter overpainted in white. The Swedish insignia of three crowns was carried on A.F.V.s at this time although it was later dropped and eventually (after 1941) superseded by a small reproduction of the Swedish flag. The colours in the signs shown in Plates 34 and 35 have been reversed in error.

U.S.S.R.

Russian tanks were usually painted in a single colour of a green or brown shade. Sometimes, but only infrequently, a disruptive pattern in a dark shade was added. A.F.V.s in winter were frequently painted or whitewashed white.

Sometimes (but rarely in combat) a red star was shown on the turret or hull. Slogans—generally of a patriotic nature—were more frequently shown on tanks in combat. Call signs, usually painted in white (black on winter-camouflaged A.F.V.s) and enclosed in a geometric shape, came increasingly to be exhibited during the Second World War.

United Kingdom

The colour most frequently used for British A.F.V.s in Europe early in 1939 was an overall shade of dark green known as Middle Bronze Green (British Standards Institution specification No. 381—1930, colour No. 23). A darker version (Deep Bronze Green, colour No. 24) was sometimes used instead.

In mid 1939 instructions were given for A.F.V.s to be camouflaged so that a disruptive pattern of the dark colour (Deep Bronze Green) was added. This was the standard scheme, but where a lighter effect was desired, larger areas were painted in Light Bronze Green (B.S.I. No. 381—1930, colour No. 22), thus leaving the Middle Bronze Green as the darker shade. In special circumstances a third colour (normally a shade of brown) could be added to either disruptive pattern.

Towards the end of 1941, a khaki brown colour, known as Standard Camouflage Colour No. 2 (later published in B.S.I. No. 987c—1942) was authorised as an alternative to Middle Bronze Green but it was laid down that the dark disruptive colour should be Standard Camouflage Colour No. 1A (also later included in

B.S.I. No. 987c)—a very dark brown. However, it appears that various lighter shades of khaki brown (such as Shade No. 4 in B.S.I. No. 987c) were sometimes used as a basic colour both before and after the War Office instruction was issued.

A.F.V.s in the Middle East were at first painted in an overall sand yellow colour but in 1940 a new scheme in radiating bands of colour was introduced. The lightest colour (sand yellow) was at the bottom, a blue-grey next and a dark colour on top. Alternatively, two or three colours were used in an irregular pattern instead of in straight lines. The colours used in these schemes appear to have been based on B.S.I. No. 381–1930, Colours Nos. 28, 34, 61 and 64, among others, and there were variations.

Formation signs were carried by British A.F.V.s, normally at the front and rear of the hull. All British units were allotted a unit code sign, usually applicable to the type of unit, which was unique *only* in conjunction with the formation sign. The code sign was a white number on a coloured square. Code numbers were usually allocated to armoured regiments in the brigade in accordance with their seniority in the Army List.

The most important of these unit code numbers for A.F.V.'s in 1939–41 were as follows:

| | 1939–40 | | 1940–1 | |
	Europe	Middle East	Europe	Middle East
Armoured Division				
Headquarters (I) Armoured Brigade	3	?	50	71
Armoured Regiment (Battalion) (1)	4	24	51	40
Armoured Regiment (Battalion) (2)	5	25	52	86
Armoured Regiment (Battalion) (3)	6	26	53	67
Headquarters (II) Armoured Brigade	7	?	60	71
Armoured Regiment (Battalion) (1)	8	28	61	40
Armoured Regiment (Battalion) (2)	9	29	62	86
Armoured Regiment (Battalion) (3)	10	30	63	67
Armoured Car Regiment	129	14	47	76
	(Army Troops)			

The coloured square of the unit code sign was red for Headquarters and armoured units of (I) Brigade and green for Headquarters and units of (II) Brigade. Colours for armoured car regiments varied. Different combinations of code numbers for Armoured Brigades in the Middle East were used from time to time in 1940–41; duplications occurred through changes caused by battle casualties, the Brigade sign being the distinguishing factor. 1st Army Tank Brigade with the B.E.F. used the same unit code numbers as for the (I) Brigade of an Armoured Division with a white bar added above the numbers. Later, various numbers were used for Army Tank Brigades.

Tanks of 6th Armoured Division did not carry unit code numbers but had instead coloured patches below the divisional sign.

Tactical signs for A.F.V.s in 1939–40 were at first in the form of coloured pennants painted on the tank and/or flown from the wireless aerial. In 1940 a more or less standardised system using hollow geometric shapes painted on turrets and/or hulls was adopted as follows:

Regimental (Battalion) Headquarters—diamond
'A' Squadron (Company)—triangle
'B' Squadron (Company)—square
'C' Squadron (Company)—circle
'D' Squadron (Company)—vertical bar

These tactical signs were in the following colours:

Senior Regiment in Brigade—red
Second Regiment in Brigade—yellow
Third Regiment in Brigade—blue
Fourth Regiment in Brigade—green

In armoured formations only armoured car regiments (after 1940) or infantry motor battalions had a fourth squadron or company and the fourth unit in an armoured brigade was usually the motor battalion.

British A.F.V.s frequently carried individual names, usually allocated in associated groups for squadrons and/or sub units, often bearing the same initial letter as the Squadron letter. In the Battalions of the Royal Tank Regiment, however, the name in most cases began with the letter equivalent to the Battalion number (e.g. 4th Battalion tank names—Destroyer, Devil, Duck, etc.).

The War Department registration number (prefixed by T for tanks, F for armoured cars and so on) was carried in white on the front and rear of the hull and/or hull or turret sides, according to the type of vehicle. Civilian registration numbers ceased to be allocated to W.D. vehicles early in the War and the plates carrying these were usually no longer displayed after 1940.

Different A.F.V. recognition signs were used at various times. In North Africa from about November 1941 onwards these consisted of vertical white/red/white strips painted on the turrets and/or hulls of tanks. In France in 1940 a white square appears to have served for this function.

Finally, British A.F.V.s nearly always carried a bridge group number, equivalent to the maximum loaded weight of the vehicle. This number was in black on a yellow disc or within a yellow ring.

U.S.A.

An overall shade of green was used, ranging from a fairly light olive colour to a quite dark green in different units and vehicles. U.S.A. vehicle registration numbers were carried on hull sides in white or sometimes pale blue.

Tanks often carried their unit number on their turrets, together with letters and numbers indicating the position of the vehicle in the unit. Vehicles supplied to the United Kingdom were, of course, painted in the British colours appropriate to the theatre of war where they were employed.

The dimensions quoted here should be taken as a rough guide only: in some cases they are approxima
It has not been practicable here to quote gun calibre lengths, but it should be borne in mind that
gun in 1939 had a far lower penetrative ability than, for example, the much longer 37-mm. guns us
In the tables 'm.g.' has been used to denote rifle-calibre machine-guns and 'h.m.g.' for weapons of a

FULL-TRACK

Ref. No.	Type	Weight tons	Length ft	in.	Width ft	in.	Height ft	in.	Armour max. m.m.	Armament
	U.K.									
39	Light, Mk. VIB	5·2	12	11½	6	9	7	3½	14	1 h.m.g., 1 m.g.
49	Cruiser, Mk. I	12·0	19	3	8	4	8	4	14	1 2-pr, (40 mm.), 3 m.g.
50	Cruiser, Mk. IIA	13·75	18	1	8	3½	8	6	30	1 2-pr, 2 m.g.
51	Cruiser, Mk. IV	14·75	19	9	8	4	8	6	30	1 2-pr, 1 m.g.
74	Cruiser, Mk. V	18·0	19	0	8	7	7	4	40	1 2-pr, 1 m.g.
40	Infantry, Mk. I	11·0	15	11	7	6	6	1½	60	1 h.m.g., *or* 1 m.g.
52	Infantry, Mk. II	26·5	18	5	8	6	8	0	78	1 2-pr, 1 m.g.
65	Infantry, Mk. III	16·0	17	9	8	7½	7	5½	65	1 2-pr, 1 m.g.
78	Infantry, Mk. IV	38·5	24	5	10	8	8	2	102	1 2-pr, 1 3-in., 1 m
25	Carrier, Bren	4·0	12	0	6	11	4	6	12	1 m.g.
	Germany									
15	PzKpfw IB	5·7	14	6	6	9	5	7	15	2 m.g.
20	PzKpfw IIc	8·7	15	7	7	0	6	6	30	1 2-cm., 1 m.g.
44	PzKpfw IIIE	19·15	17	7¾	9	7	8	0	30	1 3·7 cm., 2 m.g.
45	PzKpfw IVB	17·42	19	3	9	4	8	6	30	1 7·5-cm., 2 m.g.
60	Stu. G. III	21·65	18	0	9	8	6	4	50	1 7·5-cm.
	France									
9	AMR 35 ZT	6·0	14	2	6	0	5	10	13	1 25-mm. *or* 1 h.m. *or* 1 m.g.
8	AMC 35 ACG 1	14·5	15	0	7	4	7	8	40	1 47-mm., 1 m.g.
5	CL R.35	9·8	13	4	6	2	6	8	45	1 37-mm., 1 m.g.
6	CL H.35	11·4	14	1	6	0	7	1	34	1 37-mm., 1 m.g.
16	CL FCM.36	12·8	14	11	7	2	7	4	40	1 37-mm., 1 m.g.
3	CM D.2	20	16	10	7	3	8	10	40	1 47-mm., 2 m.g.
7	CC S.35	20	17	8	7	1	9	0	55	1 47-mm., 1 m.g.
4	CB B.1 bis	32	21	9	8	3	9	4	60	1 75-mm., 1 47-mm 2 m.g.
11	Chenillette UE	2·0	8	10	5	7	3	5	7	Nil
	Italy									
12	L.3/35	3·2	10	4	4	7	4	2	13·5	2 m.g.
63	L.6/40	6·8	12	5	6	4	6	8	30	1 20-mm., 1 m.g.
41	M.11/39	11·0	15	6	7	2	7	6½	30	1 37-mm., 2 m.g.
64	M.13/40	14·0	16	2	7	3	7	9	40	1 47-mm., 3 m.g.
	U.S.A.									
37	Light M2A4	10·8	14	7	8	4	8	4	25·4	1 37-mm., 4 m.g.
80	Light M.3	12·23	14	10	7	6	8	3	51	1 37-mm., 2–4 m.g.
	Poland									
2	TK3	2·43	8	6	5	10	4	4	8	1 20-mm. *or* 1 m.g.
17	7TP	11·0	15	1	7	11	7	1	40	1 37-mm., 1 m.g.
	U.S.S.R.									
22	T-26B	9·55	15	0	8	0½	8	4	25	1 45-mm., 1 m.g.
75	T-40A	6·2	14	0	7	8	5	8	14	1 h.m.g., 1 m.g.
32	T-28C	32·0	24	5½	9	2½	9	3	80	1 76·2-mm., 3 m.g.
23	BT-7	13·8	18	8	8	0	7	6	22	1 45-mm., 1 m.g.
61	T-34/76A	26·3	20	0	9	9½	8	0	45	1 76·2-mm., 2 m.g.
33	T-35	45	31	6	10	6	11	3	30	1 76·2-mm., 2 45-mr 5 m.g.
55	KV IB	47·5	22	3½	10	11½	10	8	110	1 76·2-mm., 3 m.g.
56	KV II	53·0	22	3½	10	11½	12	0	110	1 152-mm., 2 m.g.
	Czechoslovakia									
13	LT-35	10·5	14	10	7	0	7	2½	35	1 37-mm., 2 m.g.
30	LT-38	8·5	14	11	6	7½	7	9	25	1 37-mm., 2 m.g.
	Sweden									
35	Strv. m/39	9·0	15	0	6	6½	6	4	24	1 37-mm., 2 m.g.

·rmance figures are also approximate—they can vary widely under different conditions.
major factor in performance. Short-barrelled weapons like the French 37-mm. widely used as a tank
J.S. M2A4 and M3 Light Tanks.
5 mm., but below 20 mm.

MOURED VEHICLES 1939-41

Engine	H.P.	Speed m.p.h.	Range miles	Crew	Notes
Meadows	88	35	130	3	
.E.C.	150	25	100	6	
A.E.C.	150	16	100	5	
Nuffield Liberty	340	30	90	4	
Meadows	300	31	100	4	
Ford	70	8	80	2	
A.E.C. (diesel)	174	15	70	4	
A.E.C.	135	15	90	3	Valentine II had diesel engine
Bedford	350	15·5	90	5	Churchill II had second m.g. instead of 3-in. how.
Ford	65/85	30	160	3	U.S. or Canadian engines—85 h.p.
Maybach	100	25	90	2	
Maybach	140	25	90	3	
Maybach	300	25	137	5	
Maybach	300	25	124	5	
Maybach	300	25	101	4	
Renault	80	37	125	2	
Renault	180	25	100	3	
Renault	82	12·5	87	2	
Hotchkiss	75	17·5	81	2	
Berliet (diesel)	91	15	200	2	
Renault	150	15	96	3	
Somua	190	25	160	3	
Renault	300	17·5	87	4	
Renault	35	18	60	2	
Spa (Fiat)	43	26	75	2	
Spa	70	26	125	2	
Spa (diesel)	105	20	125	3	
Spa (diesel)	125	20	125	4	
Continental	250	37	70	4	
Continental	250	36	60	4	
Ford	40	28	125	2	
Saurer (diesel)	110	20	100	3	
GAZ(Armstrong-Siddeley)	90	17·5	140	3	
GAZ	85	26	210	2	
M-17L	500	20	110	6	
M-17T	450	45/33	310	3	Speed 45 m.p.h. on wheels, 33 m.p.h. on tracks
V-234 (diesel)	500	31	188	4	
M-17M	500	18	94	10	
V-2K (diesel)	550	22	156	5	
V-2K (diesel)	550	16	100	6	
Skoda	120	25	120	4	
Praga	125	35	125	4	
Scania Vabis	142	28	150	3	

Ref. No.	Type	Weight tons	Length ft in.		Width ft in.		Height ft in.		Armour max. m.m.	Armament
	U.K. and South Africa									
27	Morris CS9/LAC	4·2	15	7½	6	8½	7	3	7	1 anti-tank rifle, 1 m.
53	Guy I	5·2	13	6	6	9	7	6	15	1 h.m.g., 1 m.g.
54	Car, Scout, Mk I	2·8	10	5	5	7½	4	11	30	1 m.g.
67	Ironside I	2·8	14	4	6	2	6	10	12	1 anti-tank rifle *or* 1 m.g.
57	S.A. Reconn. Car, Mk. II	6·0	16	0	6	6	7	11	12	2 m.g.
	Germany									
19	SdKfz 231 (6-rad.)	5·9	18	4	6	0	7	4	14·5	1 2-cm., 1 m.g.
28	SdKfz 231 (8-rad.)	8·15	19	1	7	3	7	10	14·5	1 2-cm., 1 m.g.
58	SdKfz 222	4·7	15	6	6	7	6	9	14·5	1 2-cm., 1 m.g.
42	SdKfz 251	8·37	19	0	6	11	5	9	12	1 m.g.
59	SdKfz 250	5·61	15	0	6	5	5	6	12	1 m.g.
	France									
10	AMD Panhard 178	8·07	15	9	6	7	7	7	20	1 25-mm., 1 m.g.
	Italy									
62	AB 40	6·48	16	5	6	4	7	8	18	3 m.g.
	U.S.A.									
38	Scout Car, M3A1	5·03	18	3	6	5½	6	1	12	1 h.m.g., 1–2 m.g.
	Poland									
1	wz 34	2·2	11	10½	6	3	7	3	6	1 37-mm. *or* 1 m.g.
	U.S.S.R.									
21	BA-32	7·5	16	2	6	3	8	0	15	1 45-mm., 2 m.g.
	Sweden									
34	Pb. m/39.40	7·8	16	9	7	6½	7	3	18	1 20-mm., 3 m.g.
	Holland									
48	D.A.F.	6·0	15	2	6	7½	6	7	12	1 37 mm., 3 m.g.

Engine	H.P.	Speed m.p.h.	Range miles	Crew	Wheel arrangement	Notes
orris Commercial	96·2	45	240	4	4 × 2	
eadows	53	40	210	3	4 × 4	
aimler	55	55	200	2	4 × 4	
umber	80	45	—	3	4 × 2	
ord	95	50	200	4	4 × 4	
ee text)	65–70	37	150	4	6 × 4	
issing NAG	155	53	186	4	8 × 8	
orch	81	46	175	3	4 × 4	
aybach	100	31	186	12	½-T	
aybach	100	37	198	6	½-T	
anhard	105	45	187	4	4 × 4	
pa	80	46	250	4	4 × 4	
ercules	110	55	250	8	4 × 4	
troen	20	22	156	2	4 × 2	
AZ (Ford)	85	34	155	4	6 × 4	
olvo	135	44	—	6	4 × 4	
ord	95	37	181	6	6 × 4	

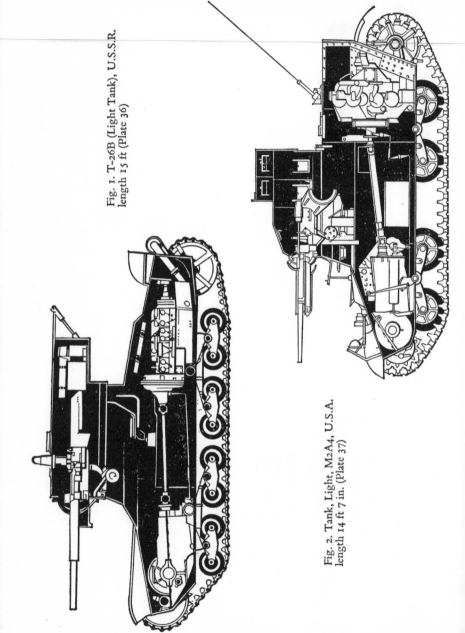

Fig. 1. T-26B (Light Tank), U.S.S.R.
length 15 ft (Plate 36)

Fig. 2. Tank, Light, M2A4, U.S.A.
length 14 ft 7 in. (Plate 37)

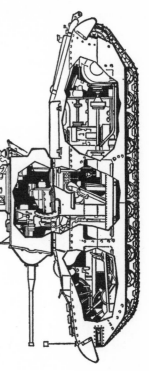

Fig. 3. Panzerkampfwagen IV, Ausf. A, Germany
length 19 ft 3 in. (Plate 45)

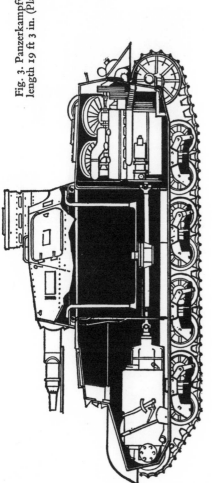

Fig. 4. Tank, Infantry, Mark II, Matilda, U.K.
length 18 ft 5 in. (Plate 52)

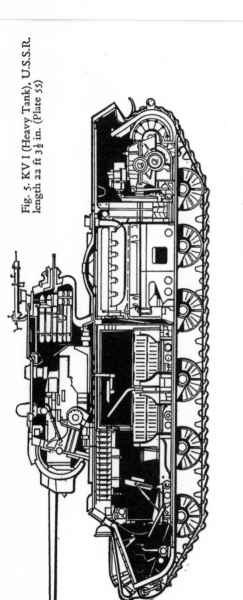

Fig. 5. KV I (Heavy Tank), U.S.S.R.
length 22 ft 3½ in. (Plate 55)

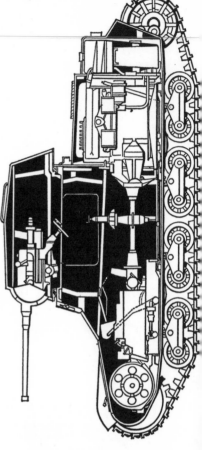

Fig. 6. Carro Armato M.13/40, Italy
length 16 ft 2 in. (Plate 64)

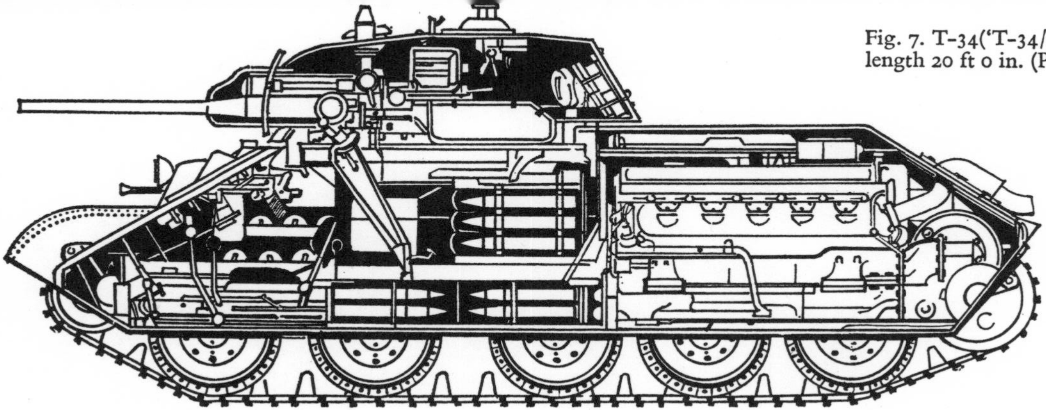

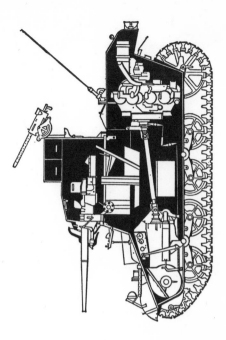

Fig. 7. T-34('T-34/76A'), U.S.S.R.
length 20 ft 0 in. (Plate 61)

Fig. 8. Tank, Light, M3 (Stuart I), U.S.A.
length 14 ft 10 in. (Plate 80)

Book II
TANKS
and other Armoured Fighting Vehicles
1942–45

Introduction to Book II: 1942–45

The war on land 1942–45

The beginning of 1942 was marked by notable success for Japanese arms, following the attack on the United States fleet in Pearl Harbor in December 1941 and the invasion of British, Dutch, French and U.S. overseas territories. The whole area was largely unsuited to the use of armour but, its use nevertheless, was more important than is generally supposed.

Unlike the Far East battles, armour had played the main part in the North African campaign where in April 1942 Axis forces were at the gateway to Cairo; fortunes changed at El Alamein in October and led to the Germans and Italians being expelled from the African continent, the final actions taking place in Tunisia in early 1943, where the British Eighth Army met up with the Anglo-American force that had landed in Morocco and Algeria in November of the previous year. The Mediterranean battles were transferred next to Sicily and then to Italy; much more difficult terrain for the employment of armour.

The great German–Soviet battles on the Eastern Front continued, but the halting of the Germans at Stalingrad in the winter months of 1942 was the turning point. The greatest tank battle of all time took place at Kursk in summer 1943, leading eventually to the Russians fighting their way into Berlin in April 1945.

In the West, the Anglo-Canadian raid on Dieppe in August 1942 showed the need for adequate preparations (including the development of special armoured vehicles) for the full scale invasion of North West Europe so that, despite Russian demands, D-Day did not take place until June 1944

The land war in the Far East was gradually won by the Allies (before its abrupt termination by the atomic bombs dropped on Japan itself) by the 1944–45 campaign in Burma and the island-hopping amphibious operations in the Pacific.

Armour Developments

The influence of the excellent Soviet medium and heavy tanks and the powerful German tanks developed to counter them was the predominant feature of tank development in 1942 and continued to be so for the greater part of the war. Although the later German tanks—exemplified by the Tiger I, Panther and Tiger II tended to have a slightly better armament/armour combination, the Russian tanks were the more reliable, thanks in part to the longer development history of their excellent diesel engines and, no doubt, to their less complex design. The German PzKpfw III and IV, although greatly improved, were continued in production longer than was desirable, but an earlier change to the new Panther would have left a dangerous shortage of medium tanks at a critical time. Production difficulties also led to the increased emphasis on the well-armed and armoured Sturmgeschütz at the expense of tanks. The turretless Sturmgeschütz was simpler to make but less flexible in use than a tank. An unwanted diversion from German battle-tank production was brought about by the need for anti-aircraft tanks due to Allied air superiority. By contrast, A.A. tanks were largely dropped from British and United States formations after 1944.

British-built tanks were generally out-gunned by German armour to the end of the war, the Comet of 1944 probably being the best all-round answer to enemy medium tanks. The Cromwell was a good fast tank for reconnaissance purposes and the Churchill series were well armoured although both types were under-gunned. The Challenger (built in small numbers) and the British-modified Sherman Firefly, both with the British 17-pr gun, were for a long time the only Allied tanks on the Western front up to tackling the Tiger at all ranges. The U.S. Pershing, equal to the Tiger, arrived in small numbers only in 1945.

The American Sherman and the Russian T-34 were the outstanding tanks of the war on the Allied side. The Sherman, reliable, easy to maintain, and capable of being up-gunned from the original 75-mm. formed the main-stay of American and British armoured formations on many fronts.

Italian armour development during the period under review in essence amounted to the M.15/42 medium, developed from the closely similar M.13/40, and a switch to the produc-tion of the Semoventi. These were well-armoured self-propelled mount-ings, akin to the German Sturmge-schütz and produced to a policy similar to that of the Germans. The only Italian heavy tank was built in small quantities before the Italian armistice.

Japanese tanks were mechanically sound and were the result of a carefully thought out development plan. The lightest tanks ('tankettes') were in-tended only as infantry carriers and the light and medium tanks were no match for their Allied counterparts. The later better-armed Japanese medium tanks were built in such small numbers as to have no influence on the war. The lack of effective opposition made it possible for the British forces in Burma in 1944–45 to make good use of American-built Lee/Grant tanks, which had made their mark in the 1942 Desert campaigns but were no longer suitable for employ-ment against the Germans.

The most outstanding British contri-bution to armour in World War II was perhaps in the design and develop-ment of specialized armour, such as anti-mine flail tanks, flamethrowers, bridging tanks, armoured searchlight tanks, engineer tanks and amphibious devices. The Japanese also showed ingenuity in producing specialized armour, although apart from amphi-bians they appear to have made rela-tively little use of it. The Pacific island battles saw wide use of American tracked landing vehicles in assault, cargo and troop-carrying roles. L.V.T.s were employed by the Allies also in Italy and in major river crossings in Germany.

Self-propelled guns were used in wide variety by Germany, often as a means of putting to good use obsolescent tank chassis to give mobility to field and anti-tank weapons. Lightly armoured compared with the Sturm-geschütz type of vehicle, these self-propelled guns gave good service, despite the logistic problem the many

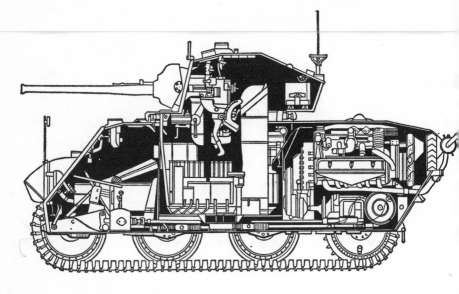

Tank, Light, Mark VIII, Harry Hopkins, U.K. — length **14′3″**

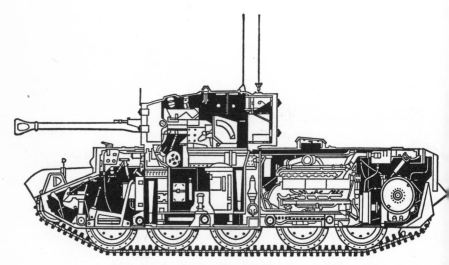

Tank, Cruiser, Cromwell VIII, U.K. — length **20′10″**

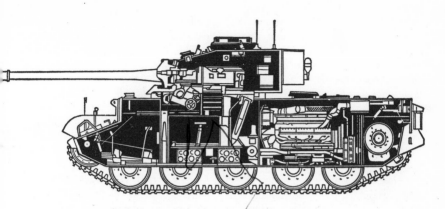

Tank, Cruiser, Comet, U.K. — length 21′6″

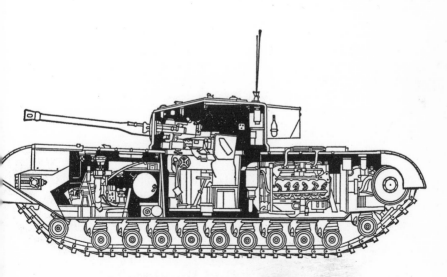

Tank, Infantry, Mark IV, Churchill III, U.K. — length 24′5″

different chassis and weapons must have created. British S.P. weapons were fewer and more standardized, the Canadian 25-pr Sexton being one of the best. American policy, after early efforts on wheeled and half-tracked chassis, was generally to standardize on tank chassis. Some American S.P.s—notably the 105-mm. (Priest) and 3-in. M.10 were also used by British forces. Powerful and well-armoured Soviet S.P. guns were mounted on T-34, KV and JS chassis.

Wheeled armoured vehicles, as in earlier stages of the war, continued to be developed in the greatest variety by the British Commonwealth countries. A version of the useful Daimler Scout Car was built in Canada (and even in prototype form in Italy, where British A.F.V.s were admired) together with light and medium armoured cars. India and South Africa also built in quantity wheeled armoured vehicles using Canadian automotive parts.

The British Daimler armoured car was probably the best Allied armoured car of World War II, being compact and manœuvrable and with a reasonably good cross-country performance as well as being better armoured and armed than most German armoured cars. The German eight-wheelers were powerful and of excellent mechanical design but clumsy by British standards.

The half-track continued to the end of the war to be a characteristic German vehicle, the armoured 1-ton and 3-ton variants still being used in large numbers, although basically infantry-carrying or support vehicles. Many comparable functions were carried out in British units by small full-tracked armoured vehicles of the Universal Carrier type. Half-tracks were also produced in small numbers by Japan and in large quantities for the Allies by the United States. The U.S. half-tracks, almost all of which were armoured, were relatively straight-forward designs but had one advantage over their German opposite numbers in having a driven front axle

This wide variety of tracked, wheeled and half-tracked armoured vehicles was produced in staggering quantities by the countries at war, production rising (even in Germany under heavy Allied air attack) to a peak in 1944–45, so that, for example, the United States alone had built by the end of the war nearly 89,000 tanks.

1
Tankette, Type 97 (Te-Ke) (*above*) and Light Tank, Type
95 (Ha-Go)

2
Medium Tank, Type 97 (Shinhoto Chi-Ha) (*above*) and
Medium Tank, Type 3 (Chi-Nu)

3
Medium Tank, Type 4 (Chi-To) (*above*) and Medium
Tank, Type 5 (Chi-Ri)

4
Gun Tank, Type 1 (Ho-Ni I) (*above*) and 15-cm. S.P.
Howitzer, Type 4 (Ho-Ro)

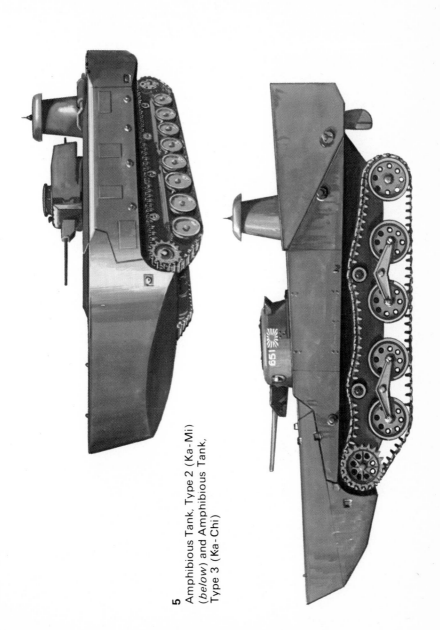

Japan

5
Amphibious Tank, Type 2 (Ka-Mi) (*below*) and Amphibious Tank, Type 3 (Ka-Chi)

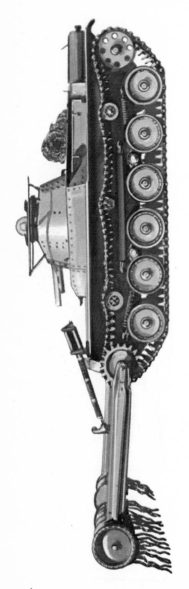

6

Flail Tank (*above*) and Engineer Vehicle—Jungle Cutter (Ho-K)

Japan

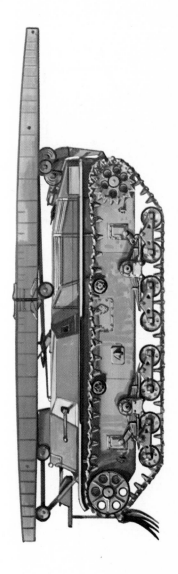

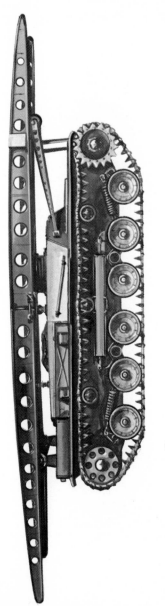

7
Tank Recovery Vehicle, Type E (*below*) and Tank Bridge-layer (Medium Type 97 chassis)

8
Armoured Personnel Carrier, Half-tracked, Type 1 (Ho-Ha)
(*below*) and Armoured Personnel Carrier, Tracked, Type 1
(Ho-Ki)

9
Light Tank M.5A1 (*below*) and 75-mm. Howitzer Motor
Carriage, M.8

10
Light Tank, M.22 (Locust) (*below*) and Light Tank, M.24
(Chaffee)

11
Medium Tank, M.3 (Lee) (*above*) and Tank, Medium,
Grant

12
Medium Tank, M.4 (typical) (*below*) and Sherman Vc

13
Medium Tank, M.26 (Pershing)

14
Heavy Tanks, M.6 (*above*) and M.6A1

15

105-mm. Howitzer Motor Carriage, M.7 (*above*), and as 'S.P. 105-mm. Priest' (*below*)

16
3-in. Gun Motor Carriage, M.10 (*above*) and 76-mm. Gun
Motor Carriage, M.18

17
Landing Vehicle, Tracked (Unarmored) Mark IV (LVT4)
(*below*) and Landing Vehicle, Tracked (Armored), Mark
IV (LVT[A]4)

18
Car, Half-Track M.2A1 (*below*) and 75-mm. Gun Motor Carriage, M.3

19
Armored Car, Staghound I
(T.17E1) (*below*) and
Armored Car, Boarhound (T.18E2)

20
Light Armored Car, M.8 (*above*)
and Armored Utility Car, M.20

U.K.

21
Tank, Light, Mark VII, Tetrarch (*below*)
and Tank, Light, Mark VIII, Harry Hopkins

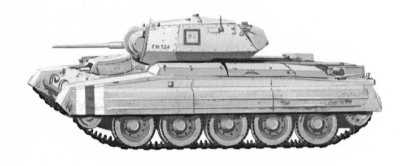

22
Tanks, Cruiser, Mark VI, Crusader I (*above*) and Crusader III

23
Tanks, Cruiser, Centaur IV (*below*) and Cromwell

24
Tank, Cruiser, Challenger

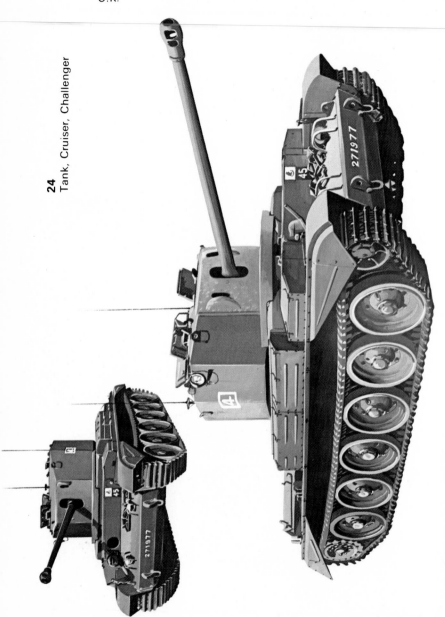

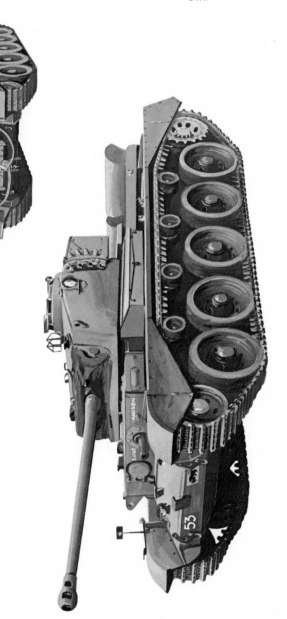

26
Tank, Cruiser, Ram II (*above*) and Armoured Personnel
Carrier, Ram Kangaroo

27
Australian Cruiser Tanks, Mark I (*above*) and Mark III

Australia

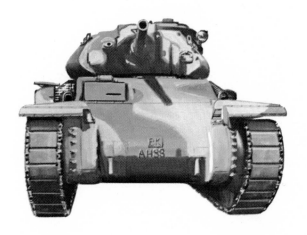

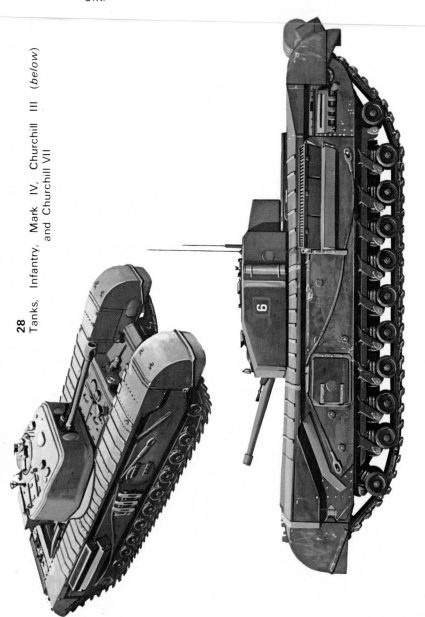

28
Tanks, Infantry, Mark IV, Churchill III (*below*) and Churchill VII

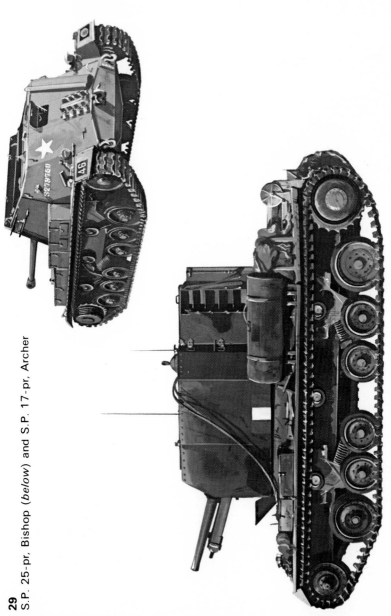

29
S.P. 25-pr, Bishop (*below*) and S.P. 17-pr, Archer

30
S.P. 25-pr, Sexton

U.K.

31
Sherman D.D.

32
Churchill VII Crocodile (*below*) and Grant C.D.L.

33
Matilda Scorpion Mark I (*below*) and Grant Scorpion Mark IV

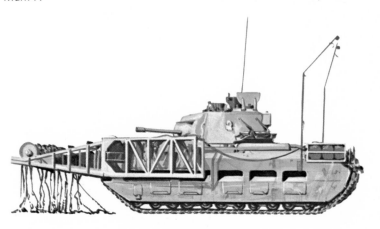

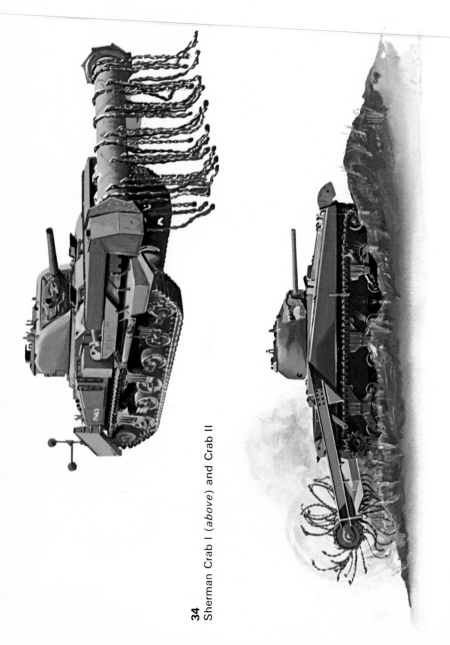

34
Sherman Crab I (*above*) and Crab II

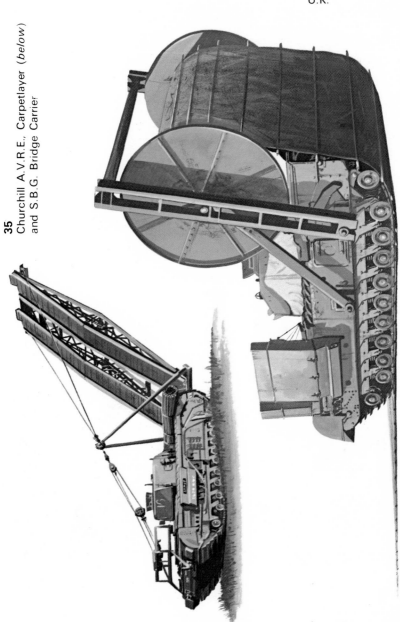

35
Churchill A.V.R.E., Carpetlayer (*below*)
and S.B.G. Bridge Carrier.

U.K.

36
Churchill A.R.V., Mark I (*below*) and Sherman B.A.R.V.

37
Carrier, Universal, Mark II (*below*) and Carrier, 2-pr, Tank
Attack (Aust.)

38
South African Armoured Reconnaissance Cars, Mark IV
(*below*) and Mark VI

U.K.

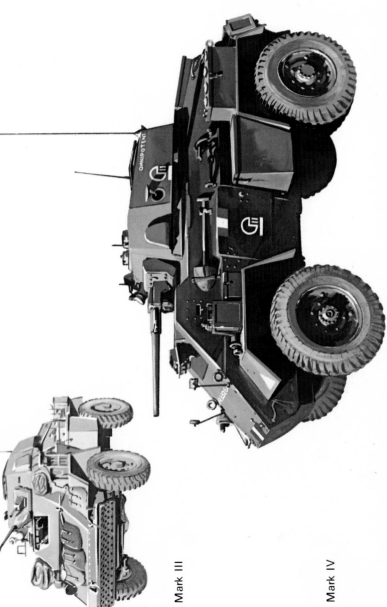

Mark III

Mark IV

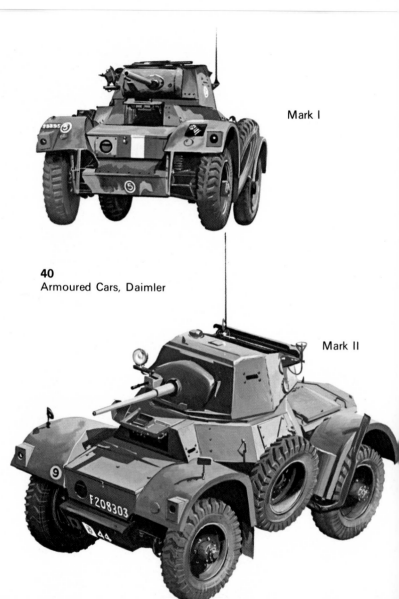

Mark I

40
Armoured Cars, Daimler

Mark II

U.K.

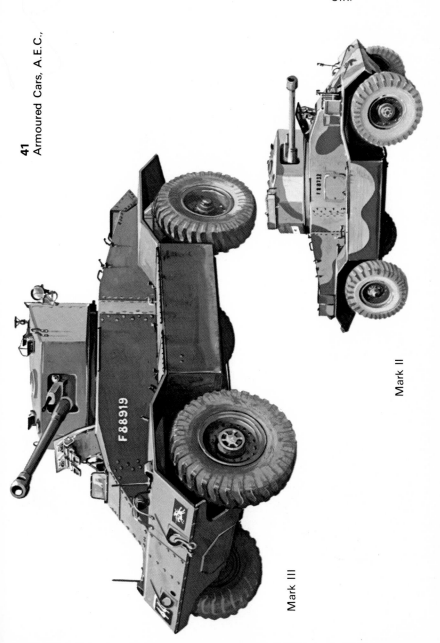

F88919

Mark III

Mark II

42
Car, Scout, Humber, Mark I

43
Car, Scout, Ford, Lynx II (*above*) and Car, Light Reconnaissance, Canadian G.M., Mark I, Otter I

44
Cars, 4 × 4, Light Reconnaissance, Humber, Mark IIIA
(*below*) and Morris, Mark II

45

Armoured Carrier, Wheeled, I.P., A.O.V.

Armoured Carrier, Wheeled, I.P., Mark IIA

46

Armoured Command Vehicle (A.E.C.) 4 × 4, Mark I

Armoured Command Vehicle (A.E.C.) 6 × 6, Mark I

47

S.P. 17-pr Gun — Straussler

Carrier, A.E.C., 6-pr Gun, Mark I (Deacon)

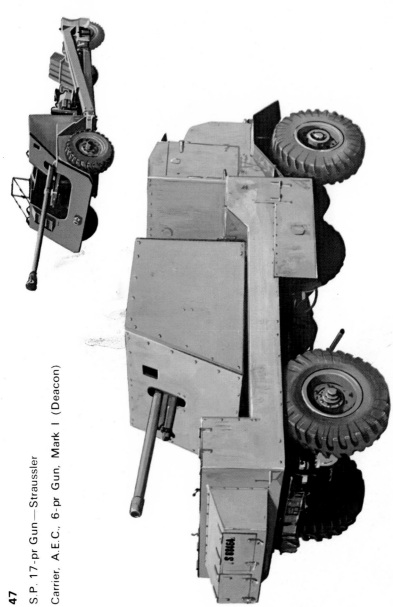

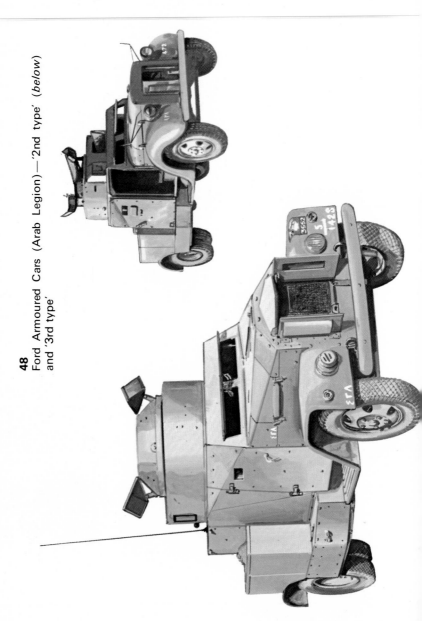

48
Ford Armoured Cars (Arab Legion)—'2nd type' (*below*)
and '3rd type'

49
Autocanon Dodge (*below*) and Autocanon 75-mm., Ford

France

50
Carro Armato M.15/42

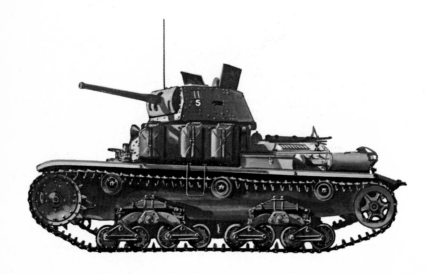

51
Carro Armato P.40

52 Semovente M.42M da 75/34 (*above*) and Semovente M.42L da 105/23

53
Panzerkampfwagen II, Ausf. L, Luchs

54
Panzerkampfwagen III, Ausf. L (*below*) and Ausf. M

Germany

55
Panzerkampfwagen IV, Ausf. H

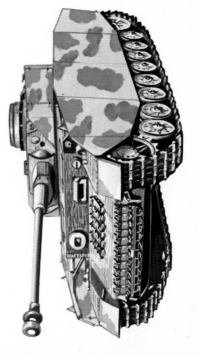

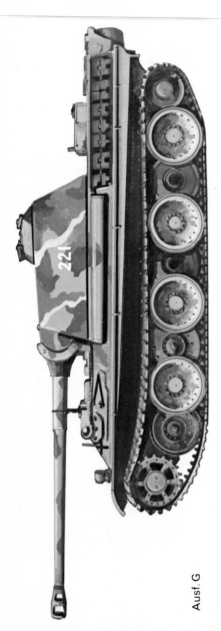

Ausf. G

56
Panzerkampfwagen V, Panther, Ausf. D

Germany

57
Panzerkampfwagen VI, Tiger I

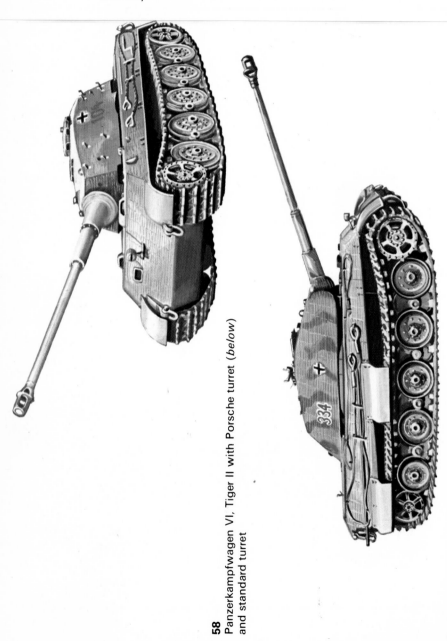

58
Panzerkampfwagen VI, Tiger II with Porsche turret (*below*)
and standard turret

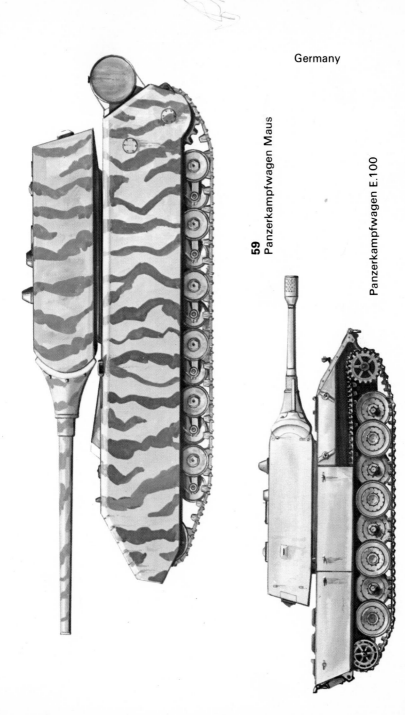

Germany

59
Panzerkampfwagen Maus

Panzerkampfwagen E.100

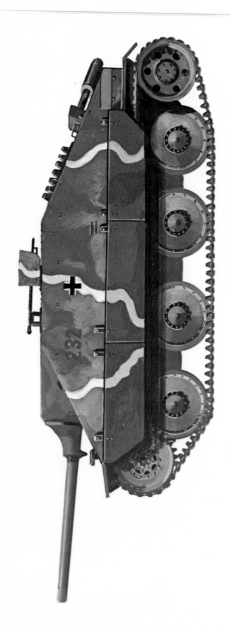

60 Jagdpanzer 38(t), Hetzer

61
Sturmgeschütz III/10.5-cm. StuH

62
Sturmpanzer IV, Brummbär (*above*) and Jagdpanzer
IV/70

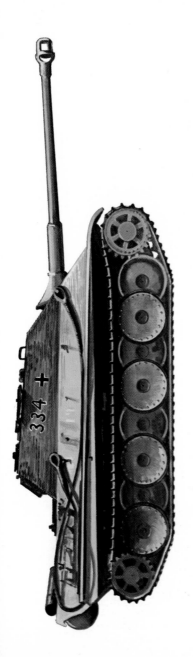

63
8.8-cm. Panzerjäger Panther-Jagdpanther

64
Jagdpanzer Tiger (P), Elefant

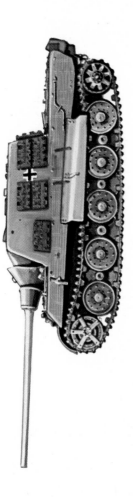

65 Jagdpanzer VI Jagdtiger with Porsche suspension (*above*) and Henschel suspension

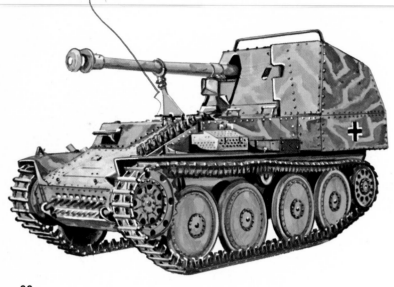

Germany

66
7.5-cm. Pak auf Gw. 38(t), Marder III, Ausf. M

67
15-cm. sIG33 auf Sf. II (*above*) and 7.62-cm. Pak auf
Gw. II, Ausf. D

68

15-cm. Pz fH 18 auf Gw. III/IV, Hummel (*below*) and
8.8-cm. Pak 43/1 (L/71) auf Gw. III/IV, Nashorn

Germany

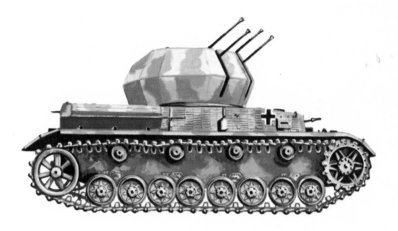

69
Flakpanzer IV (3.7-cm.), Möbelwagen (*below*) and
Flakpanzer IV (2-cm.), Wirbelwind

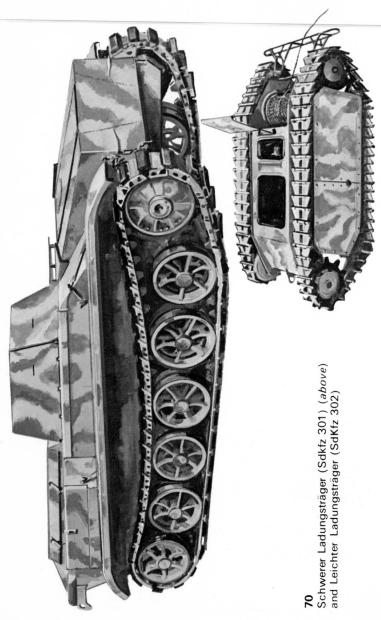

70
Schwerer Ladungsträger (Sdkfz 301) (*above*)
and Leichter Ladungsträger (SdKfz 302)

Germany

71
Leichter Schützenpanzerwagen SdKfz 250/8 (*below*) and
Leichter Schützenpanzerwagen SdKfz 250/9

72
Panzerspähwagen SdKfz 234/2 (Puma) (*above*) and
Panzerspähwagen SdKfz 234/3

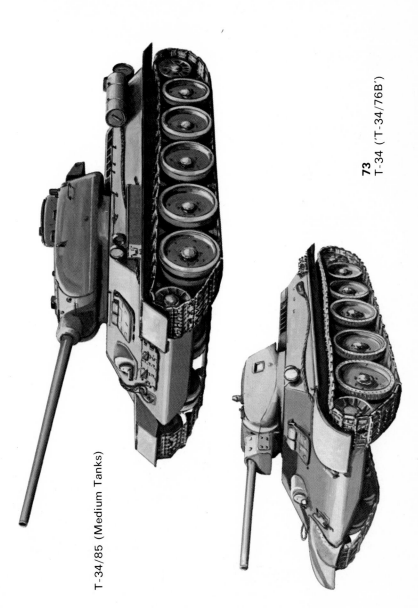

T-34/85 (Medium Tanks)

74
KV-85 (Heavy Tank) (*above*) and SU-85

75
JS-II (Heavy Tank)

76
JSU-122 (*above*) and JSU-152

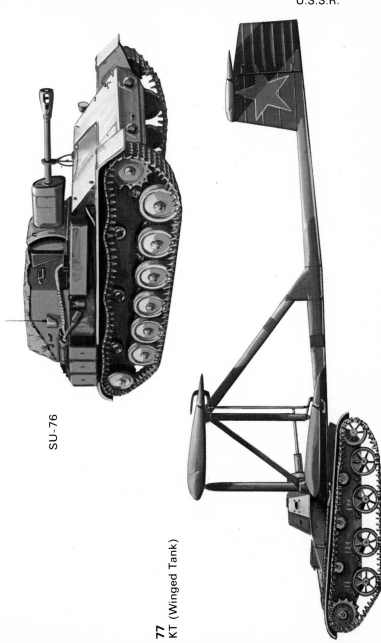

U.S.S.R.

SU-76

77
KT (Winged Tank)

78
BA-64 (Light Armoured Car)

Argentina

79
Tanque 'Narhuel', Modelo DL 43

80
Stridsvagn M/42 (*below*) and Stormartillerivagn M/43

1 **Tankette, Type 97 (Te-Ke) and Light Tank, Type 95 (Ha-Go), Japan.**

The ultra-light tank was evolved in Japan for a dual purpose—as an infantry supply vehicle (towing a trailer) and as a command and liaison vehicle for tank units. Derived originally from Carden-Loyd designs (examples of which were purchased from Britain) and developed through the Type 95 Tankette series, more emphasis was placed on the second function with the Type 97, as the Tankette was found to be quite a useful fighting vehicle, except against heavier enemy tanks. A two-man 4·25-ton vehicle, built by Tokyo Motor Industry, the Type 97 had a 60-b.h.p. Ikegai air-cooled diesel engine at the rear to the right, a centrally mounted turret with a 37-mm. gun and the driver was located at the front left-hand side. The track-driving sprockets were at the front and the suspension consisted, each side, of a large trailing idler wheel and two two-wheel bogie units on bell-crank arms restrained by a long horizontal coil spring.

The light tank was produced to meet a demand for a lighter and more mobile tank than the Type 89 Medium for use in mechanized formations. Designed by Mitsubishi Heavy Industries Ltd in 1933, the Type 95 was the first Japanese light tank classified as such and, due to delays in the introduction of later models into production, remained the principal light tank in service throughout World War II.

The official name for this tank was Ha-Go, but it was often known colloquially as 'Kyo-Go' ('ninety-five'). One of its principal features was the air-cooled diesel engine, able to function satisfactorily in the extreme cold of north Manchuria or in tropical climates. This six-cylinder unit of 110-b.h.p. was located at the rear at the right. Another feature was the use of welding in the construction of the armoured hull, which was protected on a 12-mm. basis. The armament of the Type 95 Light Tank consisted of a 37-mm. gun in the turret (manned by the commander) with, additionally, a ball-mounted 7·7-mm. machine-gun at the right side near the back and another 7·7-mm. machine-gun in a ball mounting at the front left-hand side of the hull. The third member of the crew, the driver, sat to the right of the hull machine-gunner. The transmission layout and bell-crank suspension of the Type 95 were similar to those of the Type 97 Tankette. An interesting point with the Type 95 is that tanks used in north Manchuria were modified while they were there so that the bell crank suspension arms were inverted and an extra small road wheel introduced at the centre of each arm. This was to counteract pitching encountered in the furrows of the kaolin fields of the country.

Both the Type 97 Tankette and the Type 95 Light Tank were used widely in World War II. The former was quite effective when used in comparable functions to those of the British Universal Carrier series. The latter, although obviously no match for Allied medium tanks, was a good vehicle in its class and one of the best Japanese tanks of its era.

2 Medium Tank, Type 97 (improved) (Shinhoto Chi-Ha) and Medium Tank, Type 3 (Chi-Nu), Japan.

The first tank built in Japan was a proto-type completed in 1927 which was developed into a heavy tank. A second and lighter prototype was classified as a medium, which was standardized as Type 89. The design of the latter was directly influenced to some extent by a Vickers Mark C medium tank purchased from Britain. An indirect effect was a fire in the petrol engine of the British tank, which led to the important decision by the Japanese to develop a tank diesel engine, for economy as well as its low fire risk. Air cooling of the diesel was decided on for its advantages in cold climates and in avoiding problems of water supply.

The Type 89 gave good service but by 1935 developments in other countries made it desirable to introduce a faster medium tank, better-protected without undue increase in weight.

The more successful of two competing designs was adopted in 1937 as the Type 97 medium tank or Chi-Ha. With a new suspension system of medium-sized road wheels carried on internal bell cranks controlled by horizontal coil springs, and a cleaned-up hull design, the Type 97 foreshadowed the general appearance of most modern tanks. The main armament still consisted of the short-barrelled 57-mm. gun, however, and an improved model of Type 97 was designed in which the

original turret was replaced by a new turret mounting a 47-mm. gun with a much higher velocity than the old 57-mm. gun. Type 97s were reworked with the new turret and the Type 97 modified and known as Shinhoto ('new turret') Chi-Ha became from 1942 onwards the most important Japanese medium tank of World War II. The secondary armament consisted of a machine-gun in the rear face of the turret at the left-hand side and another in the hull front, to the left of the driver.

With a 170-b.h.p. twelve-cylinder diesel engine and weighing just under 16 tons, the Type 97 (improved) had a maximum speed of 23 m.p.h.

Prior to the modifications to Type 97 described above, an improved medium tank, known as Type 1 (Chi-He) was designed. This differed little in layout and external appearance from the Type 97 (improved) except that it had a flat driver's plate, without the curved protruberance of the earlier tank. The Type 1, however, had the maximum armour protection increased from the inadequate 25-mm. of the Type 97 to 50-mm. and the engine was the new standardized air-cooled diesel of 240-b.h.p. giving an increase in speed to 25 m.p.h.

All the features of the Type 1 were included in the Type 3 medium tank of 1943, in which a more powerful gun (by then essential) was also incorporated. This new gun requiring a larger turret, made possible fortunately without major changes because of forethought in the design of the Type 97, which allowed for a larger turret ring than was immediately necessary, was a 75 mm. weapon. Early medium tanks

Type 3 had a gun based on the Type 95 field gun; later tanks a gun developed from the Type 90 field gun. The latter had a higher muzzle velocity with a consequently shorter barrel life. Welded construction introduced in the Type 97 was used largely in the Type 3 medium.

Lack of industrial capacity in Japan in 1943–45 meant that relatively few of the later types of medium tanks could be produced and so the 'new turret' Type 97 remained the chief type in use to the end of the war.

3 Medium Tank, Type 4 (Chi-To) and Medium Tank, Type 5 (Chi-Ri), Japan.

To meet the requirement for a medium tank with a more powerful gun and greater protection, the Type 4 was developed. Armour thickness was increased to a maximum of 75-mm. and the powerful Type 88 75-mm. anti-aircraft gun was adapted for tank use. These features meant increased weight up to about 30 tons, so that the chassis of the Type 97 could no longer be used and a lengthened chassis with the same type of suspension but with seven road wheels each side was designed. To ensure that performance was maintained, the 400-b.h.p. supercharged twelve-cylinder V-form air-cooled diesel engine was used. The top speed of 28 m.p.h. was, in fact, better than that of the Type 3.

Development began in 1944 of what proved to be the ultimate Japanese medium tank of World War II. This, the Medium Type 5, was an outgrowth of the Type 4 but as it was even heavier, weighing 37 tons, an extra road wheel

each side was added to the suspension, which still employed the system employed in the Type 97 medium.

The turret of the Type 5 medium had the same 75-mm. main armament as that of the Type 4 but the Type 5 had, in addition, a 37-mm. gun mounted in the front of the hull at the left-hand side. Two machine-guns completed the armament.

In order to get Type 5 mediums into the field as soon as possible, when the invasion of Japan was imminent, a German-designed BMW aircraft air-cooled petrol engine was adapted and used, pending the development of the Japanese diesel engine of the requisite horse power. The BMW engine was of 550-b.h.p. and gave a top speed of 28 m.p.h.

Only the prototype of the Type 5 medium had been completed when World War II ended. A small number of Type 4 mediums had been built and these were not sent overseas but allocated for the defence of Japan.

The illustration of the Medium, Type 5, shows the prototype as it existed without the front track guards and the turret (facing to the rear) minus the 75-mm. gun.

4 Gun Tank, Type 1 (Ho-Ni I) and 15-cm. S.P. Howitzer, Type 4 (Ho-Ro), Japan.

These two self-propelled weapons were both built on the ubiquitous chassis of the Type 97 medium tank, powered with a 170-b.h.p. air-cooled diesel engine. Both were armed with field weapons mounted behind three-sided shields, open at the rear and with only partial overhead protection.

The Ho-Ni I was equipped with a 75-mm. gun Type 90 with a muzzle velocity of 2,260 feet per second and was the only really effective anti-tank weapon available in the field in any quantity. The fixed shield permitted a total traverse of 20 degrees, elevation of 25 degrees and depression of 5 degrees.

A Type 38 15-cm. howitzer equipped the Ho-Ro. This short calibre weapon (12 calibres long) fired a 79-lb high explosive projectile to a maximum range of 6,500 yards. This vehicle formed part of the field artillery element of Japanese armoured formations.

5 Amphibious Tank, Type 2 (Ka-Mi) and Amphibious Tank, Type 3 (Ka-Chi), Japan.

Japan, an island country with widespread interests in the Pacific area in World War II, developed, as might be expected, a number of types of amphibious tanks and support vehicles. One of the most widely used amphibious tanks was the Ka-Mi, which was based on the Light Tank Type 95. The general layout of the Type 95 was retained and the suspension system was identical except that in the amphibious tank the idler was in contact with the ground. The hull, however, was made more box-like, with straight sides, thus increasing the volumetric capacity and hence, inherent buoyancy although the main amphibious capability was provided by two pontoons, one at the front and one at the rear. Propulsion in water was by means of two propellers driven by a power take-off from the engine, a six-cylinder 110-h.p. diesel. Steering in water was by means

of twin rudders attached to the rear pontoon. The freeboard in smooth water was only about 6 inches or so and a tall trunk was fitted over the engine grill as well, occasionally, as a cylindrical extension to the turret cupola. The pontoons could quickly be jettisoned once the tank came ashore.

The armament of the Ka-Mi was one 37-mm. gun and a coaxial machine-gun and the armour was to a maximum of 12-mm. A large crew (for a light tank) of five men was carried, including a mechanic to oversee the land and water power and transmission system. The tank had a speed of 23 m.p.h. on land and 6 m.p.h. on smooth water.

The Amphibious Tank, Type 3, Ka-Chi was a medium equivalent of the Ka-Mi and shared many of its characteristics. From the point of view of the armament it was equivalent to the Medium Type 97 (improved) with its 47-mm. gun and two machine-guns, although mechanically, with a lengthened suspension system with eight road wheels each side and a 240-h.p. Type 100 diesel engine, it had more in common with some of the later Japanese medium tanks. Weighing nearly 29 tons, the Ka-Chi had a water speed of 6 m.p.h. and a road speed of 20 m.p.h. Unlike the light amphibious tank, it is not known to have been employed in action.

The illustrations show both types complete with fore and aft pontoons and with engine air trunks fitted.

6 Flail Tank and Engineer Vehicle —Jungle Cutter (Ho-K), Japan.

These two interesting examples of Japanese specialized armour were both based on the widely used Type 97 medium tank.

The flail tank was intended to clear anti-tank mines by detonation through the beating action of the flail attached to the revolving drum. The type of drive used for the flails is not known, except that it was presumably by means of a power take-off from the tank's own engine, since an auxiliary engine was apparently not carried. The tank was normal in most other respects and retained its turret. This vehicle is not known to have been used in action and may not have progressed beyond the prototype stage.

The jungle cutter was a device developed only by the Japanese. It consisted of a wedge-shaped pointed attachment, rather like the bow of a speed boat in appearance, which was carried at the front of the turretless engineer vehicle. Slightly wider than the vehicle to which it was attached, the device was used for forcing a way through heavy undergrowth. The point of attachment of the jungle cutter was at two lugs on the glacis plate of the engineer vehicle. It could be raised from the normal horizontal position if necessary and is shown raised in the illustration.

An alternative attachment for the engineer vehicle was a conventional bulldozer blade.

7 Tank Recovery Vehicle, Type E and Tank Bridgelayer (Medium Type 97 chassis), Japan.

The Japanese developed several types of engineer tanks in World War II, some of which were equipped to carry out apparently on the same mission, a bewildering variety of tasks.

One of the earlier of these vehicles was the Type E, intended for tank recovery but, as adjuncts to this function, equipped as a bridgelayer, flamethrower and mine-clearer. The bridge, about 23 feet long and capable of being folded in two, was normally carried opened above the hull of the vehicle on rollers, by means of which it was launched and then finally pushed into position. Some vehicles of this type were equipped with two hinged forks, with four tines each, one fork in front of each track. These were for mine clearance and also possibly for use as earth anchors. The Type E vehicle also had provision for five flamethrowers, with one mounting at the front and two each side. There was also a machine-gun in a ball mounting in the top centre of the glacis plate. No turret was fitted: armour was to a maximum of 25-mm. It must be assumed that the Type E was intended for special tank recovery tasks in which its particular array of equipment was needed. No jib, or even a winch, seems to have been carried and it seems likely that on some occasions vehicles of this type would have been used in conjunction with other types of engineer vehicles having the necessary pulling or lifting ability.

The suspension of the Tank Recovery vehicle was, surprisingly, quite different from that of any Japanese tank and consisted of eight small road wheels each side, carried in two sets of four (each of two two-wheel bogie units), each set mounted on a semi-elliptic leaf spring. The vehicle was powered by a six-cylinder diesel engine of 140-h.p., giving a maximum speed of 18 m.p.h.

The standard Type 97 medium tank chassis was used for the second engineer vehicle shown here, which was a specialist bridgelayer. The bridge, about 30 feet long, was carried above the hull (the vehicle was turretless) on rollers. It was launched by means of rockets attached to the front end of each trackway.

The illustrations show (top) a bridge-layer facing right and a tank recovery vehicle, Type E, complete with bridge, facing left.

8 Armoured Personnel Carrier, Half-tracked, Type 1 (Ho-Ha) and Armoured Personnel Carrier, Tracked, Type 1 (Ho-Ki), Japan.

Several types of armoured personnel carriers were developed by Japan in World War II, both full-tracked and half-tracked. One of each variety is shown here and they have an affinity in that virtually the same track assembly was used in both.

The half-tracked vehicle Ho-Ha was on the general lines of the German SdKfz 251 series but somewhat larger and of far less sophisticated design. It weighed about 7 tons, was protected by armour up to 8-mm. only and could carry fifteen men. It was powered by a six-cylinder 134-h.p. diesel engine. The suspension consisted of four road wheels each side, with the drive sprockets at the front and the idler wheel at the rear.

The full-tracked armoured personnel carrier Ho-Ki used the same track assembly as the half-track vehicle

except that it had two return rollers instead of one and a rear drive sprocket, the transmission being led back from the six-cylinder 134-h.p. diesel engine mounted at the front. Weighing 6½ tons, the tracked personnel carrier could also carry fifteen men, who were protected by 6-mm. armour all round, although the rear compartment had no overhead protection. A similar vehicle was used as a field artillery tractor.

9 Light Tank, M.5A1 and 75-mm. Howitzer Motor Carriage, M.8, U.S.A.

The Cadillac Division of the General Motors Corporation entered into tank production early in 1942 with a new version of the M.3 Light Tank, known as the M.5. This tank, at the suggestion of Cadillac's, was powered by two eight-cylinder V-form Cadillac automobile engines, with Cadillac Hydramatic automatic transmission. A prototype was constructed in October 1941 by conversion of a standard M.3 and after a highly successful five-hundred mile demonstration drive, the design, subject to modifications in detail, was accepted. A total of 2,074 was built by the end of 1942, when the M.5 was succeeded by an improved model M.5A1. This tank was distinguished from the M.5 chiefly by a turret with an extension at the rear for radio. Other improvements included an escape hatch in the floor of the hull, a gun mount including a direct sight telescope, extra turret periscopes and an anti-aircraft machine-gun mount on the right-hand side of the turret protected by a curved armoured shield. The latter, however, was invariably removed on M.5A1s supplied to the British Army (by whom they were known as Stuart VIs) and sometimes, also, on U.S. Army vehicles. Production of the M.5A1 was ended in mid-1944 when 6,810 had been built.

The M.5A1 (and the M.5) was similar in most respects to the earlier M.3. It had a similar overall performance, in spite of being some 2 tons heavier, with thicker armour, but was much easier to drive than the M.3. The armament consisted of a 37-mm. gun with a coaxial 0·30-in. Browning machine-gun and another in the hull front, together with the anti-aircraft machine-gun already mentioned. An M.5A1 of the U.S. Marine Corps in the Pacific theatre of war is shown in the illustration.

A variant of the M.5 light tank was the Howitzer Motor Carriage M.8. This used the same chassis with the upper hull modified to take an open-topped turret with full traverse, mounting a 75-mm. howitzer. Few changes were found to be necessary beyond removing the ball-mounted hull machine-gun and transferring the driver's and co-driver's hatches to the glacis plate, where they would not interfere with the traverse of the turret.

Known as General Scott, 1,778 M.8s were built between 1942 and 1944 and issued mainly as close support vehicles in Headquarters companies of U.S. armoured battalions in Europe. They were also used by Fighting French troops and one belonging to the French in the Italian campaign, is shown in the illustration.

10 Light Tank, M.22 (Locust) and Light Tank, M.24 (Chaffee), U.S.A.

The M.22 was specially designed by the Marmon Herrington Company Inc. as an airborne light tank. The first pilot model was given the experimental designation T.9, and this was followed by two more modified pilot vehicles (T.9E1) late in 1942. After a number of design changes production began in April 1943 and a total of 830 was built by February 1944, by which time the tank was classified 'limited standard' as M.22.

With a layout conventional for medium tanks of the period, the M.22 had a 162-b.h.p. Lycoming engine at the rear, with a 4-speed gearbox and drive to front track sprockets. The driver sat at the front left-hand side. The turret, carrying the other two crew members, was centrally mounted and had a 37-mm. gun coaxial with a 0·30-in. Browning machine-gun. Armour protection was at a maximum of 1 in. and the top speed was 40 m.p.h.

No M.22's were used by the U.S. Army in action and by December 1944 it was decided that there was no need for an airborne light tank. Some M.22's had, however, been supplied to the United Kingdom (where they were named Locusts) and a very small number was used by the British 6th Airborne Division at the Rhine crossing operation in March 1945. Like its British counterpart, the Tetrarch light tank, the Locust's gun was fitted with a Littlejohn Adaptor, converting it to a 'squeeze gun' and greatly increasing the velocity of the projectile. It is not known if Locusts so equipped were used in action, although Tetrarchs with

Littlejohn Adaptors certainly were. A British Locust with the Littlejohn Adaptor is shown in the illustration.

The Light Tank M.24 was the replacement for the M.3–M.5 series which, by 1943, were already considered inadequate, not only in fire power but in other qualities, such as lack of crew space and poor cooling. The layout of the new tank was worked out by the Cadillac Division of the General Motors Corporation in 1943 and Cadillac later became the main producers, together with Massey-Harris —4,070 being built between April 1944 and June 1945.

The most important feature of the M.24, compared with its light tank predecessors, was the adoption of a 75-mm. gun. This was a light weight high velocity (2,050 feet per second) weapon, adapted from aircraft use. It shared a mounting in the turret with a 0·30-in. Browning machine-gun. The twin V-8 Cadillac engine power unit of 220 b.h.p. used successfully in the M.5A1, was adapted for the M.24 and the torsion bar suspension system (with five medium-sized road wheels) was that used on the M.18 gun motor carriage. A crew of five was carried, of which the driver sat at the front left-hand side, with the co-driver-cum-radio operator at the right, where he controlled a ball-mounted 0·30-in. Browning machine-gun in the glacis plate. Separate emergency driving controls were provided for the co-driver. The commander, gunner and loader occupied the turret.

Although only lightly armoured (maximum 1 inch), the Chaffee was a fast, efficient reconnaissance vehicle. During World War II they saw service only at the end of the North West European and Pacific campaigns in 1945, although they were supplied to many different countries in the post-war years. An M.24 of the U.S. Army as it appeared in snow camouflage in North West Europe in the winter of 1944–45 is illustrated.

11 Medium Tank, M.3 (Lee and Grant), U.S.A.

By 1940, the United States had developed a medium tank that was mechanically satisfactory and carried a liberal supply of machine-guns for infantry support. After study of the reports of the German campaign of that year, however, it was felt that the tank's main armament of a 37-mm. gun was inadequate and it was decided to introduce the 75-mm. gun. The existing medium tank M2A1 was taken as the basis and the design modified to carry a 75-mm. gun in the right-hand side of the hull but retaining a turret mounting a 37-mm. gun.

This tank, which in its production form became known as Medium, M.3, had the disadvantage that the 75-mm. gun in the hull had only a limited traverse, but it was accepted that this was only an interim design that would be put into production as quickly as possible in order to get appreciable numbers of new medium tanks into the hands of the troops. For the first time, the enormous resources of the American automotive industry were to be used for tank production and an initial order for 1,000 M.3s to be built at a new tank arsenal at Detroit was awarded even before the factory was built. However, the first M.3 prototype from the Detroit Tank Arsenal was completed in April 1941, only a short time after prototypes from the more traditional heavy industry tank suppliers, the American Locomotive Co. and Baldwin Locomotive works. Nearly 5,000 M.3s of the original type were built by these and other manufacturers, the last being delivered in August 1942.

In the meantime, a British purchasing mission in the United States had ordered M.3 mediums in quantity, as well as light tanks. The tanks made to British orders, and subsequently named Grants, had some special modifications, the principal of which were incorporated in the turret. This did not have the cupola, incorporating a machine-gun, on top and there was an overhang at the rear to incorporate the wireless equipment, in accordance with British practice. Lack of a command cupola and turret overhang were both considered to be deficiencies in design later in the war but the lowering of the M.3's considerable height was, no doubt, on balance an advantage, particularly in the open North African terrain where most of the tanks were to go.

The M.3 in its original (and, numerically, by far the most important) version was powered by a Continental nine-cylinder radial air-cooled engine of 340-b.h.p. and the hull was of all-riveted construction to a maximum armour thickness of 50-mm. The engine was at the rear, the transmission being led forward to a gear-box alongside the driver and the track drive was via front sprockets. The hull-mounted 75-mm. gun at the right had a total

traverse of 30 degrees and 46 rounds were carried. The turret had a full 360 degree traverse and besides the 37-mm. gun (for which 178 rounds were carried) it had a 0·30-in. Browning machine-gun, coaxially mounted. Standard M.3s also had a further Browning in the cupola on the main turret and two more in the glacis plate at the left, operated by the driver. These hull machine-guns were normally removed in all British-used vehicles and, of course, the Grant did not have the machine-gun cupola, although an anti-aircraft machine-gun was sometimes mounted on the turret roof.

The M.3s suspension used the horizontal volute system, already well tried in earlier medium and light tanks. It consisted of three twin-wheel bogie units each side.

The Medium M.3 first saw action (as the Grant) with the British forces in the Western Desert in the spring of 1942. In spite of its design shortcomings, its effective 75-mm. gun mounted in a reliable vehicle with a good degree of mobility (maximum speed 26 m.p.h.) helped considerably to redress the balance against the German armour. A Grant of the 3rd Royal Tank Regiment, one of the first units to receive them, is shown in one of the illustrations.

The U.S. Army also used the M.3 in action in North Africa—in Tunisia. This was in the standard form in which a quantity was also supplied to Britain (where they were known as the Lee) and by which name were, likewise, used in North Africa. M.3s were also employed by British Commonwealth forces in the Burma campaign of 1944; often in hybrid form, where they were commonly referred to as 'Lee/Grants', and were used also by the Australians for home defence. The other illustration shows a later production M.3 (with the longer 40 calibre 75-mm. gun) on issue to the U.S. Army training in Britain in 1942.

12 Medium Tank, M.4 (Sherman), U.S.A.

The Sherman is arguably one of the greatest tanks of World War II, even on numbers alone, because over 58,000 were built. The Sherman was a good straightforward design which proved adaptable, so that armament and armour modification could be introduced to enable it to keep level with its opponents to the end of the war.

Design work on the M.4 as the definitive 75-mm. gun-armed medium tank to replace the medium M.3 model was commenced in March 1941. Many of the elements of the M.3, such as the power unit, transmission and suspension were quite satisfactory and were adopted, but the main feature of the M.4 was the incorporation of the 75-mm. gun in a fully rotating turret. The prototype, known as T.6, was ready by September 1941 and after trials and minor design changes was approved for production commencing in early 1942.

Production of the M.4 in the numbers envisaged would have overrun the supply of Continental engines (as used in the M.3 and original M.4 designs) and so the use of alternative engines, already used in later models of the M.3, and others, was provided for. The most important of these were the General Motors 6046 twelve-cylinder diesel

(two six-cylinder truck engines geared together) used in the M.4A2, the Ford GAA V-8 petrol engine, used in the M.4A3 and the Chrysler A.57 thirty-cylinder petrol engine used in the M.4A4. The latter engine consisted of no less than five six-cylinder truck engines all driving a common crank shaft.

The basic hull shape of all Shermans included a well-sloped glacis plate but the form of construction varied, that of the M.4A1 with a cast, rounded hull being closest to the original design. The M.4 (first in designation sequence but actually the third type to enter production) had an all-welded hull with sharp edges, as did the M.4A2, M4A3 and M.4A4. Some late M.4s, however, had a cast front portion married to the welded rear part of the hull.

Armament of the Sherman consisted originally of a 75-mm. M.3 gun (although short M.2 guns with counter-weights were provisionally fitted on some of the very first tanks built) with a coaxial 0·30-in. Browning machine-gun. In the front of the hull was a Browning machine-gun in a ball mounting and, beside it, two more Brownings, fixed to fire forwards only. The latter were eliminated after the early production vehicles. Most tanks in American use had a 0·50-in. Browning machine-gun mounted on a pintle on the turret for anti-aircraft use, although this weapon was not accurate and was commonly discarded in British-used tanks. Changes in the main armament of Shermans during the course of production included the 105-mm. howitzer in place of the 75-mm. gun, and the 76-mm. gun, a long high velocity cannon. These weapons were incorporated in a proportion of tanks during the course of production and some tanks supplied to Britain were modified to take the British 17-pr gun. These were M.4A1s, M.4A3s and M.4A4s but mostly the latter, which were known as the Sherman Vc in Britain. The 105-mm. howitzer tanks were used for close support and the 76-mm. and 17-pr gun versions used to stiffen up the anti-tank fire power of the 75-mm. Shermans.

The Sherman was used by American and British forces on nearly all battle fronts from 1942 onwards and several thousand were supplied to the Russians.

One illustration shows a side view of a typical Sherman armed with the 75-mm. gun and the other a 17-pr-equipped Sherman Vc of a British armoured regiment in Normandy in 1944, where this model was first used in action.

13 Medium Tank, M.26 (Pershing), U.S.A.

Following the abandonment of heavy tanks in the U.S.A., attention was turned to the problem of mounting a 90-mm. gun in a medium tank. A series of experimental tanks was built between 1942 and 1944, trying out various suspension systems, transmissions and other components as well as various guns, including the 90-mm. This series culminated in the T.26E1 completed in January 1944. This tank with some modifications, including a muzzle brake on the 90-mm. gun and increased ammunition stowage, became the T.26E3. By this time the need for a better gun than the 76-mm., the best weapon fitted to M.4 Medium tanks,

was recognized following combat experience in Normandy. There was, therefore, a demand for a 90-mm. gun tank but the T.26E3, now reclassified as a heavy tank was not yet considered battleworthy as it had been insufficiently tested. Twenty tanks out of the first batch to be built were, however, shipped to Europe for field trials and in January 1945 were now declared battleworthy. Allotted to the 3rd and 9th Armoured Divisions of the U.S. First Army, the tanks were named the General Pershing and standardized as M.26. Production was by now well under way and 200 had been issued by the end of the war in Europe, although most arrived at the front too late to see action. Some that did—at Remagen on the Rhine—were some of the original Pershings issued to the 9th Armoured Division.

The M.26 weighed 46 (U.S.) tons. Besides the 90-mm. gun (53 calibres long) it had a coaxial 0·30-in. Browning machine-gun and another Browning in a ball-mounting in the hull glacis plate and a 0·50-in. anti-aircraft machine-gun on the turret top. The crew of five were protected by armour at a maximum of 102-mm.

The M.26's engine was a Ford Model GAF eight-cylinder V-form type of 500-b.h.p. and the transmission was Torquematic with three forward speeds, with the track drive from rear sprockets. Suspension was of the torsion bar type and a maximum speed of 30 m.p.h. could be attained.

Although arriving too late to see much action in World War II, the Pershing was the direct ancestor of a long line of post-war U.S. medium tanks.

14 Heavy Tank, M.6, U.S.A.

A tank which received much publicity in the Allied press in 1941–42 was the American M.6 heavy tank. Sometimes shown crushing motor cars, the 50-ton M.6 was of spectacular appearance and, for its time, was a powerful tank.

Called for in 1940 as a heavy tank to complement the M.3 Medium, the first pilot model, out of several designed to test alternative forms of hull construction, transmission and power unit, was completed at the end of 1941. This model, T.1E2, had a cast hull and a torque converter transmission and was later standardized as Heavy Tank M.6. The T.1E3, which appeared slightly later, had a welded hull but was otherwise similar, and was standardized as M.6A1. The third to appear, T.1E1, was ready in 1943—this model had electric transmission and a cast hull. It was usually known later as M.6A2.

All models of this heavy tank were powered by a Wright G-200 radial nine-cylinder air-cooled engine of 800-b.h.p. which gave a maximum speed of about 22 m.p.h. The main armament consisted of a 3-in. gun (a modified anti-aircraft gun) with a coaxial 37-mm. gun in the turret. (The T.1E2 had also a 0·30-in. Browning machine-gun in a separate cupola on top and a 0·50-in. machine-gun on a high-angle mounting at the right rear of the turret.) Two 0·50-in. machine-guns were mounted in the front hull plate under the control of the co-driver and the driver was responsible for two (later one) fixed machine-guns. Armour was at a maximum of 100-mm. and a crew of six was carried.

Because of disagreement over the need for a heavy tank, the large orders originally envisaged were reduced drastically to one hundred and fifteen in September 1942 and then cancelled altogether at the end of the year, although there were subsequent experiments with 90-mm. and 105-mm. guns. Consequently, no more than forty of all variants of the M.6 series, including prototypes, were built. Apart from propaganda purposes, however, the programme had involved useful work, which was not wasted, on armour design, gun stabilizers and power traverse, horizontal volute spring suspension and transmissions, as all these features of the M.6 were used in various later light and medium tanks.

The illustrations show the M.6 (T.1E2) and (below) the M.6A1.

15 105-mm. Howitzer Motor Carriage, M.7 (S.P. 105-mm., Priest), U.S.A.

In action for the first time with British forces in North Africa, where it formed an important element in the self-propelled artillery available at the Alamein battle in October 1942, the Howitzer Motor Carriage M.7 became the main field artillery component in U.S. armoured divisions during World War II.

The decision to mount a 105-mm. field howitzer on the same chassis as the M.3 Medium Tank was taken in June 1941. Production began in April 1942, so that the first ninety vehicles for British use were delivered in Egypt in September. A Priest (as they were named by the British) belonging to 11th

Regiment, Royal Horse Artillery (of 1st Armoured Division), which received its first Priests on 10 September 1942, is shown in one of the illustrations. This vehicle has the earlier type of 3-piece noseplate.

The M.7 had the 105-mm. howitzer mounted to the right of the hull centre line to fire forwards, with a total traverse of 45 degrees. The driver sat at the left, and a characteristic dustbin-shaped 'pulpit' mounting for a 0·5-in. Browning machine-gun was at the right. The Continental nine-cylinder radial engine, drive train and suspension were all similar to those of the M.3 medium. Maximum speed was about 25 m.p.h. Armour was at a maximum thickness of 62 mm. although there was no overhead protection for the crew of seven, except for the driver.

A later, but generally similar, version of the M.7, the M.7B1, using M.4 Medium Tank components replaced the former in production from March 1944 onwards until the type was gradually replaced by the M.37 in the last months of the war.

The M.7 was used widely by field artillery units in U.S. armoured divisions from 1942 to 1945 in most theatres of war, including North West Europe. An M.7 in this area as it appeared in late 1944 is shown in one of the coloured views. After the North African campaign Priests continued in American and British use in the Sicilian and Italian campaigns which followed (and during which, incidentally, a 10-in. mortar was experimentally fitted in one). They were also employed by British troops in the Burma campaign and in the opening stages of the Normandy operations.

16 3-in. Gun Motor Carriage, M.10 and 76-mm. Gun Motor Carriage, M.18, U.S.A.

It was American philosophy in 1942 that enemy tanks should be engaged wherever possible by specialized 'tank destroyers', rather than by their own tanks. The characteristics required of a tank destroyer were a powerful gun and a good speed, even if these were attained at the expense of reduced protection for the crew. The Gun Motor Carriage M.10 was an adaptation of the M.4 Medium Tank chassis based on these principles. The powerful 3-in. gun was mounted in an open-top fully rotating turret on a modified M.4 tank hull with engines, transmission and suspension, equivalent to corresponding vehicles in the M.4 series. The maximum armour thickness was only 37 mm., although the side plates of the hull were, unlike those of the M.4, sloped to give better protection. The M.10 had twin General Motors diesel engines like the Medium Tank M.4A2, and the M.10A1 (externally similar to the M.10) had the Ford GAA eight-cylinder petrol engine, like the M.4A3. In either case, the maximum speed was 30 m.p.h. A development of the M.10 series was the M.36, a similar vehicle but equipped with a 90-mm. gun—the only U.S. armoured vehicle in the field with this weapon and the only one able to tackle the German Tiger II before the advent of the M.26 heavy tank.

Some M.10's and M.10A1's were supplied to the United Kingdom, and they were used by British and Commonwealth forces in Italy and North West Europe. A British modification to a proportion of the vehicles received was the substitution of the 17-pr for the 3-in. gun.

The Gun Motor Carriage M.18 continued the idea behind the M.10 but on a more modern chassis which, because of its weight of around 19 tons with a high power/weight ratio, turned out to be the fastest tracked fighting vehicle of World War II. Up to 55 m.p.h. could be achieved.

After undergoing several changes in both armament and suspension, the M.18, later nicknamed Hellcat, in its final form consisted of a 76-mm. gun, 55 calibres long, mounted in a partly open top turret on a new chassis with torsion bar suspension, powered by a Continental nine-cylinder radial engine of 340 b.h.p. (400 b.h.p. engines in some). The driver sat at the left front of the hull and the co-driver at the right, with the three other crew members in the turret. The commander sat at the left side of the turret, where he was able to operate the 0·50-in. Browning machine-gun carried on a ring mounting on the turret top.

Between July and October 1944, 2,507 M.18's were built, and all went to the U.S. Army where they were employed, with great success, mainly in the Italian and North West European theatres of war. The M.18 chassis was also used for the development of other vehicles, including the M.24 light tank.

17 **Landing Vehicle, Tracked (Unarmored) Mark IV (L.V.T.4) and Landing Vehicle, Tracked (Armored) Mark IV (L.V.T.[A]4), U.S.A.**

The great majority of amphibious cargo carriers used in World War II were built by the United States; neither her Allies nor her enemies, apart from Japan, paying very much attention to this class of vehicle.

The type was derived from an amphibian designed by Donald Roebling, intended for rescue work in hurricanes and the swampy Everglades region of Florida. A militarized version of Roebling's 1940 model was ordered as a Landing Vehicle Tracked for the U.S. Marine Corps and known as L.V.T.1. A greatly improved model, L.V.T.2, appeared in 1943. The next development, which finally became the L.V.T.3, had twin Cadillac engines in the pontoons at either side, so enabling a rear-loading ramp to be incorporated. The L.V.T.2, which had a single seven-cylinder Continental radial engine, was also modified to provide an unobstructed hold with a rear-loading ramp by having the engine moved forward, the result being known as L.V.T4.

Armoured cargo and support versions of the L.V.T.'s were also developed, the L.V.T.(A)1 and L.V.T.(A)2, both having a similar chassis to the LVT2, the former being enclosed, with an M.3 light tank turret (37-mm. gun and 0·30-in. Browning machine-gun) mounted on the roof, the latter a cargo carrier only. The L.V.T.(A)4 was similar to the L.V.T.(A)1, except that a 75-mm. howitzer turret from the M.8 gun motor carriage was used.

All the L.V.T. series were propelled in water by means of their tracks, which on all except the original L.V.T.1 had W-shaped grousers added. The water speed for all models was between 6 and 7½ m.p.h. The L.V.T.1 had an unsprung suspension system, but all the later L.V.T.s used an interesting rubber torsion suspension. Each road wheel was mounted independently on an arm, the pivot of which was a hollow tube, fitted over a smaller tube attached to the hull. The space between the two tubes was filled with vulcanized rubber which, in resisting the movement of the tube-carrying road wheel, acted like a spring.

The production of L.V.T.s in the United States amounted to 1,225 L.V.T.1s, 3,413 L.V.T.2s and L.V.T.(A)2s, 509 L.V.T.(A)1s, 1,890 L.V.T.(A)4s and 8,438 L.V.T.4s. The L.V.T.3 appeared late in World War II and was first used in action in April 1945—2,962 were built, many of which saw service after the war. There was also an improved version of the L.V.T.(A)4, the L.V.T.(A)5 with powered turret traverse, of which 269 were built too late to see action.

All the L.V.T.s (except as mentioned above) saw extensive service with the U.S. Army and Marine Corps in the Pacific, taking part in the assaults on the Japanese-held islands. L.V.T.s were also supplied to the British Army (where they were classified as 'Amphibians, Tracked' 2 ton (L.V.T.1 and L.V.T.(A)1) or 2½ ton) by whom they were used in the marshy areas of North Italy, and (in company with American-manned L.V.T.s) in the Rhine and other river crossings in North West Europe. Most of the vehicles used by the British were L.V.T.2s and L.V.T.(A)2s—known usually as Buffalo II—and L.V.T.4 (Buffalo IV). One of the latter, carrying a Universal Carrier, is shown in one illustration. The other picture shows a L.V.T.(A)4 as used by U.S. Forces in the Pacific war theatre in late 1944.

18 Car, Half-Track, M.2A1 and 75-mm. Gun Motor Carriage, M3, U.S.A.

Half-tracks were produced extensively by the United States, as well as Germany, in World War II and used for a variety of purposes. The American vehicles were generally somewhat less sophisticated, both mechanically and in the hull design, than their German counterparts, although they did have driven front axles.

Nearly all the U.S. half-tracks of World War II were armoured and the design originated, in essence, through the addition of rear tracks (of the type developed in France by Citröen from designs by Adolphe Kégresse) to a four-wheel-drive Scout Car, M.3A1. The first standardized model was a personnel carrier for ten men known as Car, Half-Track, M.2.

The layout of the M.2 was typical of the great majority of U.S. half tracks built during World War II. The engine was in the conventional normal-control truck position and the transmission was led, via a transfer box, forward to the front wheels and back to the track drive wheels at the front of the track assembly. The track suspension consisted of four road wheels each side, carried on a single bogie unit. The tracks consisted of continuous bands, made up of steel cables covered with metal cross pieces (to avoid slip) and metal track guides. A roller was carried in front of the radiator to help prevent the vehicle 'ditching'. The armoured hull, bolted on to the chassis frame, was made up of flat plates of 6·35-mm. thickness, except for the driver's plate and the upper, hinged, parts of the side doors, which were 12·72-mm.

The engine in the M.2 was the White six-cylinder in-line type of 147 b.h.p. The armament consisted of one 0·30-in. and one 0·50-in. Browning machine-guns. These weapons could be mounted on a continuous rail which ran round the perimeter of the inside of the hull.

The M.2 was followed by a similar vehicle with a slightly longer hull, capable of carrying thirteen men, designated Personnel Carrier, Half-Track, M.3. Other differences included a rear door and the omission of the machine-gun 'skate rail', a pedestal mount being provided instead. Newer versions of both M.2 and M.3, standardized in 1943, were the M.2A1 and M.3A1, both of which had an armoured ring mount at the front left-hand side of the hull for the 0·50-in. machine-gun for use against aerial or ground targets.

To meet the demand for half-tracks, the International Harvester Company joined the production programme, and the International six-cylinder engine of 143 b.h.p. was used in the M.5 and M.9 series which were externally much like the M.2 and M.3 series.

One of the earliest of many self-propelled gun mountings on half-track chassis, and the first to be standardized, was the Gun Motor Carriage M.3. This was basically a M.3 Personnel Carrier with a 75-mm. gun, model M.1897A4 (originally a French design) mounted with a shield in the crew compartment, where it had a traverse of 19 degrees left and 21 degrees to the right. The gun was intended as an anti-tank weapon, and the projectile had a muzzle velocity of 2,000 feet per second.

U.S. half-tracked 75-mm. gun motor carriages were used in action in Tunisia and Italy before being declared obsolete in September 1944. They were also used by the U.S. Marine Corps in the Pacific theatre and one of these is shown in the illustration. Some vehicles of this type supplied to Britain were used in armoured car regiments for fire support purposes.

Half-tracked personnel carriers were used widely by U.S. forces and their allies. An M.2A1 belonging to the Fighting French is illustrated.

19 **Armored Car, Staghound I (T.17E1) and Armored Car, Boarhound (T.18E2), U.S.A.**

Relatively few armoured cars were produced in the United States during World War II, because the American preference was for tracked vehicles for most combat tasks, including reconnaissance. However, British experience in the North African desert had shown that good use could be made of armoured cars in this kind of terrain and several American armoured car designs were started in 1941–42, prompted by British needs. The first of these were the T.17 and T.17E1 commenced in June 1941. Both rear-engined armoured cars, equipped with a 37-mm. gun turret (somewhat like that of the Grant medium tank) and generally alike in layout and appearance, the T.17 was a six-wheeled vehicle (6 × 6) by Ford and the T.17E1 was four-wheeled and designed by General Motors (Chevrolet Motor Car Division). Some 3,760 T.17s and 3,500 T.17E1s were on order by June 1942, but in reviewing the overall production of armoured cars, the Special Armored Vehicle Board decided to eliminate the T.17 on the grounds that it was too heavy. Only 250 had been made and these were allocated for internal security duties in the U.S.A. The T.17E1 order was also in danger of being cancelled after 250 were built, but production was continued at the specific request of the United Kingdom, and a final total of 2,844 T.17E1s was built by December 1943, all of which were supplied to Britain or Commonwealth countries, where they were known as Staghound I.

The Staghound was without a chassis as such, the automotive components being attached direct to the armoured hull. The power unit consisted of two six-cylinder G.M.C. Model 270 engines, each of 97 b.h.p., mounted at the rear and driving all four wheels through a Hydramatic (automatic) transmission. The turret carried a 37-mm. gun and a 0·30-in. Browning machine-gun, mounted coaxially, and there was another Browning machine-gun in a ball mount in the glacis plate, controlled by the co-driver at the right. The driver, who enjoyed power steering, sat at the left. Hull armour was at a maximum of $\frac{7}{8}$ inches (22 mm.), although the turret was mainly $1\frac{1}{4}$–$1\frac{3}{4}$ inches thick.

Deliveries of Staghounds to the British forces were too late for them to be used in the Desert fighting, where they would have been ideal. Although easy to drive, they were not popular with armoured car regiments for reconnaissance duties in European terrain, where they were regarded as being too large and lacked the manoeuvrability of the smaller British Daimler armoured cars. None the less, Staghounds found useful employment as command vehicles at squadron and regimental headquarters, where their roominess and provision for a crew of five were advantages. (A Staghound belonging to the regimental headquarters of a British armoured car regiment is shown in the illustration.)

A Staghound A.A. armoured car (T.17E2) was also built for Britain and 1,000 of them were produced. This had an open top turret, designed by Frazer-Nash in England and built by the Norge Division of Borg-Warner in Detroit, mounting twin 0·50-in. anti-aircraft machine-guns. British modifications of the Staghound I included the Staghound II, in which the 37-mm. gun was replaced by a 3-in. howitzer for close support use, and the Staghound III, in which a British Crusader cruiser tank 75-mm. gun turret was mounted in place of the original turret.

The heavy armoured car T.18E2 had all the characteristics required for open desert warfare to an even greater degree than the Staghound and, like it, unfortunately was ready only when the campaign in North Africa was over. It weighed over 26 (short) tons and was over 20 feet long, but the armament was only a 6-pr gun and two 0·30-in. Browning machine-guns (one in the glacis plate). This was much inferior to that of many tanks better armoured and weighing less, although with two G.M.C. engines totalling 250 b.h.p. the T.18E2, named Boarhound by Britain, was capable of a speed of 50 m.p.h. Only 30 T.18E2s out of the original order for 2,500 were completed by the Yellow Truck and Coach Company division of General Motors. All of these were delivered to Britain where they were stored in ordnance depots, none being used in action.

20 Light Armored Car, M.8 and Armored Utility Car, M.20, U.S.A.

The best American armoured car of World War II was designed in response to a requirement by the Tank Destroyer Force for a 37-mm. Gun Motor Carriage. Intended to replace the 37-mm. Gun Motor Carriage M.6—an anti-tank gun on an unarmoured ¾-ton truck—the T.22, prototype of the M.8, was later re-classified as a light armoured car.

The T.22 was designed by the Ford Motor Co. in competition with other 6 × 4 and 4 × 4 projects by Studebaker and Fargo. Out of these and many other armoured car designs at this time (some of which had even received large production orders) only the T.17E1 and the T.22, which was completed in early 1942, modified as T.22E2 and standardized as M.8, remained to be produced in quantity after a critical survey had been carried out by the Special Armored Vehicle Board.

A six-wheeled, six-wheel-drive vehicle with a rear-mounted engine—the 110-b.h.p. six-cylinder Hercules JXD—the M.8 had a welded hull (armoured to a maximum of ¾ in.) and a circular cast turret with an open top. The armament consisted of a 37-mm. gun and a 0·30-in. Browning machine-gun in the turret with provision for a 0·50-in. heavy machine-gun to be mounted on the turret top. With a four-speed gear-box, the maximum speed of the M.8 was 55 m.p.h. The car had a four-man crew.

The Armoured Utility Car M.20 was a companion vehicle to the M.8, to which it was mechanically identical. Intended as a command vehicle or armoured personnel or cargo carrier, it differed from the M.8 in having no turret and a square, raised centre section of the hull. This was open-topped and was surmounted by a ring-mounting for a 0·50-in. machine-gun. The M.20 could carry up to six men, according to function.

A total of 8,523 M.8s was built in World War II and 3,791 M.20s. They were used in numbers by the U.S. Army—the M.8 was, in fact, the only armoured car to be employed in action by the Americans. The M.8 (but not the M.20) was also supplied to the United Kingdom for use by the British and Commonwealth armies, by whom they were employed in action chiefly in the Italian campaign towards the end of the war. Named Greyhound in British service, the M.8's characteristics were summarized by one armoured car regiment as having a magnificent cross-country performance; being hard to reverse; difficult to protect against mines (the thin hull floor armour—⅛ inch to ¼ inch—was often reinforced by sandbags) and the useful advantage in a reconnaissance vehicle of being able to cross Class 9 bridges.

The illustrations show an M.8 of the U.S. Army in North West Europe (the fifteenth vehicle in C Troop of a reconnaissance unit) with impedimenta as carried in a campaign, and an M.20 in 'parade ground' condition.

21 Tank, Light, Mark VII, Tetrarch and Tank, Light, Mark VIII, Harry Hopkins, U.K.

The Light Tank, Mark VII, was a drastic departure from earlier light tanks (culminating in the Mark VIc) designed by Vickers-Armstrongs Limited. Although owing something to the track-warping steering device of the Vickers Carriers, the Light Mark VII had an entirely new form of steering in that all four road wheels on both sides could be turned into a curve for steering in a wide radius. This warped the tracks in the direction desired, although for sharper turns steering brakes on either track were brought into action.

Developed from a prototype completed at the end of 1937, the Light Mark VII, later known as Tetrarch, although armoured only up to a maximum of 16 mm., had the main armament of a contemporary British cruiser tank—a 2-pr gun with coaxial 7·92-mm. Besa machine-gun. The Littlejohn Adaptor, to greatly increase the muzzle velocity of the 2-pr was fitted to some Tetrarchs and this device is shown on the vehicle (belonging to 6th Airborne Division) illustrated. Although the first Tetrarchs were delivered in 1940, production (by the Metropolitan-Cammell Carriage and Wagon Company Limited—a Vickers-Armstrongs subsidiary) was seriously interrupted by damage caused by an air raid on the factory and the last of the 171 vehicles built was not delivered until 1942. The first use in action of the Tetrarch was during 1942—some with the Russians, who received a small quantity, and some

forming a half squadron in the British attack on Madagascar. The remaining stock of Tetrarchs was then reserved for airborne operations.

The Tetrarch created history on the eve of D-Day 1944 by being glider-landed in Normandy. Only about half a dozen tanks were used, and mainly in a defensive role, but their fire power gave useful support to the parachute troops.

Developed from the Tetrarch and weighing a ton heavier, the Light Tank, Mark VIII, named after President Roosevelt's Lend-Lease administrator, had armour protection up to 38 mm. and the design of the hull and turret was ballistically improved. The Harry Hopkins's armament was the same as the Tetrarch's but the maximum speed was reduced from 40 m.p.h. to 30 m.p.h. Following the Tetrarch in the Metropolitan-Cammell production line, 102 Light Mark VIII's were built. They were never used in action and were the last British light tank before the advent of the Alvis Scorpion in the 1960s

22 Tanks, Cruiser, Mark VI, Crusader I and Crusader III, U.K.

The Crusader arose from a proposal by the Nuffield organization for a 'heavy cruiser' development of their earlier model, Cruiser Mark IV. This the War Office accepted: the pilot model was running in July 1939 and full scale production was under way in 1940.

Although the armour protection was increased to a maximum of 40 mm., an extra pair of road wheels added, the main turret redesigned and an auxiliary turret added, the Cruiser Mark VI had many features of the Cruiser Mark IV. These included the same form of Christie suspension, the 340 b.h.p. Nuffield Liberty engine and the same turret armament. Nevertheless, it proved to be far less reliable than its predecessor, particularly when subjected to desert conditions in North Africa. Mechanically, the engine fan drive and the air cleaner were particular sources of weakness, and the cramped auxiliary turret mounting a single 7·92-mm. Besa machine-gun was unsatisfactory. The Crusader's good speed of nearly 30 m.p.h. was an asset in the desert, though, and was a feature liked by its crews and admired by the Germans and Italians—the latter to the point of building an experimental tank of their own modelled on the Crusader.

The demand for heavier armour led to the introduction of the Crusader II, in which the frontal protection was increased to 49 mm. The auxiliary turret was usually omitted in this model, the aperture plated over and the space created used for extra stowage. (Some Crusader I's were also retrospectively modified in this way.)

The 6-pr gun having by then become available, the Crusader III was designed to use it, and the first tanks of this model came off the production lines in May 1942. Basically the same turret was used, with the mantlet redesigned, but the bigger gun meant a reduction in the crew to three (Crusader I had five men, Crusader II without the auxiliary turret had four.)

A total of 5,300 Crusaders was built by a group of firms under the parentage of Nuffield Mechanizations and Aero Limited. This total includes tanks which were later in the war converted to anti-aircraft tanks and 17-pr gun tractors and chiefly employed in action in the North West Europe campaign. The Crusader I's action was in the North African desert in 1941 and the illustration shows one in the markings used at the end of that year. Crusader III's were used by both the Eighth and First Armies in North Africa, and one belonging to a regiment of 6th Armoured Division of First Army in Tunisia in 1942 is shown.

23 Tanks, Cruiser, Centaur and Cromwell, U.K.

As a successor to the Crusader, a new cruiser tank was planned in 1940 to have much heavier armour, a 6-pr gun, and to greatly improve the power/weight ratio by using a de-rated version of the Rolls-Royce Merlin aero engine. The design was completed but as the new engine could not be ready for some time, the Nuffield organization produced an interim model, known as Cruiser Mark VII (and later as Cavalier), which employed the Nuffield Liberty engine, gearbox, transmission and radiators of the Crusader, for which they were also responsible. The Cavalier (of which the prototype appeared early in 1942) was mechanically rather unreliable and only a few hundred were built. It was, however, redesigned by Leyland Motors Limited, retaining the same engine modified and linked to a Merrit-Brown gearbox. The suspension was also improved, although the armour (a basic 76-mm. frontal protection) and the 6-pr gun, coaxial and hull 7·92-mm.

Besa machine-gun armaments were unchanged. This tank was known as Centaur I. The British 75-mm. replaced the 6-pr gun in Centaur III, and Centaur IV was a close support version armed with the 95-mm. howitzer.

Cavaliers and Centaurs were used mainly in secondary roles in the North West Europe campaign, the former only as an artillery observation post vehicle and the latter mainly as O.P., bulldozer and anti-aircraft tanks. Some eighty Centaur IV's of the Royal Marines Armoured Support Group did, however, see action as gun tanks, both in support of the landings, firing from landing craft offshore, and subsequently in continuing to give fire support inland. A Centaur IV of this formation is shown in the illustration.

The Cromwell appeared as the natural development of the Centaur, which had been designed so that the Nuffield Liberty engine could easily be replaced by the new engine, when the Meteor engine was ready for it. The first batch of Meteors (adapted from the Merlin aero engine) were built by Rolls-Royce (although other manufacturers then assumed production) and the Cromwell was produced in series from January 1943 onwards. After some changes, Leyland Motors Limited some months later became production 'parents' for the Cromwell as well as the Centaur—which was, of course, replaced on the assembly lines by the newer tank as soon as possible. Some Centaurs were later re-engined with Meteors and re-designated as Cromwells.

Running through eight basic Marks, the Cromwells I–III had the 6-pr gun, the IV, V and VII had the 75-mm., and the VI and VIII had the 95-mm. howitzer. The early Cromwells were exceedingly fast, with a maximum speed of 40 m.p.h., but this was governed down to 32 m.p.h. on later models to lengthen the life of the Christie suspension. Welded hull construction was first used in British tanks on the Cromwell V w and VII w, and in these tanks the maximum thickness was increased from 76 mm. to 101 mm. British armoured reconnaissance regiments in North West Europe in 1944–45 were equipped with the Cromwell which, additionally, equipped the armoured brigade of 7th Armoured Division in the earlier stages of the campaign. The illustration shows a Cromwell (with 6-pr gun) of 5 Troop, A Squadron, 15th/19th Hussars in 1943, when it formed part of 9th Armoured Division. This regiment, still equipped with Cromwells, became, in 1944, the Armoured Reconnaissance Regiment of 11th Armoured Division in North West Europe.

24 Tank, Cruiser, Challenger, U.K.

The Challenger was designed in 1942 as a cruiser tank to mount the new 17-pr gun. Prototypes were produced in the same year by the design firm, Birmingham Railway Carriage and Wagon Company, the use of many components of the Cromwell series easing many problems. Development of the turret was undertaken by Stothert and Pitt Ltd who were specialists in A.F.V. turret design. Problems were encountered during trials with the suspension and the turret and mounting, and then it was suggested that the 17-pr gun should be mounted in the Sherman, which was becoming available in increasing numbers to Britain.

The latter proved ultimately to be the best answer to the question of getting a powerful tank gun into the field where it could tackle the latest German tanks. Nevertheless, 200 Challengers were ordered and, the design snags eliminated, delivered during 1944. They were used chiefly by British regiments equipped with Cromwells in North West Europe, from Normandy onwards.

The illustrations show a tank of 8th King's Royal Irish Hussars, the armoured reconnaissance regiment of 7th Armoured Division.

25 Tank, Cruiser, Comet, U.K.

The Comet was the last of the line of British cruiser tanks and by far the best. It had a good gun and was fast and reliable.

Leyland Motors Limited undertook the design of the Comet: work was commenced during 1943 and the first prototype was completed in February 1944. Designed around the new 77-mm. gun—a shorter version of the 17-pr—some of the best features of the Cromwell were used, including the same Meteor engine. All-welded construction was used for the hull and turret, a system also employed with some of the later versions of the Cromwell. The Christie suspension system was again used but in a heavier form, since the Comet's weight was about 4½–5 tons heavier than that of the Cromwell.

After trials with the prototype, wider tracks were used and track return rollers (four each side) were added. A hull Besa machine-gun position like the Cromwell's was retained in the new design, and this was one point of subsequent criticism, because of the vertical plate it needed—far more vulnerable than the sloping glacis plate of the German Panther, one of the Comet's adversaries. The hull floor protection against mines was also felt to be not fully satisfactory.

The first production Comets arrived in September 1944 and, when delivered to armoured regiments towards the end of the year, met with general approval. The 77-mm. gun did not have quite the penetrative ability of the 17-pr but was very accurate and also had good high explosive ammunition. As a result of the German offensive in the Ardennes, which interrupted training, the Comet was not used in action until after the Rhine crossing in 1945. The first formation to be re-equipped with the Comet was the 29th Armoured Brigade of 11th Armoured Division, and tanks of Regimental Headquarters, 2nd Fife and Forfar Yeomanry of this brigade are shown in the illustrations.

26 Tank, Cruiser, Ram and Armoured Personnel Carrier, Ram Kangaroo, Canada.

A cruiser tank designed and produced in Canada, the Ram foreshadowed some of the features of the U.S. Sherman Medium Tank, M.4.

Using the running gear of the U.S. M.3 Medium, the hull was completely redesigned in the light of British experience and the clumsy sponson of the M.3 was eliminated so that the main armament was concentrated in the turret. As only the 2-pr gun was available to start with, this was used in the prototype, which was running in June 1941. This gun (in an adapted Valentine mounting) also equipped the first fifty production vehicles to be built, and these were named Ram I. The turret design incorporated a removable front adapter plate, however, so that when the much more powerful 6-pr gun came along later, the turret was readily changed to accept this weapon. All the subsequent vehicles (of which 1,899 were built, production ending in 1943) had the 6-pr and were known as Ram II. The Ram (in both Marks) also carried two mounted 0·30-in. Browning machine-guns—one coaxial with the main armament and the second in the hull at the front left-hand side. On all the earlier vehicles this hull machine-gun was in a small auxiliary turret, although on the final vehicles to be built a ball and socket mounting was used instead. A further Browning machine-gun was carried for anti-aircraft use.

The engine used in the Ram tanks was the nine-cylinder radial Continental, developing 400 b.h.p.; the gearbox had five speeds and the steering was of the controlled differential type. With a top speed of 25 m.p.h., the Ram had maximum armour protection of 3 inches (76 mm.).

The Ram was used widely for training Canadian armoured units, but was never used in action as a battle tank, as the American Sherman became available in large quantities and was adopted more or less as the standard medium tank of the Allied Forces. However, when there was a call in 1944 for armoured personnel carriers to carry infantry into battle in the North West Europe campaign, the Ram chassis was used. Following earlier armoured personnel carriers, improvised for use in Normandy by the removal of the guns from Priest S.P.s (Priests and Shermans were also converted in Italy) the Ram Kangaroo became the standard British armoured personnel carrier. With the turret removed, the Ram could carry an infantry section of eight men, well protected by the hull armour, although lacking overhead cover. A British and a Canadian regiment were each equipped with Ram Kangaroos by December 1944 and, with a combined strength of 300 Kangaroos, operated under 79th Armoured Division until the end of the War.

The illustrations show a Ram II as used for training about 1942, and a Ram Kangaroo based on one of the later production vehicles with the hull ball m.g. mounting and no side doors.

27 Australian Cruiser Tanks, Mark I and Mark III, Australia.

The first pilot model of the first tank ever to be built in Australia was completed in January 1942. As World War II progressed, it became an increasing possibility that supplies of fighting vehicles from Britain or other Commonwealth countries for the Australian Army could not be counted on. Several hundreds of tracked carriers, based on designs adapted from drawings received from the United Kingdom were built in 1940–41, but when it was decided to undertake the production of cruiser tanks in Australia, it was felt preferable to develop an entirely new design consistent with Australian resources. The resulting design by Colonel W. D. Watson, a tank designer on loan to Australia from the United Kingdom, was entirely original.

The hull of the A.C.I. was cast in one piece—an unusual practice, but made necessary by the lack of capacity of Australian heavy industry to undertake the manufacture of the rolled plate, which it was originally intended to use in conjunction with smaller castings. A power unit of adequate performance was the next problem and, as no engine was available in Australia, or could be imported at that time, this was made up by combining three Cadillac V-8 cylinder petrol engines to form a 330 b.h.p. unit. These were at the rear of the hull in an arrangement of two beside each other, and the third centrally placed behind them. The power from all three engines was collected in a transfer box and thence forwards by one Carden shaft to the clutch and 5-speed crash gearbox. The track drive sprockets were at the front.

It had originally been the intention to adopt a suspension system, and tracks like those of the U.S. M.3 medium tanks but, although U.S. type tracks were used, the suspension finally chosen was the American type re-designed as a horizontal-volute spring type, resulting in a similar arrangement to that of the French Hotchkiss H-35 tank. The armament for the A.C.I had to be based on weapons of British

design available in Australia, and this resulted in a turret-mounted 2-pr gun with coaxial 0·303-in. Vickers water-cooled machine-gun and another Vickers machine-gun centrally mounted in the front of the hull.

The armour was between 65 mm. and 25 mm. and, with an all-up weight of 28 tons, the A.C.I. had a top speed of 35 m.p.h. It was found to be not entirely reliable in service and, as by 1943 British and American tanks were available for Australia, no more than sixty-six A.C.I.s were built. In the meantime, however, improved Australian cruiser tanks were under development. As no heavier anti-tank gun than the 2-pr was to be had, the A.C.3 (the A.C.2 was a light cruiser design both started and abandoned in 1941) used the 25-pr field gun. A Vickers 0·303-in. machine-gun was mounted co-axially with the 25-pr. The hull machine-gun mounting of the A.C.1 was omitted, the extra space being used for stowage of the larger 25-pr ammunition.

The Cadillac engine arrangement in the A.C.3 was improved and made more compact by their being mounted in a semi-radial pattern, so that all three engines were linked to a common crankcase.

The ultimate development of the A.C.1 was the mounting of the 17-pr gun, this version to be known as A.C.4. After recoil tests with twin 25-pr guns in a special turret on an A.C.1, the 17-pr gun then produced in Australia was mounted successfully. Around 700 tanks of the A.C.3 and A.C.4 types were needed by the Australian Army, but apart from the experimental models none of these were built, because of the change in priorities in

Australian war production brought about by supplies of A.F.V.s from overseas. The A.C.1s built were, however, used by the Australian Army for many years for defence, and then training, the last of them being declared obsolete in 1956.

28 Tanks, Infantry, Mark IV, Churchill III and Churchill VII, U.K.

The first versions of the Infantry Tank Mark IV, to appear in 1941—the Churchills I and II—were equipped, of necessity, with 2-pr gun turrets. However, as a supply of 6-pr guns became available the Churchill III entered the production line, using a welded turret designed by Babcock and Wilcox Limited. Mechanically the same as its predecessors, having the 350-h.p. Bedford twelve-cylinder with a Merritt-Brown 4-speed gearbox, the Churchill III differed from the Churchill I–III mainly in the different turret and ammunition stowage. A little later, the Churchill III was joined on the production lines by a further version, Churchill IV, with the same armament but having a cast instead of a welded turret.

At the earliest opportunity, earlier marks of Churchill were reworked and had their 2-pr turrets replaced by new turrets with the 6-pr gun.

The Dieppe Raid in August 1942 was used to try out the Churchill in action for the first time. Some thirty Churchill tanks, mostly Churchill IIIs, but with a handful of Churchill Is and IIs (the latter equipped with flamethrowers), were used in support but had little chance of proving themselves, as few were able to surmount the sea wall and penetrate inland.

Some Churchill IIIs and other Marks were among the tanks supplied to the U.S.S.R. in 1942, but it was not until the Tunisian campaign of 1942–43 that the Churchill, represented mainly by Mark IIIs and IVs, really proved its worth, particularly in mountainous country.

Development in the meantime resulted in the Churchill V, a close support version equipped with a 95-mm. howitzer and the Churchill VI, similar to the Churchill IV but with a British-built 75-mm. gun in place of the 6-pr.

An entirely new version of the Churchill was designed by Vauxhall Motors Limited, the original 'parent' company for the group of Churchill tank manufacturers, to meet a new War Office specification A.22F (later renumbered A.42) for an infantry tank with 6-in. frontal armour. The new model, known as Churchill VII, although superficially similar to earlier Churchills, used a completely different form of hull construction in that a hull frame was dispensed with, the armour plate itself forming the hull. Many detailed improvements were incorporated, the most obvious being circular side doors and driver's vision port instead of the rectangular variety. A commander's turret vision cupola was introduced after the first few Churchill VIIs were built. The Churchill VII had main armament of a 75-mm. gun with a coaxial 7·92-mm. Besa machine-gun and another Besa in the hull front. A close support tank, Churchill VIII, was identical except for the 95-mm. howitzer which replaced the 75-mm. gun.

A ton heavier than earlier models, Churchills VII and VIII had a heavier suspension system and slightly lower ratios in the gearbox, and the governed top speed was reduced from about 16 m.p.h. to about 13 m.p.h.

Reliable, with heavy armour and a reasonably satisfactory gun, the Churchill VII (together with earlier models brought up to roughly the same standard) was one of the most important British tanks in both the Italian and North West Europe campaigns until the end of the war, during which 5,640 of all Marks were built.

The illustrations show a Churchill III of 142nd (Suffolk) Regiment, Royal Armoured Corps, at the time of the Tunisian campaign, and a Churchill VII in the colours of 6th (Guards) Tank Brigade.

29 S.P. 25-pr, Bishop and S.P. 17-pr, Archer, U.K.

The war in the North African desert emphasized the need for both increased mobility and protection for field and anti-tank artillery. The Bishop was designed hurriedly in 1941 in response to an urgent request from the Middle East for a self-propelled mounting for the 25-pr field gun—a weapon that had often been found to be the only effective answer to the German medium tanks. Designed by the Birmingham Railway Carriage and Wagon Company Limited, the sturdy and reliable Valentine tank chassis was used as the carrier for the 25-pr gun, which was mounted in a fixed shield with a total traverse of 8 degrees, elevation of 15 degrees and depression of 5 degrees.

One hundred Bishops were built by July 1942, and nearly all of them were used in the North African campaigns.

As a design to meet an emergency, the Bishop served its purpose but was never entirely satisfactory and, although some continued in action in Sicily and Italy in 1943, it was replaced as soon as possible by the U.S.-built Priest S.P. 105-mm. or the Canadian Sexton S.P. 25-pr.

The Bishop design was proposed as the basis of a self-propelled mounting for the new 17-pr anti-tank gun in 1942, but this was found to be impracticable. Nevertheless, the Valentine chassis was again used but this time with a rearward-facing layout for the gun. Two prototypes were completed in the first part of 1943 by Vickers-Armstrongs. After some modifications to the gun traverse system, frontal armour and other features, production began: the first vehicles were delivered in 1944, and a total of 665 of them were finished by the end of the war.

The rear-facing arrangement of the 17-pr gun in the Archer permitted a compact design—particularly useful in an anti-tank gun—and a total traverse of 45 degrees allowed reasonable flexibility in use. The welded upper hull had armour protection up to 20 mm.—effective against small arms. A 0·30-in. Browning machine-gun was carried for protection against local ground attack and aircraft.

The Bishop used the Valentine II chassis with an A.E.C. 131 b.h.p. diesel engine, but the Archer chassis was equivalent to that of the later models of Valentine tank with the

General Motors diesel of 192 b.h.p., giving a top speed of 20 m.p.h.—compared with the slightly heavier Bishop's 15 m.p.h.

Although the merits (rapid withdrawal in emergency, for one) and demerits of the rearward-facing gun were often debated, the Archer was generally acknowledged as reliable and the effectiveness of the 17-pr gun was never in doubt. The Archer was used by anti-tank regiments in North West Europe and Italy from 1944 onwards, and continued to be employed by the British Army for several years after the war. An Archer of the anti-tank regiment of 15th (Scottish) Division in Germany in 1945 is shown in the illustration. The Bishop shown is as it appeared in the Sicily campaign in 1943.

30 S.P. 25-pr Sexton, Canada.

The Sexton was probably the most important Canadian-built tracked vehicle to be used in action—it was the principal self-propelled field artillery piece employed by British and Canadian armoured formations in 1944–45.

Based on the chassis of the Canadian Ram cruiser tank (which never saw combat as a battle tank) the Sexton was designed by the Canadian Army Engineering Design Branch. Intended as a replacement in the Commonwealth Armies for the U.S. M.7 Priest S.P. 105-mm., the Sexton was not unlike the M.7 in appearance, and the suspension of both vehicles shared a common ancestry with the U.S. M.3 Medium tank.

The British 25-pr field gun was mounted slightly to the left of centre in an open-top welded armoured superstructure, where it had a traverse of 25 degrees left and 15 degrees right, and an elevation of 40 degrees. Eighty-seven high explosive and smoke shells were carried together with eighteen armour-piercing shells for anti-tank use. Two 0·303-in. Bren machine-guns were carried (but not normally mounted) for local protection, although in some vehicles a 0·50-in. Browning heavy machine-gun was mounted at the front of the hull at the left.

The nine-cylinder Continental engine of 400 b.h.p. (484 b.h.p. in later models), used in the Ram and in some models of the U.S. M.3 and M.4 medium tanks, in the Sexton gave a top speed of 25 m.p.h.

Production of the Sexton took place at the Montreal Locomotive Works Tank Arsenal, and a total of 2,150 of them was completed by the end of World War II.

The illustrations show (top) a Sexton belonging to the 5th Royal Horse Artillery (7th Armoured Division) and (below) to the 147th (Essex Yeomanry) Field Regiment, Royal Artillery (8th Armoured Brigade), both operating in the North West Europe campaign.

31 Sherman D.D., U.K.

One of the most ingenious, yet basically simple, devices of World War II was Nicholas Straussler's D.D. amphibious tank. By water-proofing the hull and raising the freeboard, it was found that an ordinary tank could be made to float without the necessity for the clumsy buoyancy chambers or pontoons, or a boat type of hull as used in earlier amphibious tanks. The means used by Straussler to increase the freeboard was to add a canvas screen around the edge of the hull. Tried out first on a 7½-ton Light Tank Mark VII in 1941, the screen was raised by means of inflatable rubber tubes and held erect by metal struts. Production of 625 D.D. tanks based on the 17-ton Valentine tank then took place and deliveries were made in 1943–44. It was, however, desired to extend the use of the D.D. device to the Sherman, virtually the standard medium tank used by the British Army, and Sherman D.D. prototypes were built and proved as successful as the earlier models, although the 30-ton tank needed higher screens to produce the buoyancy required to make it float.

As in earlier D.D. tanks, the Sherman had Duplex Drive (hence the initials)—normal propulsion on tracks on land and propellers for movement on water. The tracks of the Sherman were also run in water because the power take off to drive the twin 3-bladed propellers was implemented through stub axles on the rear idler wheels. The propellers were movable for steering, which was operated by the tank commander through either mechanical linkage to the propellers or a hydraulic system.

The water speed of the Sherman D.D. was up to 6 m.p.h. and, as the tracks were running all the time the tank was afloat, it could climb ashore the moment it touched ground. The screens could be lowered quickly, and the Sherman's armament, a 75-mm. gun and 0·30-in. Browning in the turret (the hull machine-gun had had to be eliminated in the D.D.) could then be used.

A tactical surprise was achieved with the first use of Sherman D.D. tanks in action on some Normandy beaches in 1944, because in the water they were not immediately recognized as tanks. They were also used later on in the Italian campaign (together with a small number of Valentine D.D.s) and at the Rhine crossing in March 1945.

The illustrations show a Sherman D.D. (with screens folded) of 4th Armoured Brigade in Germany in 1945, a Sherman D.D. afloat, and one on land with the screens raised.

32 Churchill VII Crocodile and Grant C.D.L., U.K.

The first British tank-borne flamethrower to be sent into action was the Churchill Oke. Three Churchill IIs with this hastily produced flamethrower equipment were among the tanks used in the raid on Dieppe in August 1942 but, as it happened, the landing craft carrying all three never reached the beach, being sunk offshore.

A more satisfactory design of tank flamethrower was already in hand and twelve pilot models were ordered by the War Office at the end of July 1942. Mounted in the Churchill IV, the flamethrowers were of the Wasp type already used successfully in Carriers. The fuel for the flame projector, which replaced the hull machine-gun, was carried in an armoured trailer and was pumped through under pressure obtained from compressed gas cylinders. A range of between 100 and 200 yards was attainable. One thousand Crocodile equipments were ordered and some 800 were completed by the end of the war. The Churchill VII was used as the basis of the production Crocodiles and a rectangular hatch in the hull floor for the mounting of the flame equipment was included as standard in all Churchill VIIs and VIIIs, so that they could readily be adapted for this role. Apart from the hull machine-gun, all the rest of the normal Churchill VIIs armament was carried in the Crocodile.

Crocodiles equipped a tank brigade in the North West Europe campaign and were also used in smaller numbers in Italy. A Churchill VII Crocodile of C Squadron, 51st Royal Tank Regiment in the latter theatre of war is shown in the illustration.

Another form of special armour used in the North West Europe campaign, the development of which began several years earlier, was the C.D.L. tank. The initials stood for Canal Defence Light—a deliberately misleading code name, since by dazzling enemy gunners the tank was intended to support attacks. The device consisted of a high intensity arc lamp, the beam of which was, by reflectors, projected through a vertical slit in the armoured face of the special turret. The dazzle effect could be enhanced by operating a shutter, causing the beam to flicker.

Originally fitted to Matilda infantry tanks, and used on training in the United Kingdom and the Middle East, the C.D.L. was later standardized on the U.S.-built Grant. The advantage in using this tank was that the main armament of a 75-mm. gun in the hull sponson could be retained, only the small 37-mm. gun turret having to be removed to fit the C.D.L. turret.

Because of the wish to keep this weapon secret for an important action in which it could be used to the best effect—and perhaps because of ignorance of its potential (or existence) by senior commanders—the C.D.L. was not used in action until nearly the end of the war, at the Rhine and Elbe river crossings. Even so they seem to have been used as little more than ordinary static searchlights, rather than in a true assault function.

The Grant C.D.L. tanks, like the Crocodiles, in North West Europe came under the aegis of 79th Armoured Division, and one belonging to that formation is shown here.

33 Matilda Scorpion and Grant Scorpion, U.K.

The most effective device for clearing minefields devised in World War II, the flail tank, was the idea of Major A. S. J. du Toit, a motor engineer serving with the South African Union Defence Force. A working model to demonstrate the idea was built, and details were given to the Middle East Mechanical Experimental Establishment, before Major du Toit was despatched to the United Kingdom where better resources for development of the device were available.

The anti-mine flail was a power-driven revolving drum to which rows of heavy chains were attached which, beating the ground in front of the vehicle to which the device was fitted, exploded mines on contact.

The Mechanical Experimental Establishment in the Middle East first fitted the device to a lorry and then, after trials, to a Matilda tank. This equipment was then called Matilda Scorpion Mark I.

The flails of the Matilda Scorpion I were made up of wire cable to the ends of which short lengths of chain were attached. The rotating drum was driven by a Ford V-8 engine, mounted in an armoured box on the right-hand side of the tank's hull. A cardan shaft took the transmission along the supporting girder to a bevel box and from it to the rotor. The flail engine was operated by an extra crew member who had the unenviable job of sitting at the rear of the armoured box behind the engine. In this position he was nearly choked by dust and fumes from the flail engine.

An order for twenty-four Matilda Scorpion Mark Is was completed in time for them to be used to help clear minefields for the Battle of Alamein in October 1942. Still beset by mechanical difficulties and with a flailing speed of only ½ m.p.h., nevertheless the Scorpions were considered reasonably satisfactory. A better version in which the flail operator was carried in the tank itself, and the design of the side girder was changed and other improvements effected, was known as the Matilda Scorpion Mark II and was ready by early 1943.

In order to take advantage of the greater mobility of the American Grant, the Scorpion Mark II flail equipment was adapted to this tank, the combination being known as Grant Scorpion Mark III. The hull-mounted 75-mm. gun had to be removed, but the 37-mm. gun turret could be retained although this was also, in fact, removed when it was necessary to reduce the overall dimensions to be carried in landing craft. Grant Scor-

pions were used in the Sicily campaign in the summer of 1943.

The final developments of the flail tank which took place in the Middle East, parallel to work in the same field in the United Kingdom, were the Grant Scorpion IV and the Sherman Scorpion. The former used two Dodge engines, mounted at the rear of the hull, driving the rotating drum by means of cardan shafts each side. This equipment was used in very similar form on the Sherman tank, and Sherman Scorpions in small numbers were used in the Italian campaign.

A Matilda Scorpion Mark I and a Grant Scorpion Mark IV are shown in the illustrations.

34 Sherman Crab I and Crab II, U.K.

From the end of 1941 onwards development of the flail tank, initiated by Major A. S. J. du Toit, took place at the works of A.E.C. Ltd in the United Kingdom. At first undertaken independently of the parallel experiments in the Middle East, later on ideas were exchanged. The best design of flail tank to enter service in World War II, the Sherman Crab incorporated ideas from both centres of development.

The first U.K. flail tank, known as Baron, used the Matilda chassis. Early models had one engine to drive the flail but the final model had two flail engines. Sixty were built in 1943 for training purposes. The next type, the Valentine Scorpion, was based on designs received from the Middle East, although the rotor was like that of the Baron. Again, only a small order

(150 vehicles) for training only was given.

Next, flail development was transferred to the Sherman tank—this had the advantage of using the same basic vehicle that was to equip many British armoured regiments.

Prototypes of three models were built in 1943, the Sherman Marquis, turretless and based on the Baron and Scorpion; the Sherman Pram Scorpion, retaining its turret and taking its flail drive from the tank's main engines; and the Sherman Crab. The latter was considered to be the best design and was the one adopted for production in quantity for employment in the forthcoming campaign in North West Europe.

Fitted to the Sherman V, powered by a Chrysler thirty-cylinder 350 b.h.p. engine, the flail was operated through a power take off on the right-hand side of the hull, leading through a universal-jointed cardan shaft to a bevel gear at the rotor. The rotor arms could be lifted by hydraulic rams to make transport in landing craft etc. easier. A lane 9 ft 9 in. wide could be cleared of mines at a maximum speed of 1¼ m.p.h. Six hundred and eighty-nine Crabs were ordered and were widely used throughout the North West Europe campaign in 1944–45, where they operated under the command of 79th Armoured Division.

A later model, Sherman Crab II (which did not become available until nearly the end of the war) was developed to overcome the fault of Crab I and all other earlier flail tanks, in that mines buried in hollows in the ground could be passed over without being detonated because the flails operated at a constant height above a level surface. The left hand hydraulic lifting ram was replaced by a counter weight attached to the rear end of the rotor arm. This enabled the rotor arm and bearing chains to maintain a constant height over the contours of the ground.

The illustrations show a Sherman Crab I with the rotor arm at beating height (attachments on the rear of the hull are station-keeping-lights—for the benefit of following vehicles—mounted above the box containing markers to indicate the swept lane) and a Sherman Crab II flailing in a depression in the ground.

35 Churchill A.V.R.E. Carpet-layer and S.B.G. Bridge Carrier, U.K.

The Dieppe Raid of 1942, in which heavy losses were sustained by both armour and infantry, chiefly because the tanks were unable to penetrate inland, indicated the need for protection for engineers working to surmount or destroy obstacles. A suggestion by Lieutenant J. J. Denovan, of the Royal Canadian Engineers, that a tank should be adapted for this purpose was followed up by the R.C.E. using a Churchill tank. The Churchill was chosen because it had a well-armoured, roomy hull. It also had a relatively large door on each side of the hull, suitable for use by sappers under fire and for loading stores and equipment. The prototype with rearranged stowage was ready by December 1942 and a spigot motor, developed separately, was ready by February 1943 and mounted in the modified turret. The spigot motor, known as Petard, could throw a 40-lb projectile (containing a 26-lb charge) up to an extreme range of 230 yards, and was capable of destroying concrete obstacles.

The Assault Vehicle, Royal Engineers, or A.V.R.E. as it was usually called, was adjudged successful after trials and modifications to the original design which took place in 1943, and production was ordered. The Churchill III or IV was used as the basis, and a total of about 700 A.V.R.E.s was built by 1945.

Most production A.V.R.E.s were fitted with brackets on the hull for the attachment of fittings for special tasks. One of these fitments was the carpet-layer device for crossing soft patches on beaches, for example. The carpet—the most common form was hessian matting reinforced by steel tubes—was carried on a large bobbin at the front of the A.V.R.E. and was unwound by the vehicle itself running over it. A number of these were employed on the D-Day landing beaches. There were several versions, and the Carpetlayer Type D (waterproofed for landing from a landing craft) is shown in the illustration.

Another important use of the A.V.R.E. was as a carrier for the Small Box Girder (S.B.G.) bridge, which could carry a 40-ton load (the weight of a Churchill tank) over a 30-ft span. This could be laid mechanically under fire.

The A.V.R.E. was used in action in Italy and in North West Europe. Three Assault Regiments, Royal Engineers, under the command of 79th Armoured Division, with A.V.R.E.s and a variety of fitments, took part in many actions from D-Day onwards. An A.V.R.E. with S.B.G. bridge as it appeared in the attack on the Le Havre fortifications is illustrated.

36 Churchill A.R.V., Mark I and Sherman B.A.R.V., U.K.

The weakness of the British organization for the recovery of disabled tanks was brought out particularly in the early campaigns in the North African desert, where the Germans proved to be well in advance in this respect.

Early in 1942, a Royal Electrical and Mechanical Engineers experimental section undertook the design of armoured recovery vehicles on tank chassis. The idea was to use adaptations as A.R.V.s of the same kinds of tanks used by the armoured regiments, in so far as the basic chassis was suitable for use also as a recovery vehicle. The three most important A.R.V. types which emerged were based on the Cromwell, Sherman and Churchill, corresponding with the principal tanks in use from 1943 onwards.

The Churchill A.R.V., Mark I, was a turretless vehicle carrying a 3-ton jib. This was stowed on the hull for travelling but was mounted between the front 'horns' when in use and was capable of lifting out tank engines or other major assemblies for maintenance and repair. A 100-ft length of heavy steel cable was carried for hauling out bogged-down A.F.V.s and a pulley block and ground anchors were available for indirect or difficult recovery jobs. The A.R.V. also carried a 4½-in. vice and oxy-acetylene and welding plant among its equipment. Sherman and Cromwell A.R.V.s, Mark I, were also built and had similar equipment to the Churchill A.R.V.

Mark II versions of the Churchill and Sherman A.R.V.s were also produced and began to become available in 1944. These had fixed turrets with dummy guns: a fixed jib (with a 9½-ton lift) was carried at the rear and a demountable 3½-ton jib at the front. Other improved equipment included a 60-ton-pull-winch, the operator of which sat in the turret.

Development of an A.R.V. to recover disabled tanks or vehicles, both in the water and on the beaches, was commenced in 1943 specially for the forthcoming invasion of Europe. Churchill and Sherman tanks were tested in this role, but the former was abandoned because of the far greater amount of waterproofing it needed. The diesel-engined Sherman III was finally selected as the standard chassis for the Beach Armoured Recovery Vehicle (B.A.R.V.). Fully waterproofed and able to operate in up to 10 feet of water, the Sherman B.A.R.V. was intended only for simple recovery operations, such as towing vehicles 'drowned' in landing from landing craft or pushing off stranded landing craft, for which wooden railway sleepers mounted on the front were provided.

The Sherman B.A.R.V.s well served their purpose in 1944 by helping to keep the D-Day beaches clear. One B.A.R.V. was inadvertently the cause of more direct alarm to the enemy because, landed in error at a very early stage of the invasion, it was taken to be a new 'secret weapon'.

The illustrations show a Churchill A.R.V., Mark I, belonging to the 3rd (Tank) Battalion Scots Guards, and a standard Sherman B.A.R.V.

37 Carrier, Universal, Mark II, and Carrier, 2-pr, Tank Attack (Aust.), U.K. and Australia.

The British Army's demand for tracked carriers of the Bren and Scout types, and for a variety of functions, remained high throughout World War II, but even by 1940 the need was felt to standardize the design as far as possible. This resulted in the introduction of the Carrier, Universal. Mechanically the same as the earlier carriers, the Universal was powered by a Ford V-8 engine which drove the tracks via rear sprockets. Steering was by lateral displacement of the front bogie unit for gentle turns, with track braking for more abrupt turns. Although the driver's and gunner's compartments were very much the same in all carriers, the position of the armoured rear compartment varied. In the Universal Carrier, the whole of the rear was armoured, providing an open-top compartment on either side of the engine.

As before, both British and imported Ford V-8 engines were used in the Universal Carrier, and the final list of these was as follows:

No. 1   British-built engine.
No. 2 and 2a American-built engines—
            models   G.A.E.   and
            G.A.E.A. respectively.
No. 3   Canadian-built engine.
The British-built engines were originally rated at 65 b.h.p., the American engines at 85 b.h.p. and the Canadian

ones at 95 b.h.p., although at the end of the war the War Office rated them all at 85 b.h.p. In any event, engines from all three sources were inter-changeable.

The Mark II version of the Universal Carrier included some improvements, such as a spare road wheel as a standard fitting, a larger kit box on the rear of the hull, and either one or two foot-step brackets each side of the hull. Some further improvements were incorporated in the Mark III Carrier. There were also other carriers such as Carriers M.M.G., Mortar, and Armoured Observation Post, but these had basically the same hull form as the Universal Carrier, with only relatively minor adaptations to fit their specialized roles.

Some 40,000 or more Carriers of the Universal and later associated types were built in the United Kingdom alone during World War II but, even so, it was felt necessary that Commonwealth countries should also undertake the production of tracked carriers. In Canada 29,000 of the Universal-type were built to a similar specification to the U.K. version (about 5,000 of the larger Windsor carriers were also built in Canada and the U.S.A. produced 14,000 T.16 series Carriers). A Carrier, Universal, Mark II, belonging to an infantry battalion of 43rd (Wessex) Division is illustrated.

In Australia and New Zealand carriers were also built. The earliest N.Z. carriers were built from plans sent from the United Kingdom, although later models were more like the Australian ones. Australian production was much greater, to meet the heavier demand in that country, and the basic U.K. carrier design was simplified mechanically in that the track displacement device for steering was omitted. Although in other respects broadly the same as the U.K. carriers, the later Australian carriers had a modified hull with a sloping glacis plate. Also, welded construction was used—a feature employed only in some models of the U.K.-built carriers.

In 1942 an experimental version of the Australian carrier with a stronger, lengthened chassis was built as a mounting for the 2-pr anti-tank gun. The Ford V-8 engine was brought forward alongside the driver and the gun, on a field mounting with shield, was on a turntable at the rear. Trials of the 2-pr carrier showed various faults; among others it rode badly, was slow and underpowered; was insufficiently strong and mechanical components failed; the driver was too cramped and the crew and gun were inadequately protected. It did not, therefore, go into series production, although the 5,600 standard Universal-type Carriers built in Australia gave useful service.

38 South African Armoured Reconnaissance Cars, Mark IV and Mark VI, South Africa.

Experience with the South African Reconnaissance Car, Mark II, on active service in East Africa and Libya in 1940–41, showed the need for further improvements and some of these were incorporated in the next model, Mark III, also using a Ford Marmon-Herrington chassis. However, neither model was armed with an anti-tank gun, and as a temporary expedient armoured car regiments often fitted heavier weapons of calibres of 20 mm. upwards, taken from captured enemy A.F.V.s or derelict British tanks.

Consequently, it was decided to build the next model to take a 2-pr gun. This vehicle, the South African Armoured Reconnaissance Car, Mark IV, once again used Marmon-Herrington automotive components but it was a complete redesign, in which the welded armoured hull acted as the chassis to which the engine, suspension, etc., were attached directly. A rear-engine layout was adopted, with the driver at the front and a central fighting compartment. Of fairly light construction, it was felt that the turret could not absorb the recoil of a tank-pattern 2-pr gun and so a 2-pr field mounting was used, with the prominent recuperator under the barrel. A coaxial 0·30-in. Browning machine-gun was added in the final standard form of the Mark IV, together with a 0·50-in. or (more usually) a 0·30-in. Browning on an anti-aircraft mount on the turret roof.

There was a strong demand for South African-built armoured cars from the War Office, as well as the Union Defence Force and, as the supply of components from Marmon-Herrington in the U.S.A. seemed unlikely to meet requirements, the design of the Mark IV was modified to employ instead automotive components from Canadian Ford F 60L 3-ton, 4-wheel drive lorries. These lorries were diverted to South Africa from War Office orders for the Middle East Forces. The Canadian F 60Ls already incorporated driven front axles of Marmon-Herrington design, so they could readily be used. The resulting vehicle was known as South African Armoured Reconnaissance Car,

Mark IV F (the 'F' probably denoting the Ford connection). In British War Office nomenclature, the two types were known as 'Armoured Car, Marmon-Herrington'—Mark IV and Mark IV F.

A total of 2,116 Mark IV and Mark IV F cars was built and, although they were used for defence in South Africa and were issued to the Arab Legion and some Allied Forces, none were received in time to be used in combat in North Africa. The same fate applied to the much larger South African Armoured Reconnaissance Car, Mark VI.

The Mark VI resulted from the strong impression created by the German eight-wheeled armoured cars, which proved to be well suited to desert conditions. Again, the well-proven Ford Marmon-Herrington components were used, this time two sets with two engines, each of 95 b.h.p. Armament and, to a degree, armour was to be of cruiser tank standard, and consisted of a 2-pr gun and a coaxial 0·30-in. Browning machine-gun, with 30-mm. maximum protection. There was also a turret ring mounting with two 0·30-in. Browning machine-guns for anti-aircraft use. The second prototype was armed with a 6-pr gun and coaxial 7·92-mm. Besa machine-gun, with a 0·50-in. Browning anti-aircraft machine-gun.

By the time that production of the Mark VI could commence—delayed as it was by a shortage of components in South Africa—the North African campaign was well-nigh over. Armoured cars from other sources were becoming available in better quantities and, as the Mark VI was considered less well suited to the European terrain, the production orders were cancelled.

The illustrations show a standard S.A. Armoured Reconnaissance Car, Mark IV, and the first prototype S.A. Armoured Reconnaissance Car, Mark VI—operating during trials before the anti-aircraft ring mounting was fitted.

39 Armoured Cars, Humber, Mark III and Mark IV, U.K.

Humber Armoured Cars were numerically the most important British-built armoured cars of World War II, well over 5,000 being produced by the Rootes Group between 1940 and 1945.

The earliest Humber Armoured Car, the Mark I, was almost identical externally to the Guy Mark IA Armoured Car, and its mechanical layout although based, of course, on Rootes components was on similar lines to that of the Guy. Service experience suggested improvements and a cleaned-up front end, incorporating the driver's visor in the glacis plate, and radiator intake improvements were introduced in the Mark II.

The Armoured Car, Humber Mark III, which entered production in 1942 had a more roomy turret than the Marks I–II, which allowed the crew to be increased to four. The first three Marks of Humber Armoured Car all had an armament of two Besa machine-guns, one of 7·92-mm. calibre and the other 15-mm. The latter was never an entirely satisfactory weapon, being prone to stoppages, and in the Humber Mark IV Armoured Car the American 37-mm. gun was introduced in its place. Because this reduced the turret

space available, the crew was reduced to three men.

All the Humber Armoured Cars weighed about 7 tons and their 90-b.h.p. six-cylinder engines gave them a top speed of 45 m.p.h. They were used by both armoured car regiments (where they tended to be used at regimental and squadron headquarters if Daimlers were also available) and Reconnaissance Regiments (of infantry divisions) in most theatres of war in which British and Commonwealth troops were engaged up to the end of the war. The illustrations show a Mark III as it appeared in the North African desert about 1942, and a Mark IV of 1st Reconnaissance Regiment in Italy in 1944.

40 Armoured Cars, Daimler, Mark I and Mark II, U.K.

Inspired to a large extent by the design of the Car, Scout Mark I, the Daimler Armoured Car was built to the 'Tank, Light, Wheeled' formula of a wheeled vehicle having performance, armour and armament comparable to that of contemporary light tanks. After some initial difficulties it turned out to be one of the best armoured cars of World War II.

The mechanical layout of the Daimler Armoured Car consisted of a rear-mounted, 95 b.h.p. six-cylinder engine from which the transmission was taken via a 'Fluid Flywheel' and pre-selector gearbox to a centrally mounted transfer box with a single differential. From this the power was transmitted via four parallel driving shafts and Tracta universal joints to each wheel, with final reduction gears in each hub. This arrangement helped to keep the height down, as there were no central transmission shafts, and a further point making for compact design was that all the automotive components were attached direct to the hull, there being no chassis as such. Although regarded as being somewhat underpowered, the Daimler Armoured Car had a good cross-country performance and a top road speed of 50 m.p.h. Two other interesting features were the early use of disc brakes, and the inclusion of a second steering wheel facing the rear, together with basic driving controls, to enable the car to be driven rapidly in reverse in emergency.

The armament of the Daimler Armoured Car was identical to that of the Tetrarch Light Tank (with which it shared the turret design), a 2-pr gun and coaxially mounted 7·92-mm. Besa machine-gun.

Some improvements suggested by experience in service of the Daimler Mark I were incorporated in the Mark II, which followed the Mark I into production towards the latter end of the war. The most important changes were a 2-speed dynamo, a driver's escape hatch in the hull roof, an improved gun mantlet, and a different radiator and grill. Both Marks of Daimler (a total of 2,694 of which was built) sometimes had Littlejohn Adaptors added to the 2-pr guns, which greatly increased their penetrative ability.

The Daimler Mark I Armoured Car was first used in action in North Africa in 1942, and subsequently with the Mark II in Europe and the Far East. Many British and Commonwealth armoured car regiments used these cars and the illustrations show a Mark I of the 1st Derbyshire Yeomanry (6th Armoured Division) in Tunisia, and a Mark II of 11th Hussars (7th Armoured Division) in Germany in 1945.

41 Armoured Cars, A.E.C., Mark II and Mark III, U.K.

The original A.E.C. Armoured Car (Mark I) was conceived by the Associated Equipment Company Limited in 1941 as a heavy armoured car with both armour and armament equivalent to that of a cruiser tank and, in fact, used the 2-pr turret of a Valentine tank. This private venture was successful and 122 of them were built, many being sent to North Africa in 1942. When British tank armament increased, the A.E.C. Mark II Armoured Car was designed to use the 6-pr gun (with a coaxial 7·92-mm. Besa machine-gun) and, at the same time, the opportunity was taken to redesign the shape of the front hull and introduce other improvements. The Mark II had a more powerful A.E.C. diesel engine of 158 b.h.p. (which gave a top speed of 41 m.p.h.) and a crew of four. It weighed 12·7 tons and the armour protection was at a maximum of 30 mm.

The next step, in the Mark III, was to substitute the British 75-mm. gun for the 6-pr. The Mark III was very similar to its predecessor in most other respects, except that it had two (rather than one) electric fans installed in the turret roof. A total of 507 Armoured Cars, A.E.C. Marks II and III was built.

Some A.E.C. Mark IIs were supplied to the Yugoslav partisans in 1944 and one of these is shown in the smaller illustration. A.E.C. Mark IIIs were used principally in the Heavy Troops of British Armoured Car Regiments in the North West Europe campaign, and a car of 2nd Household Cavalry Regiment (then in VIII Corps) is illustrated.

42 Car, Scout, Humber, Mark I, U.K.

Production of the Daimler Scout Car (introduced into service at the beginning of World War II) was continued throughout the war. Only relatively minor changes were made in the design because it was a highly successful vehicle. However, as the number built could not meet the demand, the Rootes Group was asked to design and manufacture a scout car to supplement the Daimler Scout Cars.

To avoid unnecessary production complications the Rootes Group design which became known as Car, Scout, Humber, Mark I, employed a high proportion of components used in existing Humber 4-wheel drive military vehicles, such as the Light Reconnaissance Car, but adapted for a rear engine layout. The ubiquitous Rootes 87 b.h.p. six-cylinder engine was linked to a 4-speed gearbox and gave a top speed of 60 m.p.h. Rather larger than the Daimler Scout Car and with room for three men, the Humber Scout Car was of a mechanically less sophisticated design, and the maximum frontal protection was only 14 mm. compared with the Daimler's 30 mm. For some or all of these reasons, given a choice, armoured regiments tended to use

Humbers for liaison purposes rather than scouting.

The Mark II version of the Humber Scout Car was externally similar to the Mark I but had synchromesh added to 2nd gear as well as in 3rd and 4th. A total of 4,300 Humber Scout Cars was built between about late 1942 and the end of the war.

The illustrations show vehicles belonging to 11th Armoured Division.

43 Car, Scout, Ford, Lynx I–II, and Car, Light Reconnaissance, Canadian G.M., Mark I, Otter I, Canada.

As well as manufacturing large numbers of tanks, Canadian industry made a significant contribution to the production of wheeled armoured vehicles for the Commonwealth during World War II. Many chassis were supplied for armoured vehicles built in India and South Africa, but among the most important produced complete in Canada itself were the Lynx Scout Car and the Otter Light Reconnaissance Car—products of Ford and General Motors respectively.

The drawings of the Daimler Scout Car were sent from the United Kingdom to Canada so that an equivalent vehicle could be built to supplement British production, which lagged behind demand. It would have been impracticable to undertake the extensive re-tooling and conversion of standard measurements that would have been needed to produce a replica of the Daimler Scout Car in Canada, so the Daimler's hull design was adapted to accept a Ford V-8 engine and Ford 4-

wheel drive automative components. As the Ford transmission was of the conventional pattern for 4-wheel drive vehicles, with centrally placed transmission shafts to front and rear axles, the Canadian Scout Car was of necessity nearly a foot taller than the Daimler.

Known originally in British nomenclature simply as Car, Scout, Mark III (and later as Lynx I) the early versions of this car were found to be unreliable and some components needed strengthening. Later vehicles were modified in various ways, including a revision of the radiator protection at the rear. A second model, known as Car, Scout, Ford Mark II, Lynx II, incorporated the results of both production experience with Lynx I and British operating experience with Scout cars generally, which led to the omission of the armoured roof, which was rarely used. The Lynx II was considered to be reliable and had a better performance than its predecessor. The chief external difference (apart from the roof) was the sand channels carried at the rear in the Lynx II, instead of across the front locker.

A Lynx II is shown in the illustration.

The Ford V-8 95 b.h.p. engine in the Lynx Scout cars gave a top speed of between 55 and 60 m.p.h. and the armour protection, like that of the Daimler Scout cars, was at a maximum of 30 mm. on the sloping glacis plate.

A total of 3,255 Lynx I and II Scout cars was built. They were used by the Canadian Army in Italy and North West Europe, and by British and Indian troops in the Far East.

The Canadian-built Car, Light Reconnaissance, Canadian G.M. Mark I,

Otter I was built to the same general specification as the British Humber Mark III Light Reconnaissance Car. The use of Canadian components, however, resulted in a shorter bonnet and a higher, more humped hull, although provision was made for the same armament—a Bren 0·303-in. machine-gun in the turret and a 0·55-in. Boys anti-tank rifle in the hull front beside the driver. Alternatively, a No. 19 wireless set was carried in the latter position. The six-cylinder General Motors engine developed 104 b.h.p., and gave a maximum speed of 45 m.p.h. The crew of three were protected by armour varying between 12 mm. and 6 mm.

Although of less good performance than the Humber Light Reconnaissance Car (mainly because it was over a ton heavier and lacked an auxiliary gearbox) the 1761 Otters built gave useful service in all the main theatres of war with the Canadian and British Armies (and, in addition, the Royal Air Force Regiment, which equipped some with 20-mm. cannon in the hull front and twin Browning machine-guns in the turret).

44 Car, 4 × 4, Light Reconnaissance, Humber, Mark IIIA and Car, 4 × 4, Light Reconnaissance, Morris, Mark II, U.K.

The Rootes Group were responsible for the major part of the production of Light Reconnaissance cars in the United Kingdom in World War II (3,600 in total), commencing with the Mark I (known as Ironside I) of 1940. This was followed by the Mark II which had an enclosed roof mounting a small turret, and in turn by the externally similar Mark III. This model, however, introduced 4-wheel drive. It was succeeded in 1942 by the Mark IIIA, shown here, which had various minor improvements, the most noticeable of which were extra observation ports at the front corner angles of the hull. A 3½-ton vehicle powered by an 87-b.h.p. Humber six-cylinder engine, which gave it a top speed of 50 m.p.h., the armament of the Humber Mark IIIA Light Reconnaissance Car consisted normally of a 0·303-in. Bren light machine-gun mounted in the turret, to which was sometimes added a 0·55-in. Boys anti-tank rifle usually mounted in the hull front. Often a smoke discharger was also carried. The car had a crew of three, and light armour of up to 10 mm.

The Car, 4 × 2, Light Reconnaissance, Morris, Mark I was put into production by the Nuffield Group to supplement the Humbers and the later versions of the Beaverette being built by the Standard Motor Company. A rear-engined vehicle, the Morris Mark I's cross country performance was enhanced by the smooth enclosed design of its underbelly. Nevertheless, a 4-wheel drive version, the Mark II, was introduced to take the place of the Mark I. With a 71·8 b.h.p. Morris engine and weighing slightly more at 3·7 tons and with 14-mm. armour, the specification and performance of the Morris Mark II was similar to that of the Humber Mark IIIA. The layout of the armament differed, however, in that the Boys anti-tank rifle, when carried, was operated from a hatch, to the left of the turret mounting the Bren gun, and the gunner was protected by the raised armoured hatch cover. About 2,290 Morris Marks I and II Light Reconnaissance Cars were built.

Intended originally as equipment for the Reconnaissance Corps, both the Morris and Humber Light Reconnaissance Cars were also used extensively by armoured car units of the Royal Air Force Regiment, and the Humber Mark IIIA in the illustration is one belonging to the R.A.F. Regiment in the North West Europe campaign. Both makes of car were used also for reconnoitring and liaison purposes by Royal Engineers field companies and the Morris Mark II shown is in the markings of a field company, R.E., of the 43rd (Wessex) Infantry Division.

45 **Armoured Carrier, Wheeled, I.P., Mark IIA and Armoured Carrier, Wheeled, I.P., A.O.V., India.**

The wheeled Armoured Carrier, Mark I, built in India in 1940–41, was followed throughout World War II by a series of armoured carriers of successive Marks—a total of 4,655 of them were built by the War's end.

A rear-engine layout was adopted for the Indian wheeled carriers after the Mark I. The Marks II, IIa and IIb were very similar to each other, the two latter having slightly larger tyres and the Mark IIb a slight modification to the roof plate. All employed chassis supplied direct from Canada by the Ford Motor Company of Canada. These were 4-wheel drive chassis with 95 b.h.p. Ford V-8 engines. The armour plate was designed and manufactured in India and assembly took place mainly at factories of the Tata Iron and Steel Co. and the East Indian Railway Workshops.

The Carrier, Wheeled, Mark IIC was very much like its predecessors in appearance but had a number of further improvements, including heavier springs and front axles, wider track, larger tyres and a 12-gallon auxiliary petrol tank. An Armoured Observation Vehicle version of the Mark IIC, with a small turret mounting a light machine-gun was built. This tended to be used as a light reconnaissance car, although there was also a Carrier, Mark III, which had a turret with a Boys 0·55-in. anti-tank rifle and a Bren 0·303-in. machine gun and was, in fact, specifically intended for this purpose.

The final version, Mark IV, differed from all earlier vehicles in that the driver sat separately from the rest of the crew in an armoured cab.

The Mark II series carriers were used in the North African campaigns, in Italy and in the South East Asia campaign, whereas the A.O.V. and the Marks III and IV are not known to have been employed outside Asia. The standard carriers, wheeled, were employed for a variety of purposes, in much the same way as the British tracked Universal-series carriers, by both infantry, artillery and reconnaissance units.

An Armoured Carrier, Wheeled, I.P., Mark IIA (with a Boys anti-tank rifle mounted, although a Bren light machine-gun was more often used), belonging to the Reconnaissance Unit (Indian Cavalry) of the 8th Indian Division in Italy in 1943 is shown, together with a Carrier, Wheeled, A.O.V. in Burma in 1945.

46 Armoured Command Vehicle (A.E.C.) 4 × 4, Mark I and Armoured Command Vehicle (A.E.C.) 6 × 6, Mark I, U.K.

The limited number of Guy Lizard and smaller Morris armoured command vehicles built at the beginning of World War II, was almost entirely replaced for the greater part of the war by vehicles on A.E.C. chassis.

The A.E.C. Matador chassis was used as the basis of the 4-wheeled A.C.V.—known at first officially as 'Lorry, 3 ton, 4 × 4, Armoured Command, A.E.C.' This consisted basically of an armoured body (12-mm. armour) fitted out internally for command purposes and carrying two wireless sets. These were a No. 19 H.P. and a No. 19 in the Low Power version, and an R.C.A. receiver and a No. 19 set in the High Power version. The A.C.V. Mark II (in a Low Power version only) differed in having an internal partition, dividing it into staff and wireless compartments.

Weighing nearly 12 tons, the A.E.C. 4 × 4 Armoured Command Vehicle was powered by an A.E.C. diesel engine of 95 b.h.p. which gave it a top speed of 35 m.p.h. No armament was fitted but a Bren light machine-gun was carried for defence.

A total of 416 4 × 4 A.C.V.s was built, and these were supplemented in 1944–45 by 151 vehicles of a new model—on an A.E.C. 6-wheel-drive chassis. This was very much more roomy than its predecessor, being 6 feet

289

longer, but slightly lower. It was also very much heavier at 19 tons loaded, and was powered by a more powerful A.E.C. diesel engine of 135 b.h.p. Two versions were again produced, L.P. and H.P., the former having one No. 19 H.P. wireless set and one No. 19, and the latter one No. 53 and one No. 19. Both versions were divided internally, the front compartment being for staff and the rear for the wireless equipment. As in all the earlier vehicles, eight men were carried.

The A.E.C. 4 × 4 armoured command vehicles were first used in action in the North African campaign, where, incidentally, three were captured and used by German generals, two of them by Rommel himself and his staff. These two vehicles were nicknamed 'Max' and 'Moritz', although the type was given the generic name of Mammut (Mammoth) by the Germans.

The armoured command vehicles were large and conspicuous and, of course, as they carried senior officers, valuable targets, so Major Jasper Maskelyne (a well-known stage magician in civilian life) commanding a camouflage unit of the Royal Engineers, was asked to design special camouflage for them. What he did was to disguise them as ordinary lorries, similar to the standard A.E.C. Matador gun tractors which were widely used by the British Army. This involved black shadow painting on various parts of the hull, the addition of a canvas cover to the top surfaces and an extension to the armoured noseplate. This disguise is shown in the illustration of an A.E.C. 4 × 4 A.C.V. in North Africa.

47 Carrier, A.E.C., 6-pr Gun, Mark I (Deacon) and, S.P. 17-pr Gun—Straussler, U.K.

The 6-pr gun was the best British weapon available for tackling German tanks in early 1942, and the Deacon was designed as a means of increasing its mobility, chiefly for use in the North African theatre of war. The 6-pr (on a field-type, not a tank mounting) was mounted on a turntable, with a light shield open only at the rear, and carried on an armoured A.E.C. Matador chassis. The Deacon weighed 12 tons and powered by an A.E.C. six-cylinder 95-b.h.p. diesel engine had a top speed of only 19 m.p.h. Despite their bulk and slowness, the Deacons did good work in the North African campaign, after which they were handed over to the Turkish Government. A total of 150 was built in 1942 and they were supplied ex-works already painted in a bright sand yellow. A further twenty-five vehicles without the gun and a platform body were built as armoured ammunition carriers.

In 1943, an experimental wheeled self-propelled mounting for the new and very much more powerful 17-pr anti-tank gun was designed by Nicholas Straussler. Entirely original in concept, the 17-pr gun with split trail was, in effect, added to a rectangular skeleton chassis. A motive unit, consisting of Bedford type QL lorry components, was added, the engine (at the right-hand side of the chassis) driving the two front wheels for transport. When the gun was in position, the two rear wheels could be swivelled until they were at right angles to the front wheels. The right hand rear wheel could then be driven through a power take-off from the engine, so enabling the whole carriage to be rotated through 360 degrees. Sometimes known as Monitor, the Straussler S.P. 17-pr was not adopted for service because it was felt that the mounting offered insufficient protection for the gun and its crew. The illustration shows the vehicle in its travelling position.

48 Ford Armoured Cars (Arab Legion), Transjordan.

The Arab Legion of Transjordan (now the Kingdom of Jordan) originally had the tasks of patrolling the frontier and of internal security but after the outbreak of war the Arab Legion, now including a mobile unit known as the Desert Mechanized Force, served alongside the British Army in the Middle East, and was in action in Iraq and Syria in 1941. Following the success of the Arab Legion in these operations, it was decided to expand the Desert Mechanized Force, which included only six armoured cars, into a mechanized regiment (and subsequently into a mechanized brigade of three regiments).

The original six armoured cars of the Arab Legion were purchased in Palestine and were very similar to some used by the Palestine Police. No further supplies from this source, or from Britain, were available to equip the new mechanized regiments, and it was decided that the Arab Legion should build its own armoured cars in Transjordan. Four hundred Ford commercial truck chassis were ordered from the United States, although only 250 were delivered, the ships carrying the balance being torpedoed *en route*.

The Arab Legion armoured cars were designed by their commander, Glubb Pasha (John B. Glubb), and were modelled broadly on the original six vehicles (the first type of Arab Legion armoured car), which also used Ford chassis. Glubb's original model (called here for convenience the Arab Legion 2nd type) had built-up front mudguards and bevelled edges on the bonnet and front corners of the hull, but his second model (Arab Legion 3rd type) used the original truck mudguards and had a simpler bonnet design. In both models, the turret had provision for a mounted machine-gun (usually a Vickers 0·303-in.) and a Boys 0·55-in. anti-tank rifle, and an anti-aircraft machine-gun (often a Lewis 0·303-in.). Some cars were fitted with wireless, carried in the hull behind the turret. As supplies of armour plate were not available, the armour was made up of a double skin of mild steel with a sheet of plywood sandwiched between the plates.

A total of 100 armoured cars of these two types was built, and they equipped the Arab Legion mechanized regiments until being replaced by Marmon-Herrington Mark IV F armoured cars in 1945.

49 Autocanon Dodge and Autocanon 75-mm., Ford, France.

The Fighting French contingent which fought alongside British forces in the North African campaign in 1942–43, included an armoured car unit which was equipped partly with South African built Marmon-Herrington armoured cars and partly with vehicles of French design, although based on

American or Canadian chassis. This unit was formed from what was originally an infantry regiment of soldiers from French Morocco—the 1er Regiment de marche de Spahis Marocains (R.M.S.M.).

The Marmon-Herrington armoured cars (Mark III) supplied to the Fighting French were armed with machine-guns only, but these were supported by a number of vehicles (captured from the Vichy French in Syria) that were equipped with a French short 37-mm. gun and a 7·5-mm. machine-gun coaxially mounted in a small turret, open at the rear. A further 7·5-mm. machine-gun could be mounted on a pillar mount in the body of the vehicle. The chassis used for these armoured cars was a 4 × 2 U.S.-built Dodge 1940 model. The lorry cab was retained (with the addition of light windscreen armour) and only the rear part was fully armoured, although, even so, the back portion had an open top.

Later in 1943, the R.M.S.M. received a number of vehicles with very much greater fire power, designed by one of their officers, Lieutenant Conus. This type was based on the Ford F 60L 3-ton lorry supplied by Canada for the British Army. A French 75-mm. field gun was mounted at the rear (using the turntable from a captured Italian tank) where it had a full 360 degrees traverse. The crew were protected by a three-sided shield, and the rear of the chassis and the driver's cab were also armoured, although the latter appears to have been mainly to protect the driver from the blast of the gun. An anti-aircraft pillar mounting for a machine-gun was provided on the front of the gun shield. A lorry canvas hood was carried to disguise the gun when not in action. These 'autocanons' were used in action from about October 1942 until the end of the North African campaign.

These two types of Fighting French equipment are shown in the illustrations in typical Middle East colours, the Dodge bearing a French registration number and the Ford F 60L still carrying its original British W.D. number.

50 Carro Armato M.15/42, Italy.

The Italian medium tank M.15/42 was a logical development of the M.13/40 of 1940 and its derivative the M.14/41. Very much like its predecessors in appearance, the M.15/42's 47-mm. gun was, however, of 40 calibres length (compared with 32 calibres of the earlier tanks) which gave it a far higher muzzle velocity and greater penetrative power.

The other most important change compared with the M.13/40 and M.14/41 was a more powerful engine, the S.P.A. 15TB which produced 192 b.h.p. and gave a better maximum (road) speed of 25 m.p.h., despite the increase of a ton in weight. Although the new engine provided the extra power needed, it was a petrol engine and it seems to have been something of a backward step to abandon the diesel type previously used.

Other features of the M.15/42 were a crew of four, an armament of three 8-mm. Breda machine-guns (one coaxial, two in a dual mount in the front of the hull) besides the 47-mm. gun; and maximum armour protection of 45-mm. (50-mm. on the gun mantlet).

About 2,000 M.13/40s and M.14/41s were completed (of which about the last 800 were the latter) but production of the Carro Armato M.15/42 ceased after only 82 of them were built by early 1943. Following this, Italian armoured fighting vehicle production was concentrated on self-propelled guns.

One illustration shows the fifth tank of the 1st Company, 2nd Platoon, of an Italian armoured battalion in Italy in 1943; the other an M.15/42 in desert colours.

51 Carro Armato P.40, Italy.

The only Italian heavy tank of World War II, the P.40, which entered production in 1943, had its origin in design studies commenced in 1938. One of two Ansaldo designs (in competition with two drawn up by the official Direzione della Motorizzazione) was chosen in 1940, although the first prototype to be built did not appear until early 1942.

A 26-ton vehicle, protected up to a maximum of 50 mm., a high velocity 75-mm. gun was chosen as the main armament. As the gun being developed for it was not ready when the prototype was completed, however, the 75/18 howitzer was mounted instead. This was replaced in the second prototype by the interim gun 75/32 until, with the third prototype, the 75/34, with a muzzle velocity of 610 metres per second, could be used.

The suspension of the P.40 followed the common Italian practice of two groups of four road wheels each side carried on a semi-elliptic leaf spring for each group—a somewhat crude but well-tried system. The hull and turret layout were conventional, the armament of the 75-mm. gun and coaxial 8-mm. machine-gun being concentrated in the turret—the front hull machine-gun which existed in the first two prototypes was eliminated in the final version.

The engine was at the rear, the transmission being led forward via the gearbox and clutch to track drive sprockets at the front. The prototypes used a 330-h.p. diesel but a new twelve-cylinder-V petrol engine of 420 h.p. was ready for use in the production models, to which it gave a maximum speed of 25 m.p.h.

Only twenty-one P.40s had been completed by the time of the Armistice in 1943. Two Italian tank battalions to be equipped with P.40s were in the process of formation at this time, but in the end only the Germans employed in service the few P.40s available.

52 Semovente M. 42M da 75/34 and Semovente M.42L da 105/23, Italy.

Some of the most effective Italian armoured fighting vehicles were the series of assault guns based on medium tank chassis which appeared from 1941 onwards.

These vehicles were fully armoured and enclosed, and mounted weapons ranging in power from the 75/18 (75-mm.; 18 calibres long) howitzer originally used on the M.13/40 chassis, to the 105/23 on the M.15/42 chassis.

The 75/18 Semovente was in production between 1941 and 1943: later vehicles used the M.14/41 and M.15/42 chassis. In all, 780 vehicles were built. They gave good service with the Ariete and Littorio Divisions in North Africa and later on Italian soil.

A new weapon for the P.40 tank and assault guns, the 75/34, was in the process of development in 1942. In the meantime as an interim measure the 75/32 was introduced, although only a few dozen assault guns of this type were built, by the Ansaldo concern.

The prototype for the Semovente 75/34 was completed by the end of 1942, by which time a total of 500 had been ordered. Due to problems over the design of the mounting for the 75/34, however, 75/18s or 75/32s were fitted in M.15/42 chassis intended for the new gun. In the end, only just over ninety 75/34 assault guns were built. They were intended to replace the artillery in the armoured units, the 75/18s then to be transferred to support the infantry of armoured formations. Their main use was, however, by the Germans, who acquired all those available in Italy in 1943.

The Semovente M.42M da 75/34 was considered to be a good 'tank hunter', its gun having a muzzle velocity of 610 metres per second and a range of 12½ kilometres. Apart from the longer gun, it was similar in most external respects to the early 75/18 and 75/32 assault guns on the chassis of M.13/40, M.14/41 and M.15/42 tanks, all of which had similar running gear. Weighing 15 tons, the Semovente M.42M da 75/34 was powered by a S.P.A. eight-cylinder petrol engine of 192 b.h.p. which gave it a top speed of about 25 m.p.h. The vehicle had a crew of three men and an 8-mm. machine-gun was carried for anti-aircraft defence.

The Semovente M.42L da 105/23 was in general appearance like the 75-mm. assault gun but had a much larger 105-mm., 23-calibre length, howitzer, specially developed as an assault gun. The final prototype was ready in January 1943, and firing trials took place later in that month. Deliveries began in May 1943 but, although 454 of them were finally ordered, only a relatively small number was completed. Part of the artillery group of the Ariete Division was equipped with Semovente 105/23s in the summer of 1943. Some of these assault guns were used by Italian units in the defence of Rome in September 1943. Later the Germans requisitioned all those available and employed them in Italy.

With the same 192-b.h.p. petrol engine, the Semovente 105/23 weighed somewhat more at 15·6 tons than earlier models and had a top speed of 22 m.p.h. The 105-mm. gun was a good anti-tank weapon, notably with the special ammunition developed for it and, mounted in a compact chassis, this combination represented one of the best Italian armoured fighting vehicles of World War II.

53 Panzerkampfwagen II, Ausf.L, Luchs, Germany.

The PzKpfw II as a battle tank was, as early as 1940, recognized as being outdated. Its development, as a reconnaissance vehicle was, however, continued and the final model, Ausf.L, known as Luchs (Lynx) was produced in 1942–43.

Although retaining the same general layout of the earlier vehicles of the

PzKpfw II series, the Ausf.L's design was derived mainly from Daimler-Benz prototypes (based on their earlier Ausf.D and E) rather than the M.A.N. design used for the great majority of PzKfw IIs built. The main external difference of the Ausf.L from all earlier production PzKpfw IIs was the overlapping road wheels, with torsion bar suspension, and wide tracks. With a maximum armour thickness of 30-mm. (excluding spaced armour added later to some vehicles), the armament of the Luchs consisted of a 2-cm. gun and one machine-gun, mounted coaxially in the turret. A few vehicles were fitted instead with a 5-cm. gun—a fairly heavy weapon for a vehicle of under 12 tons. The engine of the Luchs was a 178-b.h.p. six-cylinder Maybach which gave it a maximum speed of about 40 m.p.h.

54 Panzerkampfwagen III, Ausf.L and Ausf.M, Germany.

Production of the PzKpfw III, the first models of which were built in 1937, was not finally ceased until the summer of 1943, when it was still an important element in the German armoured forces. Successive increases in armament, from the 3·7-cm. gun of the early models, through the 5-cm. L/42 of 1940 to the long 5-cm. L/60 of the late models, Ausf.L and M, associated with increased armour protection, justified the retention of the PzKpfw III. Even when superseded as a tank, the Panzer III chassis remained in production as the basis of assault guns.

Among the features shared by the Ausf.L and M with earlier models of

the PzKpfw III were the transverse torsion-bar suspension system and the twelve-cylinder Maybach engine of 300-h.p. and the secondary armament of one machine-gun coaxial with the gun in the turret and one machine-gun in the right side of the hull, beside the driver. The maximum armour protection of the Ausf.L and M was 70-mm. in spaced armour at the front and the combination of the increased armour and heavier gun made it necessary to reinforce the suspension. Skirt armour on hull sides and turret was also carried on some tanks. The Ausf.L and M were almost identical in appearance but in the latter, to simplify production, some vision ports and the hull escape doors were eliminated—with the introduction of skirt armour, these were, in any case, of little use.

The final version of PzKpfw III, the Ausf.N was the same as Ausf.L or M but with the short-barrelled 7·5-cm. KwK L/24. In all, 5,644 PzKpfw IIIs were produced between 1937 and 1943.

The upper illustration shows a PzKpfw III, Ausf.M, and the lower one a PzKpfw III, Ausf.L, in winter camouflage in Russia, with the guns sheathed as protection from the cold.

55 Panzerkampfwagen IV, Ausf.H, Germany.

The Panzerkampfwagen IV, which originally entered production on a limited scale in 1937, was steadily improved in armament and armour during World War II so that it remained in production right to the end of the war, by which time about 9,000 of them had been completed. The fact that, latterly, production was continued mainly because of the urgent need for serviceable tanks in large numbers, rather than changing completely to a more modern design, is no reflection on the excellent basic design of the PzKpfw IV.

A medium tank originally specified in the 20-ton class, although in its final form at around 25 tons, the Panzer IV was powered by a 300-b.h.p. twelve-cylinder Maybach at the rear with the gearbox and final drive sprockets at the front. The suspension consisted of eight road wheels each side, suspended in pairs on leaf springs.

When the Ausf.H appeared in 1943, the main armament was the long-barrelled 7·5-cm. L/48, increasingly powerful guns having been introduced in successive models, starting with the low-velocity 7·5-cm. L/24 of the early Panzer IVs. The secondary armament remained as two machine-guns—one in the hull front and one in the turret, coaxial with the 7·5-cm. gun. The maximum armour protection was 80-mm., having been increased fourfold over that of the original version, Ausf.A. Skirting plates (or wire mesh, in some cases) were often added to the turret and hull sides to give protection against hollow charge projectiles.

The Ausf.J, which followed, the final version of PzKpfw IV, was very similar externally to the preceding model but incorporated detail changes. One of the most important (and a retrograde step) was the deletion of the turret power traverse, leaving only a 2-speed hand traverse system, in order to make room for increased fuel capacity (680 litres, compared with 470 for Ausf H) to give the extra range called for by 1944.

One of the illustrations shows a tank partly painted with 'Zimmerit', an anti-magnetic paste to repel sticky bombs; both tanks shown have both hull and turret skirting plates.

56 Panzerkampfwagen V, Panther, Germany.

The Panther, together with the Russian T-34 which was the direct cause of its inception, was one of the best tanks of World War II and one which has had much influence on post-war tank design.

Once the full effect of the T-34 was appreciated, it was at first proposed that a close copy should be built in Germany to counter it, but this was soon proved to be impracticable because of the fresh tooling that would have been required and the absence of suitable raw materials. The main features of the T.34 were, however, reproduced in the two designs submitted, ranging from the Daimler-Benz VK 3002, which was closely similar to the T.34, to the M.A.N. version, which had more traditional German features. In spite of Hitler's preference for the Daimler-Benz design, the M.A.N. model was chosen for production, which commenced in November 1942.

The Panther, as the Pzkpfw V was named, had the long sloping glacis plate of the T.34, inward sloping hull sides above track level, a turret mounting a long 7·5-cm. gun (L/70—70 calibres long) and interleaved road wheels, sprung on transverse torsion bars. Armour protection was at a maximum of 120-mm. on the turret and 80-mm. on the hull. A Maybach twelve-cylinder engine developing 642-b.h.p. (increased to 690-b.h.p. in the later models, Ausf.A and G) gave a top speed of about 28 m.p.h.

The Ausf.D was followed in production by the illogically designated Ausf.A which incorporated various improvements, one of the most obvious of which was the replacement of the unusual vertical-letter box type of mounting for the hull machine-gun by a more conventional ball-mounting. The turret was equipped with a new type of cupola and the pistol ports and loading door, present in the Ausf.D, were eliminated.

The final model of Panther, Ausf.G, had further changes, partly to compensate for shortages of raw materials and to simplify production. The driver's vision port was replaced by a rotating periscope, leaving the glacis plate clear except for the machine-gun ball mount; the hull sides were more sloped and stowage boxes at the rear were included inside the armour. This latter change was not always apparent, however, as side skirting plates were always likely to be fitted on all models of Panther. Finally, later production vehicles had all-steel road wheels with resilient hubs instead of the rubber-tyred wheels used earlier.

The illustrations show a Panther Ausf.D (bottom view) and an Ausf.G.

57 Panzerkampfwagen VI, Tiger I, Germany.

Perhaps the tank which created the greatest impression on British troops in World War II, from the time it was first encountered by them in Tunisia in 1943, was the Tiger. First used in action in September 1942 in Russia, the Tiger's design was completed before features exemplified by the Russian T.34 could be incorporated. Nevertheless, the heavy armour (at a maximum of 110-mm. on the turret and 100-mm. on the hull) and the powerful 8·8-cm. gun (KwK 36 L/55) made the Tiger a very formidable tank right to the end of the war.

Work on various heavy tank projects was started as early as 1937. These were modified with changing requirements and with the incorporation of an 8·8-cm. gun resulted in 1942 in the specification V.K. 4501, for which the design competition was won by the Henschel firm.

In spite of its size, the Tiger was fairly conventional in layout and design except that interleaved road wheels in the suspension system were used for the first time in a production tank although they were, of course, already a familiar feature in German half-tracks.

The engine—at the rear, the transmission being led forward via an 8-speed gearbox to front drive sprockets—was a V-form twelve-cylinder Maybach of 650-b.h.p., increased to 700-b.h.p. in the later vehicles to be built. This produced a top speed of 24 m.p.h., quite satisfactory for a 54-ton tank.

A total of 1,350 Tiger Is was manufactured and they were used in action in North Africa, Sicily, Italy, North West Europe and Russia.

58 Panzerkampfwagen VI, Tiger II, Germany.

Known to the Western Allies as King Tiger or Royal Tiger, the Tiger II or

Tiger Ausf. B was even more feared by its opponents than Tiger I. With an even more powerful gun (8·8-cm., 71 calibres long, compared with Tiger I's 56 calibres) thicker armour and a sloping hull glacis plate, the Tiger II had all the best features of its predecessor, together with improvements suggested by experience in Russia. Development of the type was called for in the autumn of 1942 and when the Tiger IIs were delivered to the troops in 1944 they were the most powerful tanks in service in the world, as well as the heaviest, and the position remained unchanged until nearly the end of the War.

Fortunately for its opponents, the Tiger II was mechanically unreliable, a fault perhaps due to insufficient time being allowed for development. Fourteen tons heavier than Tiger I, the King Tiger had a similar mechanical layout but the road wheels, sprung on independent torsion bars, were not interleaved, as in Tiger I, although they were overlapped. Four hundred and eighty-five Tiger IIs were built, of which the first fifty had different, more rounded, turrets than had been built for a Porsche-designed Tiger II, although the Porsche tank itself was rejected.

The relatively few Tiger IIs built were used in 1944–45 with considerable effect on both Germany's East and West fronts.

59 Panzerkampfwagen Maus and Panzerkampfwagen E.100, Germany.

These two colossal tanks, Maus and E.100, weighing around 150 tons, were produced in prototype form in Germany in 1944–45.

Maus, the earlier of the two, was the result of an instruction by Hitler to Dr Porsche in 1942 to design in conjunction with Krupp's a super-heavy tank in the 100-ton class. The first prototype (without turret and armament) was running by December 1944. The turret, mounted at the rear, with an armament consisting of a 15-cm. L/38 gun with a coaxial 7·5-m. KwK was only fitted at a late stage in development of the prototype, most test runs being carried out with a simulated turret.

The final all-up weight of Maus was no less than 185 tons, which few bridges could have withstood, so provision was made for the tank to ford rivers up to a depth of 14 feet, with air supply through a submarine-type snorkel tube. A 1200-b.h.p. Daimler-Benz petrol engine (a diesel was the ultimate type) with electric transmission was used and this produced a top speed of 12 m.p.h.

Panzerkampfwagen E.100 was the 'official' design by the Army Weapons Department for a tank in the 100-ton class and the heaviest in a proposed family of tracked fighting vehicles of between 5 and 100 tons, in which it was hoped to standardize as many components as possible. A somewhat more conventional design than Maus, being developed by Adler from the basis of the Tiger series, the E.100 was rather like a scaled-up Tiger II in appearance, with a 15-cm. gun and a coaxial 7·5-cm. gun in the turret, which was mounted centrally. The engine was a 700-b.h.p. twelve-cylinder Maybach for trials, although a 1,200-b.h.p.

version was proposed and was needed to produce the required performance.

The suspension system, like that of Maus, abandoned the torsion bars used for the later German medium and heavy tanks. It used a form of coil springing—Belleville washers. The weight of E.100 was about 138 tons and the maximum armour protection for both Maus and E.100 was 240-mm.

Two prototypes of the Maus were completed and tested in 1944–45; the E.100 prototype was never finished. Although overcoming engineering problems in the design of such heavy vehicles, the tactical value of tanks of this size was questionable as was, to an even greater degree, the diversion of A.F.V. design and production effort. There was certainly little excuse at all for two separate and competing designs at a critical stage of the war for Germany.

60 Jagdpanzer 38(t), Hetzer, Germany.

The Jagdpanzer 38(t) Hetzer ('Baiter') was one of the best self-propelled mountings for its size of World War II, being compact, well-armoured and mobile, with a top speed of about 25 m.p.h. The gun—the 7·5-cm. Pak 39 (L/48) was mounted in the right-hand side of the sloping glacis plate, which was armoured to a maximum of 60-mm. The driver sat at the left, the 150-b.h.p. six-cylinder Praga engine being at the rear. The suspension was of the leaf spring variety, the large road wheels being sprung in pairs.

An interesting feature of the Jagdpanzer 38(t) was the type of machine-gun mounted on the roof in some vehicles. This was fitted with a deflection device which enabled it to 'fire round corners', thus making it more effective in close-up defence.

The last type on the Czech LT-38 chassis to go into production, 1,577 Hetzers were built in 1944 and the design was considered good enough to be adopted by the Swiss Army in the post-war years.

61 Sturmgeheschütz III/10·5-cm. StuH, Germany.

The Sturmgeschütz III was one of Germany's most enduring armoured fighting vehicles, production of which commenced in 1940 and continued right through to the end of the war, when over 10,500 vehicles had been built.

In its standard form the StuG III was originally equipped with the low-velocity 7·5-cm. L/24 gun, suitable for close support of infantry. This was replaced in 1942 by the much more powerful L/43 and L/48 weapons which were also capable of tackling tanks. Also developed in 1943 was a new version for the close support role, but with a much heavier gun—the 10·5-cm. howitzer. The first vehicles had the 1eFH18 (light field howitzer) but the StuH.42 (assault howitzer) was soon standardized for the majority of 10·5-cm. StuG. III that were produced.

The chassis of the StuG III remained throughout production that of the contemporary model of Pzkpfw III, although the tank itself was eventually withdrawn from production in favour of the assault gun. The armour protection in the later StuG III was at a maximum of 80-mm. and side skirting plates were usually fitted. The total weight was nearly 24 tons, although the maximum speed of 24 m.p.h. remained the same as in earlier models.

The upper illustration shows a vehicle with 'Zimmerit' finish and skirting plates.

62 Sturmpanzer IV, Brummbär and Jagdpanzer IV/70, Germany.

Two self-propelled mountings developed from the Stu.G III concept, but taking advantage of the greater scope offered by the larger Pz IV chassis, the Brummbär (Grizzly Bear) appeared in 1943 and the Jagdpanzer IV/70 in 1944. Armed with the short (12 calibres) heavy 15-cm. StuH.43, the Brummbär was armoured to a maximum of 100-mm. on the front plate. Weighing over 28 tons the chassis was overloaded, although a top speed of 25 m.p.h. was attainable. Only 315 of them were built and to compensate for a shortcoming discovered in service, the last ones produced had a machine-gun added in a ball-mounting at the left-hand side of the sloping front plate.

The Jagdpanzer IV/70 was the outcome of the policy to produce heavily armoured turretless self-propelled anti-tank guns at the expense of tank production—a token of the realization of Germany's need for vehicles suited more for defence than attack. In addition, production of turretless vehicles rather than tanks helped to increase the total number available. Earlier vehicles on the PzKpfw IV chassis used the 7·5-cm. L/48 in a superstructure like that of the Stu.G III until the redesigned Jagdpanzer IV appeared. At first also armed with the 7·5-cm. L/48, the final version had the powerful 7·5-cm. L/70—the same gun as the Panther's. This exceptionally long weapon caused nose heaviness, resulting in heavy wear on the rubber tyres of the front two road wheels each side. Accordingly, steel-tyred resilient road wheels were substituted in these positions. Also, to simplify the suspension, only three, instead of four, return rollers each side were used in the later vehicles built. Output of Jagdpanzer IV with both the L/48 and L/70 guns (mostly the former) amounted to over 1,500 vehicles.

63 8.8-cm. Panzerjäger Panther-Jagdpanther, Germany.

Like the tank on which it was based, the Jagdpanther was a formidable vehicle. Following the standard German practice of using a tank chassis to mount a heavier gun in a limited traverse mounting, thus keeping the weight within reasonable bounds, the Panther chassis was used to create a highly mobile heavily armed 'tank hunter'.

The running gear and lower chassis of the Panther (Ausf.G) was retained but the hull was increased in height and the gun—the 8·8-cm. L/71 (71 calibres long)—was mounted in the centre of the sloping glacis plate. A ball-mounted machine-gun was retained but higher up the glacis than in the tank.

Produced in 1944 the Jagdpanther was considered by some at the time to be an undesirable dilution of Panther production, but in the defensive operations of 1944–45, the Jagdpanther was probably an even more effective weapon than the tank.

64 Jagdpanzer Tiger (P), Elefant, Germany.

Dr Ferdinand Porsche's design to the V.K. 4501 specification—the Tiger tank—had interesting and unusual features, such as petrol-electric drive and longitudinal torsion-bar suspension, but the more conventional Henschel design was chosen for the production order for the Tiger. Nevertheless, a limited order for ninety Porsche Tiger chassis was awarded. Five were completed at the Nibelungenwerke in Austria as tanks (and used for trials only) and the rest were modified at the Alkett concern in Berlin as 'tank hunters'. This involved the addition of a fixed superstructure (armoured to a maximum of 200-mm.) in which an 8·8-cm. Pak L/71 was mounted, with a limited traverse. The original engine intended by Porsche was replaced by two twelve-cylinder Maybach engines, totalling 640-b.h.p. but the electric transmission was retained. Weighing 67 tons, the top speed was only 12½ m.p.h.

Named at first Ferdinand (after Dr Porsche) and later Elefant, these Jagdpanzers were employed at first in Russia and later, in reduced numbers, in Italy. Experience in Russia showed that the lack of a hull machine-gun was a serious fault, and one was incorporated later.

65 Jagdpanzer VI—Jagdtiger, Germany.

In accordance with the usual German practice, a companion 'tank hunter' version of Tiger II was produced, in which the rotating turret was replaced by a fixed superstructure mounting a heavier gun than that carried in the tank. This was the Jagdtiger, armed with a 12·8-cm. Pak 44 L/55—the most powerfully armed fighting vehicle to go into production in World War II, although Germany's circumstances in 1944 made it possible for a total of only forty-eight to be built. With a similar power train and suspension (although lengthened) to that of Tiger II, the Jagdtiger was protected to a maximum thickness of no less than 250-mm., weighed 70 tons and had a top speed of 23 m.p.h. It was the heaviest and one of the most formidable fighting vehicles of its era to enter service.

During the course of its short production life, the suspension of the Jagdtiger was changed from the Henschel system of transverse torsion bars used in Tiger II to a longitudinal torsion bar system, designed by Ferdinand Porsche, in which the wheels were mounted in four pairs each side. In the illustrations a vehicle with the Porsche suspension is shown at the top, and a Jagdtiger with the Henschel system, which had nine overlapped wheels each side instead of eight, at the bottom.

66 7·5-cm. Pak auf Gw. 38(t), Marder III, Ausf.M, Germany.

The Czech LT-38 tank was continued in production after the German take-over of Czechoslovakia. By 1942, the Pzkpfw 38(t), as it was then called, was outclassed as a battle tank, but it was thought well worth while to continue output of the reliable, sturdy and easily maintained chassis as a mounting for self-propelled weapons.

The earlier self-propelled mountings (Geschützwagen—Gw.) used the chassis with the original layout in which the engine was located at the rear. The later versions, built in 1943–44, had the engine (a six-cylinder 150-b.h.p. Praga) moved forward to a position alongside the driver, and were designated Ausf.M (M = mitte [middle]), the earlier version being Ausf.H = heckmotor [rear engine]). Apart from better weight distribution, a lower silhouette was possible with the engine relocated and there were advantages in the crew having access to the gun from the rear.

The weapon used was the 7·5-cm. Pak 40/3, of a calibre length of 46, and mounted behind a shield open at the rear and with no overhead protection. One machine-gun was usually carried for local defence.

Seven hundred and ninety-nine Marder III, Ausf.M were built in 1943–44, together with four hundred and eighteen of the earlier Ausf.H in 1942–43.

Two views of different vehicles are shown in the illustrations.

67 15-cm. sIG33 auf Sf. II and 7·62-cm. Pak auf Gw. II, Ausf. D, Germany.

These two self-propelled mountings both used the chassis of different models of the PzKpfw II. The heavy infantry gun (sIG) carrier was, however, by far the better vehicle, being low and inconspicuous and the addition of an extra road wheel each side in the later version (which appeared in 1943) gave a better weight distribution and more space for crew and ammunition. With

a crew of five and a loaded weight of about 13 tons this self-propelled gun (Selbstfahrlafette—Sfl.), which was powered by the standard six-cylinder 140-b.h.p. Maybach engine, had a top speed of 25 m.p.h. Vehicles of this type on both lengthened and normal PzII chassis were used in North Africa and Russia.

The 7·62-cm. Pak—a captured Russian anti-tank gun, rechambered to take German ammunition—on the Pzkpfw II Ausf. D (also Ausf. E) chassis was, by contrast, one of the crudest of the improvised self-propelled mountings produced by the Germans in World War II. Nevertheless, it served its purpose in helping to get the greatest possible number of anti-tank guns into the field in the shortest possible time. The long-barrelled gun, protected by its own shield, was mounted towards the rear of the vehicle on top of the armoured superstructure with the end of the barrel projecting over the front. The Ausf.D of Pzkpfw II had a 180-b.h.p. six-cylinder Maybach engine and the Gw II for the 7·62-cm. Pak weighing 11·5 tons had a top speed of about 35 m.p.h.

68 15-cm. Pz. fH 18 auf Gw. III/IV, Hummel and 8.8-cm. Pak43/1 (L/71) auf Gw. III/IV, Nashorn, Germany.

A modified Panzer IV chassis, incorporating features of the Panzer III, was used between 1942 and 1944 for the production of two specially designed heavily armed but relatively lightly armoured self-propelled mountings. Known as Geschützwagen III/IV, the chassis had the Panzer IV suspension with the engine (300-b.h.p. twelve-cylinder Maybach) moved forward to allow room for a fighting compartment at the rear.

Hummel (Bumble Bee) was the 15-cm. field Howitzer (Pz.H.18) on this chassis: 666 vehicles were built in 1943–44, together with 150 similar vehicles without guns for use as armoured ammunition carriers.

The 8·8-cm. Pak 43/1 (L/71) on the same chassis with minor variations for the gun mounting, ammunition stowage etc. was known at first as Hornisse (Hornet) and later as Nashorn (Rhinoceros). Four hundred and seventy three were made in 1943–44 and although, like Hummel, armoured only to a maximum of 30-mm., the powerful gun made them a formidable weapon.

69 Flakpanzer IV (3·7-cm.), Möbelwagen and Flakpanzer IV (2-cm.), Wirbelwind, Germany.

The overwhelming Allied air superiority by 1943 made it increasingly necessary for Germany to direct a greater proportion of armoured fighting vehicle production to the output of anti-aircraft tanks.

The Pzkpfw IV chassis was used for some of the more important of the A.A. tank designs which entered service in 1943–44. The commonest of the lighter weapons were the quadruple 20-mm. and the single 3·7-cm. guns. The earlier design for both of these mountings (called Möbelwagen—furniture van—in the case of the 3·7-cm. mounting) consisted of the guns with their normal shield, surrounded by a hinged four-sided square armoured structure, which folded flat, when required, to give unimpeded all-round traverse.

The later design, again generally similar for both 20-mm. and 3·7-cm. guns called Wirbelwind (Whirlwind) for the former and Ostwind (East Wind) for the latter, dispensed with the clumsy folding shields and used instead a multi-sided pot-shaped turret, open at the top. Although only lightly armoured (16-mm.) this turret gave better protection to the gun crew.

In addition to the anti-aircraft weapon, Wirbelwind and Ostwind (unlike the Möbelwagen types) retained the front hull machine-gun of the standard Pzkpfw IV.

70 Schwerer Ladungsträger (Sdkfz 301) and Leichter Ladungsträger (SdKfz 302), Germany.

These two machines, heavy and light demolition vehicles, were more commonly known as B.IV and Goliath, respectively. The B.IV, designed by the Borgward company of Bremen and produced from 1942 onwards, carried a 500 kg. explosive charge in a wedge-shaped bin at the front. With a seat for one man, the B.IV could be driven close to the scene of the action. In the attack, the vehicle was radio controlled. At the target, the bolts holding the demolition charge were destroyed by an electrically detonated charge, allowing the explosive bin to slide to the ground. The vehicle was then reversed away before the demolition charge was detonated. Powered by a petrol engine, the B.IV could be controlled by radio up to distances of about 1¼ miles. The first model, Ausf. A, shown in the illustration, weighed 3·6 tons. A total of 1,193 B.IVs (in three models) was produced between 1942 and 1944. They were used chiefly by heavy tank units to help destroy fixed defences.

The lighter demolition vehicle SdKfz 302 or 'Goliath' was, unlike the B.IV, expendable. About 5 ft 4 in. long, the Goliath (Ausf. A) carried a 60 kg. explosive charge. Driven by one electrical starter motor for each track, the vehicle was guided, and detonated when it reached its target, through a 3-core electric cable, of which about 670 yards was carried on a drum at the rear. In front of the drum was a compartment containing the control gear and the explosive was in a third compartment. Some 2,650 Goliaths of this type were built between 1942 and 1944 together with 5,079 (between 1943 and 1945) of a later and slightly heavier model, Ausf. B or SdKfz 303, powered by a Zündapp petrol engine. The employment of Goliaths was similar to that of the B.IV.

In the illustration of a Goliath (Ausf.A) the cover over the rear compartment is shown raised, revealing the electric control cable reel.

71 Leichter Schützenpanzerwagen SdKfz 250/8 and Leichter Schützenpanzerwagen SdKfz 250/9, Germany

The light armoured semi-tracked armoured personnel carrier SdKfz 250 which first appeared in action as a troop carrier in 1940, had by the end of the war appeared in twelve main variants, many of which were support vehicles for the basic infantry carrier.

The SdKfz 250/8 was a self-propelled mounting for the 7·5-cm. KwK L/24—the gun used in the earliest versions of the Sturmgeschütz III although in a 6-ton vehicle only light protection could be afforded. The gun was mounted just behind the driver together with a machine-gun (MG 42) both for ranging the 7·5-cm. KwK and for general targets.

Virtually a semi-tracked light armoured car (Panzerspähwagen) the SdKfz 250/9 had the same turret as the Leichter Panzerspähwagen SdKfz 222. This turret carried a 2-cm. gun and machine-gun on a mounting also capable of anti-aircraft fire: the only overhead protection was a hinged wire mesh frame to guard against grenades.

With good mobility and a high top speed of nearly 40 m.p.h., the SdKfz 250 series were powered by a Maybach six-cylinder engine of 100-b.h.p., which drove the tracks via front drive sprockets. The front wheels were for steering only and were not driven. An efficient vehicle, although with a somewhat complicated suspension and track design making heavy demands on maintenance time, the SdKfz 250 and its larger counterpart the SdKfz 251 was not replaced in production by semi-tracks of simpler design until 1944.

72 Panzerspähwagen SdKfz 234/2 (Puma) and Panzerspähwagen SdKfz 234/3, Germany.

An improved version of the successful German eight-wheeled armoured car, first issued in 1938, appeared in 1944. Although the chassis was basically unaltered and only minor changes were made to the armoured hull, the use of a diesel engine of greatly increased power (the Czechoslovakian Tatra twelve-cylinder V-form of 220-b.h.p.) led to improved performance. An air-cooled diesel engine was specified in 1940, when the design work began, with the object of facilitating operation in hot countries but this type of engine was also an advantage in subsequent operations in the cold weather in Russia and the fuel economy of the diesel resulted in a much wider range.

The first model of the new eight-wheeled armoured car, SdKfz 234/1, was armed only with a 2-cm. KwK and one machine-gun in an open-topped turret—no more than that of the 5-ton light armoured car SdKfz 222, and very inadequate for a vehicle of this size. The next model, SdKfz 234/2, was equipped with a 5-cm. (L/60) gun and a machine-gun in an enclosed turret, which made it capable of engaging tanks, although it was still intended only as a reconnaissance vehicle.

Two further models of the SdKfz 234 were produced as self-propelled mountings with guns mounted to fire forwards, with only limited traverse. The SdKfz 234/4 was a highly mobile 'tank hunter' with a 7·5-cm. Pak L/48 and the SdKfz 234/3—shown in one of the illustrations, together with SdKfz 234/2—was a close support vehicle with the low velocity 7·5-cm. Stu.K L/24.

73 T-34 ('T-34/76B') and T-34/85 (Medium Tanks), U.S.S.R.

The immense superiority of the T-34 over its opponents when it first appeared in action in 1941 was countered by the Germans with the introduction of the Panther and Tiger, and by up-gunning the PzKpfw IV. Nevertheless, successive improvements in the armament and protection of the T-34 kept it in the forefront of medium tanks throughout the rest of the war.

These improvements were accompanied by various other changes, although the main basic features of the T-34's design were retained throughout its long life. All this was achieved without undue interruption to the production flow although it led to many transitional models. The Russians did not allocate model numbers at all but the main differences between T-34 variants were, however, classified by the Western Allies and the Germans, and the model letters they allotted have been used here.

The original production version of the T-34, the T-34/76A, as it became known outside the Soviet Union, had a turret design which was unsatisfactory in some respects. This was replaced in the T-34/76B by a new turret incorporating a 76·2-mm. gun with a length of 41·2 calibres (compared with the earlier gun's 30·5 calibres) and increased muzzle velocity. Vision arrangements were improved and the 'pig's head' type of mantlet was replaced by a bolted one of more angular shape in which the gun was mounted relatively higher. (This incidentally resulted in the depression of the gun being no more than 4 degrees, one of the weaker points of the T-34's design, but accepted because one solution—raising the height of the turret roof—would have increased vulnerability). The earlier turrets of Model B were of rolled plate, welded, but during 1942 a cast version was introduced and this pattern is shown in the illustration.

Good as it was, it became necessary to increase the hitting power of the T-34 and during the summer of 1943, A. A. Morozov, who had taken over as chief designer from M. I. Koshkin, who died in 1940, redesigned the tank to accept a new turret armed with an 85-mm. gun. The gun was an adaptation of a pre-war anti-aircraft gun and was in a turret designed for the KV-85 heavy tank, so, once more, introducing standardization between the two classes of Russian tank. Later, though, this turret was re-designed and the second model of the T-34/85, using the new turret is shown in the illustration in this book.

The T-34/85's roomier turret enabled a five-man crew to be used and the protection was increased to a maximum of 75-mm. at the front. The main essentials of all T-34s remained, however, including the V-12 cylinder diesel engine of 500 h.p. driving rear sprockets and the Christie suspension of large road wheels on pivot arms controlled by long coil springs. Although many improvements had been introduced since 1940, the T-34 was still basically a simple and rugged but effective design, well suited to mass production. Nearly 40,000 T-34s of all types were built during World War II.

74 KV-85 (Heavy Tank) and SU-85, U.S.S.R.

The need to improve the armament of the KV-1 heavy tank was emphasized

during the great battle of Kursk in 1943, in which the Soviet tanks encountered the German Tiger tanks in appreciable numbers. The 85-mm. gun in a new turret was fitted to the KV-1 in that year and the first of the new tanks, designated KV-85, were in action by the Autumn of 1943. The new combination was roughly equivalent to the German Tiger I (although more lightly armoured) and the Russians took the opportunity of reworking existing KV-1s to the new standard in order to make available quickly larger numbers of tanks capable of taking on the Tiger on equal terms. By Russian standards only small numbers of KV-85s were built—but the design was used as the basis of the Stalin tank which succeeded the KV series.

Roughly at the time the KV-85 appeared in service in 1943 and when a heavy tank with a more powerful gun than the 85-mm. was already envisaged, the SU-85 was designed. This SU (the initials stand for Samachodnya Ustanovka—self-propelled [gun] mounting) was intended as a 'tank hunter' and carried the high velocity 85-mm. gun in a mounting with limited traverse in a low (and hence less conspicuous) well-armoured hull on the T-34 chassis. This device, of using a standard (or, sometimes, obsolescent) chassis to to mount a heavier gun and, at the same time, achieve better protection and/or mobility than with the same weapon on a tank, was widely used by the Germans in World War II.

Often used in conjunction with T-34/76s, the SU-85 was in production from about the end of 1943 for about a year, when it gradually began to be replaced by the SU-100, with a more powerful gun, which used the same chassis and which was similar in appearance. Another widely used self-propelled gun on the T-34 chassis was the SU-122, a 122-mm. low velocity howitzer, which was in service from early 1943 onwards.

75 JS-II (Heavy Tank), U.S.S.R.

The Josef Stalin or JS-II heavy tank with its long 122-mm. gun was one of the most powerful tanks to go into service with any army in World War II.

A tank which traced its ancestry directly back to the KV series, the JS-II was another product of the design team headed by General Z. A. Kotin. Taking the KV-85 as a base, the best points were retained but others, including the suspension and transmission, were redesigned. A two-stage planetary transmission, combined with an improved engine led to better manœuvrability and overall performance. At the same time, the opportunity was taken of rearranging the internal layout in a more compact form, allowing for armour increases while decreasing the total weight compared with KV-85.

The earliest JS tanks had the same 85-mm. gun as the KV. This was then replaced by a 100-mm. weapon and then, finally, by the 122-mm. gun. As this gun needed a wider turret ring, the hull at that point had to be extended out over the tracks each side but to avoid increasing the height, the top run of the track was lowered, although in most other respects the torsion bar suspension of the JS was similar to that of the KV's.

Known as JS-I or JS-122, the first 122-mm. gun-armed Stalin tanks entered service in late 1943. The JS-II which followed was generally similar but had the hull redesigned to give greater protection, notably in the better slope on the glacis plate.

The 122-mm. gun on the JS-II had a 7·62-mm. machine-gun as a coaxial weapon. The tank was served by a crew of four. The combat weight was 45 tons and with a 600-b.h.p. twelve-cylinder-V diesel engine had a top speed of 23 m.p.h. Armour was at a maximum thickness of 120-mm.

Over 2,000 JS-IIs were produced during the war, before being superseded by even the better JS-III, which became one of the most formidable tanks of the post-war years.

76 JSU-122 and JSU-152, U.S.S.R.

Two powerful self-propelled guns based on the Stalin heavy tank chassis, the JSU-122 and JSU-152 both entered service in 1944. Superseding similar weapons mounted on the earlier KV chassis (known as SU-122 and SU-152) to which they bore a strong resemblance, these two self-propelled guns had a better mechanical performance and, among other detail improvements, improved fire control arrangements.

The 122-mm. gun used in the earlier JSU-122s (one of which is shown in the illustration) was 45 calibres long and had a range of over 14,000 yards. Later models had a 43-calibre gun with a muzzle brake. The 152-mm. gun (29 calibres long) of the JSU-152 was a howitzer with a range of well over 9,000 yards. The ammunition (weighing 96 lb for high explosive and 107 lb per round for armour piercing) was so bulky, however, that only twenty rounds could be carried.

Carrying a crew of four (five if the vehicle was fitted with radio) the two JSUs were mechanically the same as their heavy tank counterparts and had much the same performance. This was important, because they were generally employed integrally with heavy tank regiments equipped with JS tanks.

77 KT (Winged Tank) and SU-76 U.S.S.R.

By the end of 1942, the Russians were already beginning to regard light tanks as a class as obsolete and although the type was developed from the T-40 of 1941 through the T-60 and T-70 to the T-80 of 1943, production of light tanks was tailed off in that year and had ceased before the war ended. At one time regarded mainly for their amphibious qualities, the Russians also gave some consideration to the potential of the light tank as an airborne vehicle. One of the most interesting tank experiments by any country in World War II was the Russian design for a Kyrliatyi Tank (KT) or 'winged tank'.

This design, by a team led by O. Antonov, consisted of a T-60 light tank, more or less in standard form, to which biplane wings, twin booms and a tail assembly were attached. These aerodynamic structures were made of wood, mainly, it seems, because of the shortage of aircraft alloys for experiments of this kind. Rudimentary flying controls were led from the wings and tail to the tank, which formed the 'fuselage' of the machine.

The first test flight took place in 1942 and was curtailed only because of a fault in the engines of the towing aircraft. The winged tank apparently performed satisfactorily, but eventually the project had to be cancelled because of a shortage of the four-engined towing aircraft that would have been needed in some quantity to justify production of the tank gliders.

The T-60 light tank, as used in this experiment, was a 6-ton vehicle armed with a 20-mm. gun and a 7·62-mm. machine-gun. Maximum armour protection was 20-mm. and a 70-b.h.p. GAZ—202 six-cylinder petrol engine gave the tank a top speed of about 27 m.p.h.

The successor to the T-60 light tank was the T-70, which weighed 9 tons and had a 45-mm. gun and 7·62-mm. machine-gun. Several thousand were produced in 1942–43. Before production ceased, however, it had already been decided to utilize the T-70 chassis as the basis of a self-propelled mounting for the 76·2-mm. anti-tank gun.

The vehicle which emerged, the SU-76, used automotive and running gear similar to that of the T-70, although an extra road wheel each side was added to accommodate the longer hull needed as a self-propelled mounting. The power unit, mounted at the right-hand side of the hull, consisted of two engines, GAZ-202 of 70-b.h.p. each in earlier vehicles and GAZ-203 of 85-b.h.p. each in late production vehicles. Independent torsion bars for each road wheel were used for the suspension. The 76·2-mm. gun, 41·5 calibres long, was mounted at the rear in an open-topped compartment with a total traverse of 32 degrees. The relatively light armour and absence of overhead protection made the SU-76 less suitable as an anti-tank vehicle once the gun began to be outranged by more powerful German weapons. It was replaced by the SU-85 as an anti-tank vehicle, therefore, and switched to the infantry support role.

The SU-76 shown in the illustration is one of the earlier production vehicles.

78 BA-64 (Light Armoured Car), U.S.S.R.

Armoured car development in the Soviet Union in World War II was very limited indeed because, apart from improvements to the two main pre-war designs, only one new model appeared. This was the BA-64, which went into production in 1942. A light armoured scout car with 4-wheel drive, said to have been inspired by the German SdKfz 222, to which it bore a slight resemblance, the BA-64 had a crew of two—the driver and the commander, who had a small open top multi-sided turret equipped with a machine-gun. This was normally a 7·62-mm. weapon, mounted in the turret face, or on top for anti-aircraft use, but alternatively a heavy 14·5-mm. machine-gun on a pintle mount could be carried.

Weighing about 2½ tons, the BA-64 was powered by a four-cylinder 50-b.h.p. GAZ petrol engine, which gave it a maximum speed of 31 m.p.h.

79 Tanque 'Narhuel', Modelo DL 43, Argentina.

Designed in Argentina in 1943 and produced in that country, the 'Narhuel' was a medium tank weighing 35 tons. The name 'Narhuel' is a South American Indian name for the jaguar. Although owing much in inspiration and configuration to the United States M.4 Medium, the 'Narhuel' was otherwise entirely original in design. The main armament consisted of a 75-mm. gun. A machine-gun was mounted coaxially with the 75-mm. gun on the left side and there were up to three others in the hull glacis plate, with another for anti-aircraft use.

The crew consisted of five men and with a 500-h.p. engine the maximum speed was 25 m.p.h. and the range was about 150 miles. The maximum armour protection was 80-mm.

Only sixteen of these tanks were built, the need for further production of medium tanks in Argentina ceasing to exist after 1944 when supplies of U.S. M.4 mediums and other equipment became available.

80 Stridsvagn M/42 and Storm-artillerivagn M/43, Sweden.

Swedish armoured fighting vehicle development during World War II followed a policy of steady progress in mechanical improvement and up-gunning, as far as was possible with the resources available.

The 22½-ton Strv. M/42, designed by Landsverk, had a family resemblance to that concern's earlier, much lighter, series taken into Swedish Army service as Strv. M/38, M/39 and M/40. The latter were armed only with 37-mm. guns, however, which by 1942 were inadequate, and it was decided to adopt a short calibre 75-mm. gun for the Strv. M/42. With a crew of four and armour protection to an 80-mm. maximum, the Strv. M/42 was powered by an eight-cylinder Volvo water-cooled engine developing 380 b.h.p. which produced a top speed of 29 m.p.h. Two 8-mm. machine-guns were mounted to the right of the 75-mm. gun in the turret and a third machine gun was in the front of the hull.

In 1945 the Strv. M/42 was re-designated Infanterikanonvagn 73 (Ikv 73) to reflect the new role for this tank as an infantry support vehicle.

The Stormartillerivagn M/43 (Sav. M/43), which appeared in 1944, used the chassis of the Czech-designed LT-38 built under licence in Sweden by Scania-Vavis A.B. as Stridsvagn M/41. This assault gun mounted a 10·5-cm. howitzer in a fixed, enclosed armoured superstructure. Weighing 12 tons and with a crew of four, the Sav. M/43 had a six-cylinder Scania-Vabis engine of 140 b.h.p., which gave it a maximum speed of about 27 m.p.h. The Strv. M/41 design, on which the Sav. M/43 was based, had a very long life for a fighting vehicle, incidentally, because in 1962 chassis of this type were rebuilt as armoured personnel carriers.

Appendix to Book II

Armoured Fighting Vehicle Camouflage and Markings 1942-45

The artist in conjunction with the author has tried to show camouflage colours as they are likely to have appeared, and tactical and other markings for specific vehicles have been included where practicable. However, in some cases, information has been unobtainable or incomplete: black and white photographs, for example, are an unreliable guide as to whether a vehicle is painted a medium brown or medium green colour. Even reproductions of colour photo transparencies are often very misleading—for example, one photograph in colour of a Churchill tank which was reproduced in a journal showed it as something very much like middle bronze green, whereas the original transparency, which the author has examined, proves that the tank in question was actually khaki brown!

Apart from the difficulties of colour reproduction in a book, the colours used on the actual vehicles often varied for many reasons—the exact colours for camouflage were not always considered important and wide discretion was allowed to unit and tank commanders; the quality control on paints issued—always difficult to maintain—sometimes allowed quite wide variations; and colours, once applied, could sometimes be changed out of all recognition by ageing, frequently helped by terrain such as desert sand. References to official colour standard specifications are given below in some cases and these are the surest basis of information available today on exact shades as they were supposed to be applied. Even so, allowance has to be made for variations from causes such as those mentioned above and it must always be borne in mind that, for example, a dark colour, particularly in bright sunlight, will appear much lighter when spread over a wide surface and, of course, the reverse applies to a light colour in deep shadow.

For those wishing to pursue the subject, useful articles discussing the problems involved as well as details of actual colour schemes have appeared in the journals *Tankette* and *A.F.V. News*.

Argentina

The colour for fighting vehicles was either plain olive green or, where necessary, a three-colour disruptive pattern of olive green, brown and dark green.

Australia

Camouflage and markings were on similar lines to those used by the United Kingdom except that for A.F.V.s in Australia itself a two- or three-colour scheme using shades better matching the local terrain was used. For operations in New Guinea and Borneo, tanks were painted 'Jungle green'—a very dark green.

Tactical signs were as for the United Kingdom, except that independent squadrons used an inverted triangle symbol.

Canada

See under United Kingdom.

France (Fighting France)

Vehicles in the Western Desert were usually sand colour, as for contemporary British vehicles. Original French vehicles had French registration numbers, vehicles supplied by the British usually carried the original W.D. numbers. When American equipment was provided in the Italian campaign and for use in France itself in 1944–45, U.S. camouflage colours (usually olive drab) were used.

Germany

In 1942 grey, ranging from medium to dark was in general use, except in North Africa where sand yellow was normally used. A mottled pattern of green or brown was sometimes added in North Africa, more often in Tunisia near the end of the campaign.

An order dated 18 February 1943 instructed that all A.F.V.s leaving the factories should be finished in a standard dark sand (yellow) colour, although in 1944, perhaps due to paint shortages, some vehicles again left the factories in a grey finish. Tank crews in the field were issued with a supply of paint (diluted with water or petrol before use) for each vehicle—usually reddish-brown, olive drab and dark yellow—so that a camouflage pattern appropriate to the terrain could be added to the basic colour.

Thus the degree of dilution of the paint applied in the field and/or the skill and whims of the crews resulted in a very wide range of colours and patterns in German A.F.V. camouflage. A German expert has said that exceptions to the rule were very common. The German black cross, on hull and/or turret sides and rear, outlined in white, was shown on most A.F.V.s.

The basic colours used were allotted RAL numbers by the department responsible for paint standards and although a full list is not available, some of these were as follows (an asterisk following the number denotes that the colour is still a published standard in West Germany in 1975)—RAL 6006* (dark green), RAL 6007* (medium-dark green), RAL 7016* (very dark bluish-grey), RAL 7017 (very dark brownish grey), RAL 7021* (very dark grey), RAL 8002 (khaki-brown), RAL 8020 (dark cream).

A tactical number was usually carried on most German A.F.V.s, although more often omitted on armoured cars and half-tracks. This number was usually in black or red, outlined in white, or sometimes in white or white outline only. The system for allocating these numbers was usually as follows, although there were exceptions to the general rule.

R 01	regimental commander
R 02	regimental adjutant
R 03	ordnance or signals officer
R 04 etc.	regimental staff etc.
I 01	commander of I battalion
I 02	adjutant of I battalion
I 03	ordnance officer of I battalion
I 04	staff of I battalion
II 01 etc.	commander of II battalion etc.
101	officer commanding Ist company, I battalion
102	2nd in command 1st company I battalion
111	Leader, 1st platoon, 1st company, I battalion
112	2nd vehicle, 1st platoon, 1st company, I battalion
133	3rd vehicle, 3rd platoon, I battalion
201 etc.	officer commanding 2nd company
301–801 etc.	Panzer battalions consisted of three or four companies and the above system was continued up to 801 etc. for the 8th company of the II battalion.
901	
1001	Tiger battalion of a special Panzer division, such as the 'Grossdeutschland' in 1944. Also independent Tiger or Sturmgeschütz company (9th) of some divisions or reconnaisance companies (10th and 11th) in others.
1101 etc.	

The system included even higher serials in some special cases. Only the final digit, denoting the individual vehicle in the platoon, was used in some instances.

A battery letter (in plain or Gothic letters) was sometimes carried on self-propelled guns, denoting the battery to which the vehicle belonged.

Small symbolic signs indicating the type of unit and the sub-unit within that unit were carried on some armoured vehicles, but not often on tanks.

Small divisional signs, usually in yellow, but white or black was also used, were sometimes stencilled on A.F.V. hulls or turrets.

Vehicle registration serial numbers, prefixed by WH for the Army, by the double lightning flash for the SS, and WL for the Luftwaffe (e.g. Hermann Göring Division) were carried on armoured cars and half tracks but not on full tracked A.F.V.s. The letters/numbers were in black on a white background.

India

See under United Kingdom.

Italy

Sand yellow, with or without a darker disruptive pattern, in North Africa; dark greenish-grey in Europe, with sometimes a shadowy or sharp reticulated pattern added.

Tactical markings consisted firstly of the regimental number in white arabic figures and the battalion number in white Roman figures. These were usually carried on rear surfaces of the tank's fighting compartment. Battalion command tanks were denoted on the turret or hull by a rectangle divided vertically into red, blue and yellow strips or, where there were only two companies in the battalion, red and blue only. The company signs, carried on the sides and rear of the turret (or hull, in turretless vehicles) were as follows:

    1st company—red rectangle
    2nd company—blue rectangle
    3rd company—yellow rectangle
    4th company—green rectangle

Platoons were indicated by one, two or three vertical white bars on the company sign, indicating 1st, 2nd or 3rd platoon respectively. The position of the individual tank in the platoon was shown by an arabic number in white or the company colour above or below the company sign.

These markings were generally used in Africa, less frequently so in Europe.

A vehicle registration number was usually carried at front and rear. The number was in black on a white background, preceded by RoEto (Regio Esercito = Royal Army) in red.

Japan

A three-colour camouflage scheme was generally used, consisting of a sand (yellow) colour, brown and dark green, although dark green alone also appeared.

314

Tactical signs were not standardized and were used only in some units. Sometimes these consisted of large Western figures in white on hull or turret, with or without Japanese characters. A red sun symbol, with or without the rays, sometimes was used and appeared on turret, nose plates or front mudguards of tanks. A yellow star was sometimes embossed or painted on the glacis plate of tanks.

Registration plates, when carried on tanks, appeared on the rear plate of the hull only. These showed a white star, Japanese characters and a number in Western figures.

Jordan

Arab Legion armoured cars were a mustard colour to which sometimes a disruptive pattern was added. British-style geometric tactical signs were sometimes carried. The vehicle number usually appeared in both Western and Arabic figures on the mudguards on opposite sides.

South Africa

See under United Kingdom.

Sweden

A camouflage system of grey, brown, green and black, in patches. In winter, vehicles were overpainted in white.

A small reproduction of the Swedish flag was generally carried on A.F.V.s after 1941.

Large tactical numbers in black, outlined, were sometimes carried on A.F.V.s, including armoured cars.

U.S.S.R.

Russian tanks were usually painted in a single colour of green or brown shade. Sometimes, but only infrequently, a disruptive pattern in a dark shade was added. A.F.V.s in winter were frequently painted over in white.

Sometimes (but rarely in combat) a red star was shown on the turret or hull. Slogans—generally of a patriotic nature—were rather more frequently shown on tanks in combat. Call signs, usually painted in white (black on snow-camouflaged vehicles) and enclosed in geometric shapes, often came increasingly to be shown. Large white numbers on turrets or hulls of A.F.Vs were also sometimes shown towards the end of the war.

United Kingdom

British A.F.V.s in the United Kingdom at the beginning of 1942 were permitted to be painted in a basic colour of either a shade of dark green, Middle Bronze Green (British Standards Institution specification No. 381—1930, colour No. 23 or B.S.I. 987c Shade No. 7) or a khaki brown colour, known as Standard Camouflage Colour No. 2 (published in B.S.I. No. 987c—1942). Khaki brown predominated, however, and appeared also in various lighter shades, including Shade No. 4 in B.S.I. 987c—1942. Nevertheless, several Regimental histories of British armoured regiments in the Eighth Army refer to the dark green of the First Army vehicles (newly out from the United Kingdom) encountered in Tunisia in 1943 or of repainting their own desert-camouflaged vehicles in green for the forthcoming campaign in Italy.

If a dark disruptive colour was to be added to either the green or the brown basic colour, the War Office instructed that this was to be the very dark brown known as Standard Camouflage Colour No. 1A (also published in B.S.I. 987c—1942).

In 1944, a new instruction laid down that the brown Standard Camouflage Colour No. 2 should be replaced by olive drab, officially known as Shade No. 15, an amendment to B.S.I. 987c—1942. This colour was much like the green used in 1942 but somewhat duller. It was similar to the U.S. Army standard 'olive drab'. Also in 1944, the use of a dark disruptive colour was no longer authorized.

British armoured fighting vehicles in North Africa (except those of the First Army in Tunisia) were painted in various sand colours, ranging from yellow through various stone-coloured shades to pink. To these were added, when required, various darker disruptive shades. In some regiments with cruiser tanks with large road wheels, the inner wheels were painted black to make them 'disappear' and so cause the tank to look more like a lorry—an effect heightened by the use of 'sun shields' (canvas on iron hoops) to conceal the turret and upper surfaces.

Armoured fighting vehicles of British and Indian formations in Burma were painted 'jungle green'. This was, contrary to some belief, a very dark colour, an olive drab darker than that used in Europe. In 1942 it would have been Shade No. 13 in B.S.I. 987c—1942, replaced in 1945 by Shade No. 16, 'Very Dark Drab'. Australian tanks in New Guinea and Borneo were also painted in a dark 'jungle green'.

Formation signs were carried by British A.F.V.s, normally at the front and rear of the hull. All British units were allotted a unit code sign, usually applicable to the type of unit, which was often unique *only* in conjunction with the formation sign. The code sign was a white number on a coloured square. Code numbers were usually allocated to armoured regiments in the brigade in accordance with their seniority in the Army List. The main exception to these rules were signals units which had the code number in red on a square divided horizontally white over blue. The code numbers used were of those of the headquarters of the formation served by the signals unit.

The most important of these unit code numbers for A.F.V.s in Armoured Divisions in 1942-45 were as follows:

	Europe 1942-45	Libya 1942
Armoured Division Headquarters	40	49
Headquarters (I) Armoured Brigade	50	71
Armoured Regiment (Battalion) (1)	51	40
Armoured Regiment (Battalion) (2)	52	86
Armoured Regiment (Battalion) (3)	53	67
Headquarters (II) Armoured Brigade (a)	60	
Armoured Regiment (Battalion) (1)	61	
Armoured Regiment (Battalion) (2)	62	
Armoured Regiment (Battalion) (3)	63	
Armoured Car Regiment (b)	44	76
Armoured Reconnaissance Regiment (c)	45	

Notes
  (a) The second armoured brigade was deleted during the course of 1942 although in North Africa, divisions still often had two or even three armoured brigades on an *ad hoc* basis. These extra brigades sometimes had the same unit code numbers as the (I) brigade, although they were usually distinguished by their brigade signs.
  (b) At first 47 in the United Kingdom. Deleted from armoured divisions to become Corps Troops in 1943, but restored in 1945.
  (c) Added to armoured division in 1943.
The coloured squares for the unit code signs were black for Divisional Headquarters, red for Headquarters and units of (I) Brigade, and green for Headquarters and units of (II) Brigade. The unit code numbers of the latter, incidentally, were taken over by the Lorried Infantry Brigades after the 1942 reorganization. For armoured car regiments the colours varied, although at first black in the U.K. and finally, in 1945, as for Armoured Reconnaissance Regiments, namely blue and green, divided horizontally.

Independent tank brigades and armoured brigades used various code-sign numbers (155, 156, 157 for the three tank units of the 34th Tank Brigade in 1944 for example) although the numbers were standardized as 51, 52, 53 (as in the armoured

317

divisions) by 1945. White bars to denote allocation to a higher formation—above the code sign for Corps Troops, below the sign for Army Troops, and diagonally for Army Group—were added as appropriate.

Tactical signs were standardized by 1942 as the following hollow geometric shapes, painted on turrets and/or hulls, as follows:

Regimental (Battalion) Headquarters—diamond
'A' Squadron (Company)—triangle
'B' Squadron (Company)—square
'C' Squadron (Company)—circle
'D' Squadron (Company)—vertical bar

Canadian units sometimes used an inverted triangle for 'A' Squadron. These tactical signs were in the following colours:

Senior Regiment in Brigade—red
Second Regiment in Brigade—yellow
Third Regiment in Brigade—blue
Fourth Regiment in Brigade—green

In armoured formations, only armoured car regiments or infantry motor battalions had a fourth squadron or company and the fourth unit in an armoured brigade was usually the motor battalion. From about 1943 onwards some British armoured regiments adopted a numbering system to supplement or replace the tactical signs. Large serial numbers were shown on hull or turret sides and rear. Unlike the German system, this did not denote battalion, company and platoon but ran through the unit, the order differing between regiments, although pains were usually taken to avoid numbering regimental headquarters tanks with the lowest numbers, and thus make them stand out.

British A.F.V.s frequently carried individual names, usually allocated in associated groups for squadrons and/or sub units, and/or bearing the same initial letter as the squadron letter. They were often names associated with regimental tradition or links, such as battle honours, recruiting towns or districts. In the battalions of the Royal Tank Regiment, the World War I tradition of naming all tanks with a letter equivalent to the battalion number (e.g. 4th Battalion tank names—Destroyer, Devil, Duck etc.) was continued in World War II.

The War Department registration number (prefixed by T for tanks, F for armoured cars, and so on) was carried in white (or black for light-painted vehicles) on the front and rear of the hull and/or hull or turret sides, according to the type of vehicle.

Varying A.F.V. recognition signs were used at different times. The white/red/white strips adopted in the Middle East in late 1941 were abandoned about March 1942 to be followed by a white St Andrew's cross on upper surfaces (principally for air recognition) and then in turn by R.A.F.-type roundels (blue, white and red—the

318

latter in the centre). In the United Kingdom, red/white/red strips were painted on A.F.V.s in March 1942 as a recognition sign and this applied also to the First Army vehicles in Tunisia and was later used in Italy until mid-1943. The white five-pointed star (with or without an enclosing ring) first used by American forces in the North African landings in 1942 was adopted by the War Office for general use as an 'Allied Star' by British forces in June 1943. Usually shown on top surfaces as an air recognition sign, it also appeared sometimes on hull or turret sides, particularly on tanks in the Far East.

Finally, a bridge group number was usually carried by British A.F.V.s. This denoted the maximum loaded weight of the vehicle in tons and the figure was in black on a yellow disc or within a yellow ring, shown at the front.

U.S.A.

The most common basic colour finish for U.S. A.F.V.s was green, although the shade varied widely. In 1942, however, the dark green commonly used (U.S. Army Ref. No. 320, similar to the British B.S.I. 987c—1942, shade No. 7) was generally superseded for Army vehicles by olive drab (Ref. No. 319). A range of other basic colours, suited to different terrains, was available, though, and recommended styles of application of darker disruptive patterns (in one or two colours) were published by the U.S. War Department. The U.S. Marine Corps also came to use olive drab as the basic colour, although forest green (a colour not dissimilar to olive drab but less brown) was standard. Landing Vehicles Tracked were sometimes finished in naval grey. Disruptive patterns, sometimes somewhat bizarre, were used, but not consistently.

A system of tactical signs including full details from formation down to company level was introduced in 1943. This consisted of small white numbers, symbols and letters, carried at front and rear, of which 7 △ 31 △ B-13 is an example, denoting 7th Armored Division, 31st Armored Battalion, B company, 13th vehicle (actually a Sherman tank). (In the Cavalry, the signs represented squadron and troop, and in the Artillery battalion and battery.) Prior to this, only the Company and vehicle designator was usually shown (sometimes in conjunction with the divisional sign, though), but even late in the war, where security necessitated it, other symbols were painted out leaving only the company and vehicle sign. The U.S. 1st Armored Division in Tunisia in 1942 used a permutated system of white geometric shapes denoting battalion, company and platoon, with a number added to indicate the individual tank.

United States Marine Corps vehicles sometimes carried geometric shapes (diamond, semi-circle, rectangle etc.) surrounding a number indicating regiment, battalion and company. Tactical letters and numbers or larger numbers alone also were used on A.F.V. hulls and/or turrets.

Vehicle registration letters were shown in white or pale blue prefixed by 'USA' (for Army vehicles) usually, on tanks, on the hull sides near the rear. The first digits were standardized for the type, tanks always having 30 (e.g. USA 3031428—an M.4 Medium tank), half tracks and tracked vehicles except tanks (such as S.P. guns) —40; armoured cars—60; tracked tractors (including L.V.T.s)—9. U.S. Marine Corps vehicles did not conform to this system and carried the prefix 'U.S.M.C.'.

The general recognition sign of a five-pointed star was used by the U.S. forces from 1942 onwards. This was normally white, with or without a white outer ring.

The bridge group sign of a black figure (denoting the maximum laden weight in tons) on a yellow disc was often carried at the front of U.S. armoured vehicles in Europe.

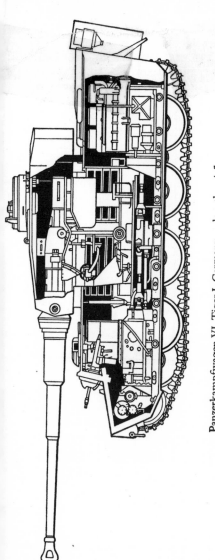

Panzerkampfwagen VI, Tiger I, Germany — length 20′4″

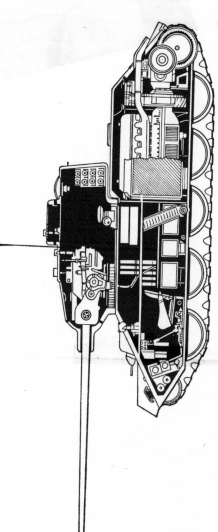

T-34/85 (Medium Tank), U.S.S.R. — length 19′8″

The dimensions and weights given here should be taken as a rough guide only: in some cases they are tions. Most of the specialized armoured vehicles are not included in these tables, because in most cases they the standard vehicles from which they have been developed and due allowance has to be made for the effect

Gun calibre lengths are not shown here but these should always be taken into account (and also the ment' column, 'm.g.' has been used to denote machine-guns of rifle calibre and 'h.m.g.' for weapons of

FULL-TRACKED

Ref. No.	Type	Weight tons	Length ft in.		Width ft in.		Height ft in.		Armour max. mm.	Armament
	Japan									
1	Tankette, Type 97	4·25	12	0	5	11	5	10	12	1 37-mm.
1	Light, Type 95	7·50	14	1	6	11	7	3	12	1 37-mm., 2 m.g.
2	Medium, Type 97 (new turret)	15·80	18	1	7	8	7	11	25	1 47-mm., 2m.g.
2	Medium Type 3	19·00	18	6	7	8	8	7	50	1 75-mm., 2 m.g.
3	Medium Type 4	30·00	20	9	9	5	9	5	75	1 75-mm., 2 m.g.
3	Medium, Type 5	37·00	24	0	10	0	10	0	75	1 75-mm., 1 37-mm, 2 m.g.
5	Amphibious, Type 2	12·50	24	7	9	2	7	6	12	1 37-mm., 2 m.g.
5	Amphibious, Type 3	28·80	33	9	9	10	12	6	50	1 47-mm., 2 m.g.
8	Armoured Personnel Carrier, Type 1	6·5	15	1	6	11	8	3	6	—
	U.S.A.									
9	Light M.5A1	15·13	15	10	7	6	7	10	67	1 37-mm., 3 m.g.
10	Light M.22	7·32	12	11	7	4	5	8	25	1 37-mm., 1 m.g.
10	Light M.24	18·08	18	0	9	4	8	1	63	1 75-mm., 3 m.g.
11	Medium M.3	26·80	18	6	8	11	10	3	51	1 75-mm., 1 37-mm., 3 m.g.
12	Medium M.4	29·69	19	4	8	7	9	0	51	1 75-mm., 1 m.g.
13	Medium M.26	41·52	20	9	11	6	9	1	102	1 90-mm., 3 m.g.
14	Heavy M.6	56·48	24	9	10	2	9	10	82	1 3-in.., 1 37-mm., 4 m.g.
9	75-mm. H.M.C. M.8	15·44	14	7	7	4	7	6	44	1 75-mm., 3 m.g.
15	105-mm. H.M.C. M.7	22·60	19	9	9	5	8	4	62	1 105-mm., 1 m.g.
16	3-in. G.M.C. M.10	29·46	19	7	10	0	8	1	63	1 3-in., 1 m.g.
16	76-mm. G.M.C. M.18	16·80	17	10	9	5	8	5	25	1 76-mm., 1 m.g.
17	L.V.T.(A)4	18·30	26	2	10	8	10	2	13	1 75-mm.
17	L.V.T. 4	16·25	26	1	10	8	8	1	—	1 m.g.
	U.K., Canada and Australia									
21	Tetrarch	7·50	13	6	7	7	6	11	16	1 2-pr, 1 m.g.
21	Harry Hopkins	8·50	14	3	8	10	6	11	38	1 2-pr, 1 m.g.
22	Crusader I	19·00	19	8	8	8	7	4	40	1 2-pr, 2 m.g.
22	Crusader III	19·75	19	8	8	8	7	4	51	1 6-pr, 1 m.g.
23	Centaur IV	27·50	20	10	9	6	8	2	76	1 95-mm. how., 1 m.g.
23	Cromwell	28·00	20	10	10	0	8	2	76	1 75-mm. or 6-pr., 2 m.g.
24	Challenger	31·50	26	4	9	6	8	9	102	1 17-pr, 1 m.g.
25	Comet	32·50	21	6	10	0	8	9	101	1 77-mm., 2 m.g.
26	Ram II (Canada)	29·50	19	0	9	10	8	9	76	1 6-pr, 2 m.g.
27	Aust. Cruiser A.C.I	28·00	20	9	9	1	8	5	65	1 2-pr, 2 m.g.
28	Churchill III	39·00	24	5	10	8	9	0	102	1 6-pr, 2 m.g.
28	Churchill VII	40·00	24	5	11	4	9	0	152	1 75-mm., 2 m.g.
29	Bishop	17·20	18	2	8	7	9	1	60	1 25-pr
29	Archer	16·00	21	11	9	0	7	4	60	1 17-pr
30	Sexton (Canada)	25·4	19	3	8	11	8	0	32	1 25-pr
37	Carrier, Universal Mk II	3·95	12	4	6	11	5	3	12	1 m.g.
37	Aust. 2-pr. Carrier	5·15	13	11	6	10	6	5	12	1 2-pr
	Italy									
50	M.15/42	15	16	7	7	4	7	9	42	1 47-mm., 2 m.g.
51	P.40	25	18	8	9	1	8	3	50	1 75-mm., 2 m.g.
52	Semovente 75/34	15	16	7	7	3	6	1	42	1 75-mm., 1 m.g.
52	Semovente 105/23	15·7	16	8	7	11	5	9	50	1 105-mm., 1 m.g.

pproximations. Performance figures are also approximate—they can vary widely under different condi-
o not lend themselves to tabular description. However, their basic characteristics are similar to those of
n performance of the special equipment carried.
unction of the weapon) when comparing guns of the same calibre (i.e. diameter of the bore). In the 'arma-
round 12–15 mm., but below 20-mm.

ARMOURED VEHICLES 1942–45

Engine	b.h.p.	Speed m.p.h.	Range miles	Crew	Notes
kegai diesel	65	26	155	2	
Mitsubishi diesel	110	28	155	3	
Type 97 diesel	170	24	130	4	
Type 100 diesel	240	25	130	5	
Type 4 diesel	400	28	155	5	
B.M.W. (petrol)	550	28	125	5	
Mitsubishi diesel	110	23	200	5	Water speed 6 m.p.h.
Type 100 diesel	240	20	200	7	Water speed 6 m.p.h.
diesel	134	25	—	15	
Cadillac	220	40	100	4	
Lycoming	162	35	110	3	
Cadillac	220	35	175	5	
Continental	340	26	120	6	Grant, height 9 ft 4 in.
Continental	400	24	120	5	
Ford	470	20	75	5	
Wright	800	22	100	6	
Cadillac	220	40	100	4	
Continental	340	25	105	7	
General Motors	375	30	200	5	
Continental	340/400	55	105	5	Length including gun 21 ft 10 in.
Continental	250	16	150	6	Water: speed 7 m.p.h., range 100 miles.
Continental	250	20	150	7	Water: speed 7·5 m.p.h., range 75 miles.
Meadows	165	40	140	3	2-pr gun = calibre 40-mm.
Meadows	148	30	125	3	
Nuffield Liberty	340	27	100	5	
Nuffield Liberty	340	27	100	3	6-pr gun = calibre 57-mm.
Nuffield Liberty	395	27	165	5	
Rolls-Royce	600	32	165	5	
Rolls-Royce	600	32	105	5	17-pr gun = calibre 76-mm.
Rolls-Royce	600	29	123	5	Length including gun 25 ft 1 in.
Continental	400	25	144	5	
Cadillac (×3)	330	30	200	5	
Bedford	350	15·5	90	5	
Bedford	350	12·5	90	5	
A.E.C. diesel	131	15	90	4	
General Motors diesel	192	20	140	4	
Continental	400	25	180	6	484 b.h.p. engine on some
Ford	85	32	160	4–5	
Ford	95	20	160	4	
P.A.	190	25	140	4	
P.A.	330	25	175	4	
P.A.	190	25	140	3	
P.A.	190	24	95	3	

Ref. No.	Type	Weight tons	Length ft in.		Width ft in.		Height ft in.		Armour max. mm.	Armament
	Germany									
53	PzKpfw. Luchs	11·8	14	6	8	2	7	0	30	1 2-cm., 1 m.g.
54	PzKpfw. III, Ausf. L-M	21·95	18	1	9	8	8	3	50+20	1 5-cm., 2 m.g.
55	PzKpfw IV, Ausf. H.	24·61	19	4	10	8	8	10	80	1 7·5-cm., 2 m.g.
56	PzKpfw Panther (Ausf. G)	44·10	22	7	11	3	9	10	80	1 7·5-cm., 2 m.g.
57	PzKpfw Tiger I	54·13	20	4	12	3	9	5	100	1 8·8-cm., 2 m.g.
58	PzKpfw Tiger II	68·6	23	10	12	4	10	2	150	1 8·8-cm., 2 m.g.
59	PzKpfw Maus	185	29	8	12	1	12	0	200	1 15-cm., 1 7·5-cm., 1 m.g.
59	PzKpfw E.100	137·79	28	6	14	8	10	11	200	1 15-cm., 1 7·5-cm., 1 m.g.
60	JgPz 38(t) Hetzer	15·75	16	0	8	8	6	11	60	1 7·5-cm., 1 m.g.
61	Stu. G. III/10·5 cm. Stu.H.	23·52	18	4	9	9	7	0	50+30	1 10·5-cm., 1 m.g.
62	Stu. Pz. IV, Brummbär	27·75	19	4	10	2	8	2	100	1 15-cm.
62	JgPz IV/70	25·8	19	9	10	6	6	1	80	1 7·5-cm., 1 m.g.
63	8·8-cm. PzJg Jagdpanther	44·78	22	7	10	9	8	11	80	1 8·8-cm., 1 m.g.
64	JgPz Elefant	66·93	22	4	11	3	9	9	200	1 8·8-cm.
65	JgPz VI, Jagdtiger	70·57	25	7	11	11	9	3	250	1 12·8-cm., 1 m.g.
66	7·5-cm. Pak auf Gw. 38(t) Marder III (Ausf. M)	10·80	14	9	7	1	7	11	25	1 7·5-cm., 1 m.g.
67	7·62-cm. Pak auf Gw. II, Ausf D.	11·50	15	3	7	7	6	8	30	1 7·62-cm.
68	8·8-cm. Pak auf Gw. III/IV, Nashorn	23·62	19	0	9	8	8	8	30	1 8·8-cm.
68	15-cm. PzfH auf Gw. III/IV, Hümmel	23·5	19	0	9	7	9	3	30	1 15-cm.
69	FlakpanzerWirbelwind	22·0	19	4	9	7	9	1	80	4 2-cm.
69	Flakpanzer Möbelwagen	25·0	19	4	9	7	10	2	80	1 3.7-cm.
	U.S.S.R.									
77	T-60	5·75	13	1	7	6	5	9	20	1 20-mm., 1 m.g.
73	T-34/76B	28·00	20	0	9	10	8	0	70	1 76·2 mm., 2 m.g.
73	T-34/85	31·5	19	8	9	10	7	10	75	1 85-mm., 2 m.g.
74	KV-85	46·00	22	4	10	8	9	6	110	1 85-mm., 3 m.g.
75	JS-II	45·00	21	9	10	3	8	11	120	1 122-mm., 3 m.g.
77	SU-76	11·55	15	3	8	9	6	8	35	1 76·2-mm.
74	SU-85	29·00	19	5	9	10	8	1	75	1 85-mm.
76	JSU-122	45·5	22	4	10	1	8	2	90	1 122-mm., 1 m.g.
76	JSU-152	46·00	22	4	9	10	8	3	90	1 152-mm., 1 m.g.
	Sweden									
80	Strv. m/42	22·50	20	0	8	0	8	6	80	1 75-mm., 3 m.g.
80	Sav. m/43	12·00	15	1	8	3	7	7	25	1 10·5-cm.

Engine	b.h.p.	Speed m.p.h.	Range miles	Crew	Notes
aybach	178	40	155	4	
aybach	300	25	124	5	Length including gun 21 ft
aybach	300	24	124	5	Length including gun 23 ft
aybach	700	28	110	5	Length including gun 29 ft 1 in., turret max. 120-mm.
aybach	700	24	62	5	Length including gun 27 ft, turret 110-mm.
aybach	700	24	68	5	Length including gun 33 ft 8 in., turret 185-mm.
aimler-Benz	1200	12	118	6	Turret 240-mm.
aybach	1200	24	130	6	700 b.h.p. engine fitted, turret 240-mm.
aga	150	25	111	4	Length including gun 20 ft 7 in.
aybach	300	25	98	4	Length including gun 20 ft 2 in.
aybach	300	24	124	5	
aybach	300	25	124	4	Length including gun 28 ft 3 in.
aybach	700	28	130	5	Length including gun 32 ft 4 in.
aybach (×2)	640	12·5	93	6	Length including gun 26 ft 9 in.
aybach	700	23	105	6	Length including gun 35 ft
aga	125	30	150	4	Length including gun 18 ft 8 in.
aybach	140	34	93	4	Length including gun 18 ft 6 in.
aybach	300	24	124	5	Length including gun 27 ft 8 in.
aybach	300	24	124	6	Length including gun 21 ft 11 in.
aybach	300	26	124	5	
aybach	300	24	124	6	
AZ-202	70	27	380	2	
-2-34 diesel	500	31	188	4	Length including gun 21 ft 7 in.
-2-34 diesel	500	31	140	5	Length including gun 24 ft 7 in.
-2K-S diesel	600	22	156	4	Length including gun 27 ft 10 in.
-2-IS diesel	513	23	150	4	Length including gun 31 ft 6 in.
AZ-202 (×2)	140	28	280	4	
-2-34 diesel	500	34	220	4	Length including gun 25 ft 9 in.
-2-IS diesel	513	25	137	5	Length including gun 31 ft 4 in.
-2-IS diesel	513	25	137	5	Length including gun 28 ft 9 in.
olvo	380	29	—	4	
cania-Vabis	140	27	—	4	

Ref. No.	Type	Weight tons	Length ft in.		Width ft in.		Height ft in.		Armour max. m.m.	Armament
8	*Japan* Armoured Personnel Carrier, ½-tracked, Type 1	7·00	20	0	6	11	6	7	8	—
	U.S.A.									
19	T.17E1 (Staghound)	13·70	18	0	8	10	7	9	32	1 37-mm., 2 m.g.
19	T.18E2 (Boarhound)	23·70	20	6	10	1	8	7	51	1 6-pr, 2 m.g.
20	M.8	7·80	16	5	8	4	7	4	19	1 37-mm., 1 m.g.
20	M.20	5·27	16	5	8	4	7	7	19	1 h.m.g.
18	Car, ½-track M.2A1	7·90	19	7	6	5	7	5	13	1 h.m.g., 1 m.g.
18	75-mm. G.M.C., M.3	9·40	20	5	7	1	8	3	16	1 75 mm.
	U.K., Canada, India and S. Africa									
39	Humber Mks III–IV	7·1	15	0	7	2	7	10	15	1 h.m.g., 1 m.g.
40	Daimler Mks I–II	7·5	13	0	8	0	7	4	16	1 2-pr, 1 m.g.
41	A.E.C. Mks II–III	12·7	17	10	8	10	8	10	30	1 6-pr, 1 m.g.
38	S.A. Mk IV	6·12	15	0	6	0	7	6	12	1 2-pr, 1 mig.
38	S.A. Mk VI	11·00	18	8	7	3	—		30	1 2-pr, 1 m.g.
42	Scout Car, Humber	3·39	12	7	6	2	6	11	14	1 m.g.
43	Scout Car, Lynx II	4·00	12	1	6	1	5	10	30	1 m.g.
44	Light Recce Car, Humber Mk IIIA	3·50	14	4	6	2	7	1	10	1a.t.r., 1 m.g.
44	Light Recce Car, Morris Mk II	3·70	13	3	6	8	6	2	14	1 a.t.r., 1 m.g.
43	Light Recce Car, Otter I	4·80	14	9	7	0	8	0	12	1 a.t.r., 1 m.g.
45	Carrier, I.P. Mk IIA	5·70	15	6	7	6	6	6	14	1 a.t.r., 1 m.g.
45	Carrier, I.P., A.O.V.	6·87	15	6	7	7	8	2	14	1 m.g.
47	Deacon	12·00	21	1	8	1	9	6	25	1 6-pr
47	Straussler S.P. 17-pr	8·00	26	5	9	5	5	4	25	1 17-pr
	Germany									
71	SdKfz 250/8	6·00	15	0	6	5	6	9	14·5	1 7·5-cm., 1 m.g.
71	SdKfz 250/9	6·00	15	0	6	5	6	11	14·5	1 2-cm., 1 m.g.
72	SdKfz 234/2 Puma	11·00	20	1	7	10	7	8	100	1 5-cm., 1 m.g.
72	SdKfz 234/3	10·50	20	1	7	10	7	0	30	1 7·5-cm., 1 m.g.
	U.S.S.R.									
78	BA-64	2·4	12	0	5	0	6	3	10	1 m.g. or 1 h.m.g.

Engine	b.h.p.	Speed m.p.h.	Range miles	Crew	Wheel arrange-ment	Notes
esel	134	31	190	15	½-track	
neral Motors (two)	194	55	450	5	4 × 4	
neral Motors (two)	250	50	250	5	8 × 8	
ercules	110	55	350	4	6 × 6	
ercules	110	55	350	6	6 × 6	
hite	147	45	200	10	½-track	
hite	147	45	220	5	½-track	
ootes	90	45	250	4	4 × 4	Mk IV has crew of 3 and 37-mm. gun instead of h.m.g.
aimler	95	50	205	3	4 × 4	
E.C. diesel	158	41	250	4	4 × 4	Mk III: length 18 ft 5 in., 75-mm.
ord	95	50	200	3	4 × 4	
ord (two)	190	35	200	3	8 × 8	Width 8 ft 8 in. over spare wheels
umber	87	60	200	2-3	4 × 4	
ord	95	57	200	2	4 × 4	
umber	87	50	250	3	4 × 4	a.t.r. = 0·55 in. Boys anti-tank
orris	72	50	250	3	4 × 4	
neral Motors	104	45	260	3	4 × 4	
ord	95	50		3-6	4 × 4	Typical armament given
ord	95	50		—	4 × 4	
E.C. diesel	95	19		5	4 × 4	
edford	72	30	200	5	4 × 2	Third wheel also driven for gun traverse
aybach	100	37	186	3	½-track	SdKfz = Sonderkraftfahrzeug
aybach	100	37	186	3	½-track	(Special Motor Vehicle)
tra	220	53	375	4	8 × 8	—Prefix to ordnance
tra	220	53	375	5	8 × 8	numerical designations.
AZ	50	31	375	2	4 × 4	